The
East Anglia
Bus H

British Bus Publishing

Body codes used in the Bus Handbook series:

Type:

B	Single-deck service bus - standard floor.
C	Coach-Tour coach
D	Low floor double-deck bus (4-metre)
DP	Express or rural service bus with high-back seating
G	Articulated vehicle
H	Full-height double-deck
L	Low-height double-deck (usually with sunken gangway)
M	Minibus
N	Low-floor bus
O	Open-top bus (CO = convertable)
P	Partial open-top

Seating capacity is then shown. For double-decks the upper deck first,

Door position:-

C	Centre entrance/exit
D	Dual doorway
F	Front entrance/exit
R	Rear entrance/exit (no distinction between doored and open)
T	Three or more access points

Equipment:-

L	Lift for wheelchair
T	Toilet

e.g. - H32/28F is a high-bridge bus with thirty-two seats upstairs, twenty-eight down and a front entrance/exit.
B43D is a bus with two doorways.

Re-registrations:-

Where a vehicle has gained new index marks the details are listed at the end of each fleet showing the current mark, followed in sequence by those previously carried starting with the original mark.

Other books in the series:

The Scottish Bus Handbook
The Ireland & Islands Bus Handbook
The North East Bus Handbook
The Yorkshire Bus Handbook
The Lancashire, Cumbria and Manchester Bus Handbook
The Merseyside and Cheshire Bus Handbook
The North and West Midlands Bus Handbook
The East Midlands Bus Handbook
The South Midlands Bus Handbook
The North and West Wales Bus Handbook
The South Wales Bus Handbook
The Chilterns and West Anglia Bus Handbook (New Summer in 1998)
The East Anglia Bus Handbook
The South West Bus Handbook
The South Central Bus Handbook (New Summer in 1998)
The South East Bus Handbook (New in Autumn 1998)

Annual books are produced for the major groups:

The 1998 Stagecoach Bus Handbook
The 1998 FirstBus Bus Handbook
The 1999 Arriva Bus Handbook (New in Autumn 1998)

Associated series:

The Hong Kong Bus Handbook
The Leyland Lynx Handbook
The Model Bus Handbook
The Toy & Model Bus Handbook - Volume 1 - Early Diecasts
The Fire Brigade Handbook (fleet list of each local authority fire brigade)
The Fire Brigade Handbook - Special Appliances Volume 1
The Fire Brigade Handbook - Special Appliances Volume 2

Contents

The East Anglia Bus Handbook

The East Anglia Bus Handbook is part of the Bus Handbook series that details the fleets of stage carriage and express coach operators. Where space allows other significant operators in the areas covered are also included. These handbooks are published by *British Bus Publishing* and cover Ireland, Scotland, Wales and England outside central London. The current list is shown on page 2. These provide comprehensive coverage of all the principal operators' fleets in the British Isles.

Quality photographs for inclusion in the series are welcome, for which a fee is payable. The publishers unfortunately cannot accept responsibility for any loss and request you show your name on each picture or slide. Details of changes to fleet information are also welcome. The writers and publisher would be glad to hear from readers should any information be available which corrects or enhances that given in this publication.

More information on the Bus Handbook series is available from:

British Bus Publishing,
The Vyne,
16 St Margaret's Drive
Wellington
Telford,
Shropshire TF1 3PH

Series Editor and type-setting: Bill Potter

Principal Editors for *The East Anglia Bus Handbook:* Colin Lloyd & Keith Grimes

Acknowledgements:
We are grateful to David Donati, Steve Sanderson, Jef Johnson, the PSV Circle and the operating companies included in this edition for their assistance in the compilation of this book.
To keep the fleets up to date we recommend *Buses*, published monthly by Ian Allan while the news-sheets of the PSV Circle provide more in-depth information.

The front cover photograph features the Ray Stenning-designed livery now applied to Harris Bus. The frontispiece shows former Volvo demonstrator, J295TWK, a Leyland Lynx 2 and one of three operating with Essex-based Hedingham & District.

Contents correct to May 1998
ISBN 1 897990 38 3
Published by *British Bus Publishing*
The Vyne, 16 St Margarets Drive,
Wellington, Telford, TF1 3PH
Fax & Evening orderline - 01952 255669

© British Bus Publishing, May 1998

AMBASSADOR TRAVEL

Ambassador Travel (Anglia) Ltd, James Watt Close, Gapton Hall Industrial Estate, Great Yarmouth. Norfolk, NR31 0NX

106	F106CCL	Volvo B10M-61	Plaxton Expressliner	C49FT	1989	
107	G107HNG	Volvo B10M-60	Plaxton Paramount 3500 III	C49FT	1989	
108	G108HNG	Volvo B10M-60	Plaxton Paramount 3500 III	C49FT	1989	
109	G109HNG	Leyland Tiger TRCL10/3ARM	Plaxton Paramount 3500 III	C53F	1990	
111	G111HNG	Leyland Tiger TRCL10/3ARM	Plaxton Paramount 3500 III	C53F	1990	
112	G512MNG	Volvo B10M-60	Plaxton Paramount 3500 III	C53F	1990	
113	TJI5403	Volvo B10M-60	Plaxton Paramount 3500 III	C53F	1990	
133	PIJ4317	Volvo B10M-60	Plaxton Première 350	C53F	1992	Ex Park's, Hamilton, 1993
134	TJI5401	Volvo B10M-60	Plaxton Première 350	C53F	1992	Ex Park's, Hamilton, 1993
135	TJI5402	Volvo B10M-60	Plaxton Première 350	C53F	1992	Ex Park's, Hamilton, 1993
137	L978UAH	Volvo B10M-62	Plaxton Première 350	C48FT	1994	
138	PIJ3379	Volvo B10M-62	Plaxton Excalibur	C28FT	1994	

139-144		Volvo B10M-62	Plaxton Première 350	C49FT	1995	
139	M741KJU	**141** M743KJU	**142** M330KRY	**143** M331KRY	**144** M332KRY	
140	M742KJU					

145	N940RBC	Volvo B10M-62	Plaxton Premiere 350	C49FT	1996	
146	N950RBC	Volvo B10M-62	Plaxton Premiere 350	C49FT	1996	
147	P413MDT	Volvo B10M-62	Plaxton Premiere 350	C49F	1997	
148	P411MDT	Volvo B10M-62	Plaxton Premiere 350	C46FT	1997	
149	P412MDT	Volvo B10M-62	Plaxton Premiere 350	C46FT	1997	
190	K68BKG	Volvo B10M-60	Plaxton Première 350	C53F	1994	Ex Bebb, Llantwit Fardre, 1997
191	M23JDW	Volvo B10M-61	Plaxton Première 350	C47FT	1994	Ex Bebb, Llantwit Fardre, 1996
192	M34KAX	Volvo B10M-62	Plaxton Première 350	C49FT	1995	Ex Bebb, Llantwit Fardre, 1997
193	M35KAX	Volvo B10M-62	Plaxton Première 350	C49FT	1995	Ex Bebb, Llantwit Fardre, 1997
194	M32KAX	Volvo B10M-61	Plaxton Première 350	C53F	1994	Ex Bebb, Llantwit Fardre, 1998
201	M325VET	Scania K113CRB	Van Hool Alizée HE	C49FT	1995	
202	N822DKU	Scania K113CRB	Van Hool Alizée HE	C49FT	1996	
203	N823DKU	Scania K113CRB	Van Hool Alizée HE	C49FT	1996	
204	N824DKU	Scania K113CRB	Van Hool Alizée HE	C49FT	1996	
205	P105GHE	Scania K113CRB	Van Hool Alizée HE	C49FT	1996	

Plaxton Excalibur-bodied Volvo B10M PIJ3379 is operated by Ambassador Travel and was converted to twenty-eight seats for Norwich City Football Club. The only Excalibur in the fleet, it is a model which Plaxton retained at the top-of-the-range until 1997 when the style was made available to a lower specification.
Philip Stephenson

Ambassador Travel 506 is one of six 9.9-metre Volvo B6 buses with Alexander Dash bodywork purchased new in 1994. They are used exclusively on the Norwich Airport Park and Ride service for which they carry a base livery of all-over green with red and orange high-lighting and appropriate lettering.

| 500 | L938ORC | | Mercedes-Benz 811D | | Plaxton Beaver | | B31F | | 1994 | | | |

501-506			Volvo B6-9.9M		Alexander Dash		B41F		1994			
501	L67UNG	**503**	L69UNG	**504**	L71UNG	**505**	L73UNG	**506**	L74UNG
502	L68UNG								

878-886			Leyland Leopard PSU3G/4R		Eastern Coach Works B51	C51F		1982	Ex Eastern Counties, 1984		
878	HCL927Y	**882**	HEX47Y	**884**	HEX52Y	**885**	CAH885Y	**886**	CAH886Y
881	HCL957Y	**883**	PIJ8513						

1001	JOX467P	Leyland Leopard PSU3C/4R	Plaxton Supreme III Express	C49F	1976	Ex Midland Red West, 1992
1002	RDA670R	Leyland Leopard PSU3E/4R	Plaxton Supreme III Express	C49F	1977	Ex Midland Red West, 1992
1003	XRR622M	Leyland Leopard PSU3B/4R	Plaxton Elite III Express	C53F	1973	Ex Barton, 1992
1004	GNN221N	Leyland Leopard PSU3B/4R	Plaxton Elite III Express	C53F	1973	Ex Barton, 1992
1007	ONN279M	Leyland Leopard PSU3B/4R	Plaxton Elite III Express	C53F	1974	Ex Barton, 1993
1008	RRB118R	Leyland Leopard PSU3D/4R	Duple Dominant I	C49F	1977	Ex Trent, 1993
1009	UVO123S	Leyland Leopard PSU3E/4R	Duple Dominant I	C49F	1977	Ex Trent, 1993
1010	RRB120R	Leyland Leopard PSU3D/4R	Duple Dominant I	C49F	1977	Ex Trent, 1993

1011-1015			Leyland Leopard PSU3B/4R		Plaxton Elite III Express	C53F		1973-74 Ex Barton, 1994		
1011	RNN982N	**1012**	RNN984N	**1013**	OAL631M	**1014**	XRR629M	**1015**	XRR613M

Previous registrations:-

HCL927Y	CAH878Y, PIJ5751	PIJ4317	J437HDS
HCL957Y	CAH881Y, PIJ3379	PJI8513	CAH883Y
HEX47Y	CAH882Y, PIJ9274	TJI5401	J431HDS
HEX52Y	CAH884Y, PIJ4317	TJI5402	J432HDS
PIJ3379	L977UAH	TJI5403	G609MVG

Livery :- White (Cosmos) 134-7, 147; white and red (Globus) 139, 140, 143; white (Insight) 202; white, red and blue (National Express) 108, 113, 148, 192; white and green (Norwich City FC) 138; green, red and orange (Park & Ride) 501-506

The East Anglia Bus Handbook

AMBER BUS & COACH COMPANY

G P Webster, Unit 6 Bakers Court, Paycocke Road, Basildon, Essex, SS14 3EH

NEL119P	Bristol VRT/SL3/501	Eastern Coach Works	DPH41/29F	1976	Ex Stephenson, Rochford, 1996
XRN718R	Bedford YMT	Duple Dominant II	C53F	1977	Ex Super Simien Coaches, Canvey, 1996
IAZ6387	Leyland Leopard PSU5C/4R	Duple 320 (1989)	C53F	1979	Ex Thamesway, 1996
SVM182W	Volvo B58-61	Plaxton Supreme IV	C53F	1980	Ex Super Simien Coaches, Canvey, 1996
LDA637W	Ford R1114	Duple Dominant IV	C53F	1980	Ex Evergreen, Blackheath, 1997
RNK317W	Ford R1114	Duple Dominant IV	C53F	1981	Ex Super Simien Coaches, Canvey, 1996
HNM201Y	Ford R1114	Duple Dominant IV	C53F	1983	Ex Super Simien Coaches, Canvey, 1996
B884AJX	DAF SB2300DHTD585	Plaxton Paramount 3200	C53F	1985	Ex Apple, Slough, 1996
C133PPE	Leyland Tiger TRCTL11/3RH	Berkhof Everest 370	C49FT	1985	Ex Speedlink, 1996
D868VKE	Mercedes-Benz 609D	Reeve Burgess	C23F	1987	Ex Hailstone Travel, Basildon, 1997
D138WCC	Freight-Rover Sherpa	Carlyle	B20F	1987	Ex Super Simien Coaches, Canvey, 1996

Previous registrations:-

D868VKE	D161HML, CSU907
IAZ6387	AFH192T, MKH487A, AEP253T, 999BCY, ATH58T, 278TNY, ATH110T
LDA637W	AUY533W, LIW4871
SVM182W	LPJ726W, FSU356

Livery:- White with orange and red.

J AMOS & SON

W G Amos, The Bungalow, Belchamp St. Paul, Essex, CO10 7BS

HRT530N	Bedford SB5	Duple Dominant	C41F	1975	Ex Burton, Haverhill, 1990
SWO70N	Bedford YRQ	Plaxton Panorama Elite III	C45F	1975	Ex Davian, Enfield, 1990
VFT935T	Bedford YLQ	Duple Dominant II	C45F	1978	Ex Kendrock, Sutton-in-Ashfield, 1993
JAR484Y	Ford Transit 150	Ford	M12	1983	Ex Essex CC, 1993
C764NRC	Ford Transit 150	Ford	M11	1986	Ex Andrew, Spalding, 1994

Livery:-Cream, red and beige.

A typical scene in Sudbury Bus Station finds Amos of Belchamp St.Paul's HRT530N. This Duple Dominant coach is built on the increasingly rare Bedford SB5 chassis.
Richard Godfrey

ANDREWS COACHES

A J Miller, 22 Cambridge Road, Foxton, Cambridgeshire, CB2 6SH

MSJ385P	Seddon Pennine 7	Alexander AT	C24DL	1976	Ex Primrose Coaches, Hayle, 1994
ESU914	Bedford YMT	Plaxton Supreme III	C53F	1977	Ex Miller, Foxton, 1992
ESU912	AEC Reliance 6U3ZR	Plaxton Supreme IV	C57F	1979	Ex Miller, Foxton, 1992
UHH267	MAN SR280	MAN	C49FT	1980	Ex Walker, Beeston, 1996
JDB934V	Ford R1114	Plaxton Supreme IV	C53F	1980	Ex Mil-Ken, Kentford, 1995
MMJ538V	Bedford YMT	Duple Dominant II	C53F	1980	Ex Coach Services, Thetford, 1995
ESU910	Ford R1014	Plaxton Supreme IV	C31F	1980	Ex Miller, Foxton, 1992
HSV193	Ford R1014	Plaxton Supreme IV	C31F	1980	Ex Pettit, Sawston, 1994
HSV192	Volvo B10M-61	Plaxton Viewmaster IV	C47FT	1981	Ex Miller, Foxton, 1992
HSV197	Bedford YNT	Plaxton Supreme IV	C47DL	1981	Ex Miller, Foxton, 1992
KHB29W	Ford R1114	Plaxton Supreme IV Express	C53F	1981	Ex Fargo Coachliner, Rayne, 1996

Previous registrations:-

ESU910	CEB138V	HSV193	CEB140V
ESU912	XER134T	HSV197	MEW152W
ESU914	PEB126R	UHH267	GPA609V
HSV192	FVA146W		

Livery:- White with red and blue relief.

Andrews Coaches is a successor to the former Millers Coaches business which sold its bus interests to Cambus in 1992. Certain vehicles were retained and these form the base of the new operation. Plaxton Viewmaster IV coachwork is carried by Volvo B10M HSV192, seen here in the livery of Andrews Coaches of Foxton. The Viewmaster was a high floor version of the Supreme, and was replaced by the 3500 version of the Paramount. It is seen approaching Epsom racecourse on Derby Day 1997. *Kevin Vincent*

ANGLIAN COACHES

Anglian Coaches Ltd, Beccles Road, Loddon, Norfolk, NR14 6JJ

w	WDB551S	Ford R1114	Duple Dominant II	C53F	1978	Ex Webb & Smith, Stowmarket, 1992
w	UVG846	Ford R1114	Plaxton Supreme IV	C53F	1979	Ex Horton, Ripley, 1994
	PJI7229	DAF MB200DKTL600	Plaxton Supreme IV	C50F	1980	Ex Griffiths, Y Felin Heli, 1996
	NBX862	DAF MB200DKTL600	Plaxton Supreme IV	C57F	1980	Ex County, Brentwood, 1997
	OTG551	Volvo B10M-61	Van Hool Aragon	C50F	1980	Ex Dunn-Line, Nottingham, 1996
	OXK395	Volvo B58-61	Duple Dominant	B53F	1980	Ex Black Prince, Morley, 1997
	KSU412	Ford R1114	Plaxton Supreme IV	C53F	1981	Ex Norfolk, Gt.Yarmouth, 1985
	MJI4487	Ford R1114	Plaxton Supreme IV	C51F	1981	Ex Moss, Sheffield, 1986
	CSK282	Ford R1114	Plaxton Supreme IV	C53F	1981	Ex Wallace Arnold, 1987
	LTG272X	Ford R1114	Plaxton Supreme IV	C53F	1981	Ex Sanders, Holt, 1993
	LTG274X	Ford R1114	Plaxton Supreme IV	C53F	1981	Ex Sanders, Holt, 1993
	G289UFB	Mercedes-Benz 609D	Made-to-Measure	C24F	1989	Ex Buzzlines, Ashford, 1997

Previous registrations:-

CSK282	PNW318W		
KSU412	SVF510W	OXK395	NGD19V
MJI4487	PNB788W	PJI7229	ECF590V
NBX862	MNM45V, LAT266, POI2905, 7947RU, MNM45V	UVG846	FTV546V

Livery:- Red, yellow and blue; white (Norwich City College Park & Ride) G289UFB

Anglian of Loddon recently re-introduced service vehicles into their fleet in the shape of OXK395, a Duple Dominant bodied Volvo B58. It is seen in Norwich on the company's Norwich to Loddon service during September 1997. *Richard Godfrey*

ARRIVA EAST HERTS & ESSEX

Arriva East Herts & Essex Ltd, 15th Floor, Terminus House, Terminus Street,
Harlow, Essex, CM20 1YD

AN248	KPJ248W	Leyland Atlantean AN68B/1R	Roe	H43/30F	1980	Ex Luton & District, 1993
BOV595	G545JOG	Bova FHD12.290	Bova Futura	C46FT	1990	Ex WMT (Smiths), 1995
BOV596	JIW3696	Bova FHD12.290	Bova Futura	C47FT	1988	Ex WMT (Smiths), 1995
DIB56	J56GCX	DAF SB220LC550	Ikarus CitiBus	B48F	1992	Ex South London, 1997
DIB124	K124TCP	DAF SB220LC550	Ikarus CitiBus	B48F	1992	Ex Cowie South London, 1997
DI754	P754RWU	DAF DE33WSSB3000	Ikarus Blue Danube396	C53F	1997	Ex Cowie Leaside, 1997
DI926	J926CYL	DAF SB220LC550	Ikarus CitiBus	B48F	1992	Ex Grey Green, 1997
DI927	J927CYL	DAF SB220LC550	Ikarus CitiBus	B48F	1992	Ex Grey Green, 1997
DI928	J928CYL	DAF SB220LC550	Ikarus CitiBus	B48F	1992	Ex Grey Green, 1997
DP753	P753RWU	DAF DE33WSSB3000	Plaxton Première 350	C53F	1997	Ex Leaside, 1997
DPL551	N551LUA	DAF DE33WSSB3000	Plaxton Première 350	C49FT	1996	Ex Leaside, 1997
DPL552	N552LUA	DAF DE33WSSB3000	Plaxton Première 350	C49FT	1996	Ex Leaside, 1997

DP301-313

Dennis Dart 9SDL3002*   Plaxton Pointer   B35F   1991   309 rebodied 1992
*302-7/13 are 9SDL3011

301	J301WHJ	304	J304WHJ	307	J307WHJ	310	J310WHJ	312	J312WHJ
302	J302WHJ	305	J305WHJ	308	J308WHJ	311	J311WHJ	313	J313WHJ
303	J303WHJ	306	J306WHJ	309	J309WHJ				

DP318-323

Dennis Dart 9SDL3011   Plaxton Pointer   B35F   1992

318	K318CVX	320	K320CVX	321	K321CVX	322	K322CVX	323	K323CVX
319	K319CVX								

DP324-334

Dennis Dart   Plaxton Pointer   B34F   1996

324	P324HVX	327	P327HVX	329	P329HVX	331	P331HVX	333	P833HVX
325	P325HVX	328	P328HVX	330	P330HVX	332	P332HVX	334	P334HVX
326	P326HVX								

DP545	K545ORH	Dennis Dart 9SDL3016	Plaxton Pointer	B34F	1992	Ex Cowie Leaside, 1996
DP546	K546ORH	Dennis Dart 9SDL3016	Plaxton Pointer	B34F	1992	Ex Cowie Leaside, 1996
DP951	M951LYR	Dennis Dart 9.8SDL3040	Plaxton Pointer	B40F	1995	Ex Grey Green, 1996

Five DAF SB220 buses with Ikarus Citibus bodywork are used on routes 310 and 310a serving the Hertford Road corridor. These routes are operated jointly by Arriva East Herts and Essex and MTL London. Currently, all of the buses carry a dedicated red and cream livery and route branding. DI927 turns into Waltham Cross Bus Station in late 1997.
Colin Lloyd

DPL405-414 — Dennis Dart 9.8SDL3017 — Plaxton Pointer — B40F — 1993

405	K405FHJ	407	K407FHJ	409	K409FHJ	411	K411FHJ	413	K413FHJ
406	K406FHJ	408	K408FHJ	410	K410FHJ	412	K412FHJ	414	K414FHJ

DPP416-431 — Dennis Dart SLF — Plaxton Pointer — N36F — 1997

416	R416COO	420	R420COO	423	R423COO	426	R426COO	429	R429COO
417	R417COO	421	R421COO	424	R424COO	427	R427COO	430	R430COO
418	R418COO	422	R422COO	425	R425COO	428	R428COO	431	R431COO
419	R419COO								

DW64	J64BJN	Dennis Dart 9SDL3012	Wright Handybus	DP40F	1992	Ex West's, Woodford Green, 1997
DW65	J65BJN	Dennis Dart 9SDL3011	Wright Handybus	B35F	1992	Ex West's, Woodford Green, 1997
DW314	J314XVX	Dennis Dart 9SDL3011	Wright Handybus	B35F	1992	
DW315	J315XVX	Dennis Dart 9SDL3011	Wright Handybus	B35F	1992	
DW316	J316XVX	Dennis Dart 9SDL3011	Wright Handybus	B35F	1992	
DW317	J317XVX	Dennis Dart 9SDL3011	Wright Handybus	B35F	1992	
DW761	K761JVX	Dennis Dart 9SDL3017	Wright Handybus	B40F	1992	Ex West's, Woodford Green, 1997
DW762	K762JVX	Dennis Dart 9SDL3017	Wright Handybus	B40F	1992	Ex West's, Woodford Green, 1997
DWL401	J401XVX	Dennis Dart 9.8SDL3012	Wright Handybus	B40F	1992	
DWL402	J402XVX	Dennis Dart 9.8SDL3012	Wright Handybus	B40F	1992	
DWL403	J403XVX	Dennis Dart 9.8SDL3012	Wright Handybus	B40F	1992	
DWL404	J404XVX	Dennis Dart 9.8SDL3012	Wright Handybus	B40F	1992	
DWL415	L415NHJ	Dennis Dart 9.8SDL3025	Wright Handybus	B40F	1994	

LR1-23 — Leyland Olympian ONTL11/1R — Roe — H43/29F — 1982

1	TPD101X	4	TPD104X	9	TPD109X	15	TPD115X	23	TPD123X
2	TPD102X	7	TPD107X	10	TPD110X	17	TPD117X		

LX251-258 — Leyland Lynx LX2R11C15Z4S — Leyland Lynx — B49F — 1990

251	H251GEV	253	H253GEV	255	H255GEV	257	H257GEV	258	H258GEV
252	H252GEV	254	H254GEV	256	H256GEV				

LX888	E888KYW	Leyland Lynx LX1126LXCTZR1S	Leyland Lynx	B47F	1987	Ex Grey Green, 1996
LX889	E889KYW	Leyland Lynx LX1126LXCTZR1S	Leyland Lynx	B47F	1987	Ex Grey Green, 1996

M1-9 — MCW Metrobus DR101/6 — MCW — H43/30F — 1979 — Ex Cowie Leaside, 1997

1	GBU1V	4	GBU4V	5	GBU5V	8	GBU8V	9	GBU9V

M80	JBO80W	MCW Metrobus DR102/20	MCW	H46/31F	1981	Ex Newport, 1994
M170	BYX170V	MCW Metrobus DR101/12	MCW	H43/28D	1979	Ex Leaside, 1997
M175	BYX175V	MCW Metrobus DR101/12	MCW	H43/28D	1979	Ex Leaside, 1997
M266	BYX266V	MCW Metrobus DR101/12	MCW	H43/28D	1979	Ex Arriva London North, 1998
M366	DTG366V	MCW Metrobus DR102/15	MCW	H46/31F	1980	Ex Grey Green, 1997
M367	DTG367V	MCW Metrobus DR102/15	MCW	H46/31F	1980	Ex Grey Green, 1997
M372	DTG372V	MCW Metrobus DR102/15	MCW	H46/31F	1980	Ex Grey Green, 1997
M491	GYE491W	MCW Metrobus DR101/12	MCW	H43/28D	1979	Ex Arriva London North, 1998
M537	GYE537W	MCW Metrobus DR101/14	MCW	H43/28D	1981	Ex Leaside, 1997
M544	GYE544W	MCW Metrobus DR101/14	MCW	H43/28D	1979	Ex Arriva London North, 1998
M573	GYE573W	MCW Metrobus DR101/14	MCW	H43/28D	1981	Ex Leaside, 1997
M625	KYO625X	MCW Metrobus DR101/14	MCW	H43/28D	1981	Ex Leaside, 1997
M649	KYV649X	MCW Metrobus DR101/14	MCW	H43/28D	1981	Ex Leaside, 1997
M1248	B248WUL	MCW Metrobus DR101/14	MCW	H43/28D	1984	Ex Leaside, 1997
M1367	C367BUV	MCW Metrobus DR101/14	MCW	H43/28D	1985	Ex Leaside, 1997
M1379	VLT88	MCW Metrobus DR101/14	MCW	H43/28D	1985	Ex Leaside, 1997
M1398	C398BUV	MCW Metrobus DR101/14	MCW	H43/28D	1985	Ex Leaside, 1997
M1437	VLT12	MCW Metrobus DR101/14	MCW	DPH43/24F	1986	Ex Leaside, 1997
MB45	D45OKH	Iveco Daily 49.10	Robin Hood City Nippy	DP19F	1987	Ex East Yorkshire, 1989
MB52	E352NEG	Iveco Daily 49.10	Robin Hood City Nippy	DP19F	1988	Ex Premier Travel, 1989
MB53	E353NEG	Iveco Daily 49.10	Robin Hood City Nippy	DP19F	1988	Ex Premier Travel, 1989
MB54	E354NEG	Iveco Daily 49.10	Robin Hood City Nippy	DP19F	1988	Ex Premier Travel, 1989
MB115	F115JGS	Iveco Daily 49.10	Robin Hood City Nippy	B25F	1988	Ex Sampsons, Hoddesdon, 1988
MB154	F154DKV	Iveco Daily 49.10	Reeve Burgess Beaver	B25F	1988	Ex Iveco demonstrator, 1989
MB706	E296VOM	Iveco Daily 49.10	Carlyle Dailybus 2	B25F	1988	Ex Southend, 1992

MB707-712 — Iveco TurboDaily 59.12 — Dormobile Routemaker — B25F — 1993

707	K707FNO	709	K709FNO	710	K710FNO	711	K711FNO	712	K712FNO
708	K708FNO								

Arriva East Herts & Essex' first batch of Super Low Floor (SLF) Dennis Darts were delivered to the former County Bus and Coach, and consisted of three Wright Crusader bodied examples for Hertford local route 395. SLF416 (P416HVX) is based at Ware garage and is seen in Hertford in the summer of 1997. *Tony Wilson*

MB717-729 — Iveco TurboDaily 59.12 — Marshall C31 — B25F — 1994

717	L717OVX	720	M720UTW	723	L723PHK	726	M726UTW	728	M728UTW
718	L718OVX	721	M721UTW	724	L724PHK	727	M727UTW	729	M729UTW
719	M719UTW	722	L722OVX	725	M725UTW				

MB730-744 — Iveco TurboDaily 59.12 — Marshall C31 — B25F — 1995

730	M730AOO	733	M733AOO	736	M736AOO	739	N739AVW	742	N742AVW
731	M731AOO	734	M734AOO	737	M737AOO	740	N740AVW	743	N743AVW
732	M732AOO	735	M735AOO	738	M738AOO	741	N741AVW	744	N744AVW

MB748	E448TYG	Iveco Daily 49.10	Robin Hood City Nippy	DP23F	1988	Ex Keighley & District, 1993
MB795	F795JKX	Iveco Daily 49.10	Reeve Burgess Beaver	B21F	1988	Ex Sovereign, 1992
MB796	F796JKX	Iveco Daily 49.10	Reeve Burgess Beaver	B21F	1988	Ex Sovereign, 1992

MB918-938 — Mercedes-Benz 709D — Reeve Burgess Beaver — B23F — 1989-92

918	G918UPP	926	G926WGS	930	G930WGS	933	J933WHJ	936	J936WHJ
919	G919UPP	927	G927WGS	931	G931WGS	934	J934WHJ	937	J937WHJ
924	G924WGS	928	G928WGS	932	G932WGS	935	J935WHJ	938	J938WHJ
925	G925WGS	929	G929WGS						

MB939	P939HVX	Mercedes-Benz 711D	Plaxton Beaver	DP25F	1997

MBV940-952 — Mercedes-Benz Vario O810 — Plaxton Beaver 2 — B27F — 1998

940	R940VPU	943	R943VPU	946	R946VPU	949	R949VPU	951	R951VPU
941	R941VPU	944	R944VPU	947	R947VPU	950	R950VPU	952	R952VPU
942	R942VPU	945	R945VPU	948	R948VPU				

MBT713	L713OVX	Iveco TurboDaily 59.12	Marshall C31	B18FL	1994
MBT714	L714OVX	Iveco TurboDaily 59.12	Marshall C31	B18FL	1994
MBT715	L715OVX	Iveco TurboDaily 59.12	Marshall C31	B18FL	1994
MBT716	L716OVX	Iveco TurboDaily 59.12	Marshall C31	B18FL	1994

The majority of Arriva East Herts & Essex' Mercedes-Benz fleet carry Reeve Burgess Beaver bodywork. One of the exceptions is Mercedes-Benz MB939, P939HVX, which is fitted with the later Plaxton-built version. This vehicle carries a livery for the West Anglia Great Northern railway feeder service linking Ware rail station with the local area. Wearing the distinctive yellow white and blue livery, it is seen on lay-over soon after delivery. *Colin Lloyd*

MBT801	L801KNO	Peugeot-Talbot Freeway	TBP	B18FL	1993	
MBT802	L802KNO	Peugeot-Talbot Freeway	TBP	B18FL	1993	
MBT803	L803KNO	Peugeot-Talbot Freeway	TBP	B18FL	1993	
MBT804	L804KNO	Peugeot-Talbot Freeway	TBP	B18FL	1993	
MBT805	L805OVX	Peugeot-Talbot Freeway	TBP	B18FL	1993	
MBT865	P865VTJ	LDV Convoy	Whitacre	M8L	1997	
MC540	D40MAG	Iveco Daily 49.10	Robin Hood City Nippy	DP16F	1987	Ex West Yorkshire, 1989
MCW75	JBO75W	MCW Metrobus DR102/20	MCW	H46/31F	1981	Ex Newport, 1994
MCW80	JBO80W	MCW Metrobus DR102/20	MCW	H46/31F	1981	Ex Newport, 1994

MD601-612

		Mercedes-Benz 811D	Reeve Burgess Beaver	B28F	1991

601	J601WHJ	605	J605WHJ	607	J607WHJ	609	J609WHJ	611	J611WHJ
603	J603WHJ	606	J606WHJ	608	J608WHJ	610	J610WHJ	612	J612WHJ
604	J604WHJ								

MD613	L613LVX	Mercedes-Benz 811D	Dormobile Routemaker	B31F	1993	
MD614	L614LVX	Mercedes-Benz 811D	Dormobile Routemaker	B31F	1993	
MR367	F367CHE	MCW MetroRider MF150/110	MCW	B33F	1988	Ex West's, Woodford Green, 1997
MR667	E667YDT	MCW MetroRider MF150/65	MCW	B33F	1988	Ex West's, Woodford Green, 1997
MR713	F713CWJ	MCW MetroRider MF150/110	MCW	B33F	1988	Ex West's, Woodford Green, 1997
MR714	F714CWJ	MCW MetroRider MF150/110	MCW	B33F	1988	Ex West's, Woodford Green, 1997
MR715	F715CWJ	MCW MetroRider MF150/110	MCW	B33F	1988	Ex West's, Woodford Green, 1997
MR718	F718CWJ	MCW MetroRider MF150/110	MCW	B33F	1988	Ex West's, Woodford Green, 1997
MR719	F719CWJ	MCW MetroRider MF150/110	MCW	B33F	1988	Ex West's, Woodford Green, 1997
OD621	G621YMG	DAF SB220LC550	Optare Delta	B47F	1989	Ex West's, Woodford Green, 1997
OD760	K760JVX	DAF SB220LC550	Optare Delta	B49F	1992	Ex West's, Woodford Green, 1997

PDL201-209

		DAF DE02GSSB220	Plaxton Prestige	DP37F	1997

201	R201VPU	203	R203VPU	205	R205VPU	207	R207VPU	209	R209VPU
202	R202VPU	204	R204VPU	206	R206VPU	208	R208VPU		

RMC1453	453CLT	AEC Routemaster R2RH	Park Royal	H32/25RD	1962	Ex Cowie Leaside, 1997
RMC1464	464CLT	AEC Routemaster R2RH	Park Royal	O32/25RD	1962	Ex Cowie Leaside, 1997

RV1	GJG750D	AEC Regent V 2D3RA	Park Royal	H40/32R	1966	Ex Cowie Leaside, 1997
SLF165	R165GNW	Dennis Dart SLF	Wright Crusader	N36F	1997	
SLF169	R169GNW	Dennis Dart SLF	Wright Crusader	N41F	1997	
SLF170	R170GNW	Dennis Dart SLF	Wright Crusader	N41F	1997	
SLF266	M266VPU	Dennis Lance SLF	Wright Pathfinder	N40F	1994	
SLF267	M267VPU	Dennis Lance SLF	Wright Pathfinder	N40F	1994	
SLF268	M268VPU	Dennis Lance SLF	Wright Pathfinder	N40F	1994	
SLF269	M269VPU	Dennis Lance SLF	Wright Pathfinder	N40F	1994	
SLF416	P416HVX	Dennis Dart SLF	Wright Crusader	N37F	1996	
SLF417	P417HVX	Dennis Dart SLF	Wright Crusader	N37F	1996	
SLF418	P418HVX	Dennis Dart SLF	Wright Crusader	N37F	1996	

SLF419-431

		Dennis Dart SLF	Plaxton Pointer	N42F	1996

419	P419HVX	422	P422HVX	425	P425HVX	428	P428HVX	430	P430HVX
420	P420HVX	423	P423HVX	426	P426HVX	429	P429HVX	431	P431HVX
421	P421HVX	424	P424HVX	427	P427HVX				

T69	70CLT	Leyland Titan TNLXB2RRSp	Park Royal	O44/26D	1979	Ex Cowie Leaside, 1997
T83	CUL83V	Leyland Titan TNLXB2RRSp	Park Royal	O44/26D	1979	Ex Cowie Leaside, 1997
T100	CUL100V	Leyland Titan TNLXB2RRSp	Park Royal	O44/26D	1979	Ex Cowie Leaside, 1997
TDB61	F61SMC	Leyland Tiger TRBTL11/2RP	Duple 300	B55F	1988	Ex Sovereign, 1989
TDB62	F62SMC	Leyland Tiger TRBTL11/2RP	Duple 300	B55F	1988	Ex Sovereign, 1989
TDB63	F63SMC	Leyland Tiger TRBTL11/2RP	Duple 300	B55F	1988	Ex Sovereign, 1989
TDL54	C254SPC	Leyland Tiger TRCTL11/3RH	Duple 320	C53F	1986	Ex London & Country, 1993
TDL55w	C255SPC	Leyland Tiger TRCTL11/3RH	Duple 320	C49F	1986	Ex London & Country, 1993
TDL60	C260SPC	Leyland Tiger TRCTL11/3RH	Duple 320	C49F	1986	Ex London & Country, 1993
TDL65	C265SPC	Leyland Tiger TRCTL11/3RH	Duple 320	C53F	1986	
TPL1	124CLT	Leyland Tiger TRCTL11/3ARZM	Plaxton Paramount 3200 III	C53F	1989	Ex Cowie Leaside, 1997
TPL2	361CLT	Leyland Tiger TRCTL11/3ARZM	Plaxton Paramount 3200 III	C53F	1989	Ex Cowie Leaside, 1997
TPL8	H643GRO	Leyland Tiger TRCT10/3ARZA	Plaxton Paramount 3200 III	C53F	1991	Ex Cowie Leaside, 1997
TPL518	530MUY	Leyland Tiger TRCTL11/3ARZ(Vo)	Plaxton Paramount 3500 III	C51FT	1988	Ex Alan's Cs, Saffron Walden, 1993
VDL185	185CLT	Volvo B10M-61	Duple 320	C53F	1988	Ex Grey Green, 1997
VDL205	205CLT	Volvo B10M-61	Duple 340	C53F	1988	Ex Grey Green, 1997
VP564	E564BNK	Volvo B10M-56	Plaxton Derwent II	B54F	1988	Ex Sampsons, Hoddesdon, 1989
VP565	E565BNK	Volvo B10M-56	Plaxton Derwent II	B54F	1988	Ex Sampsons, Hoddesdon, 1989
VPL3	C874CYX	Volvo B10M-61	Plaxton Paramount 3200 II	C53F	1986	Ex Cowie Leaside, 1997
VPL4	C876CYX	Volvo B10M-61	Plaxton Paramount 3200 II	C53F	1986	Ex Cowie Leaside, 1997
VPL501	L501MOO	Volvo B10M-60	Plaxton Première 350	C49FT	1993	
VPL503	H903AHS	Volvo B10M-60	Plaxton Paramount 3500 III	C53F	1991	Ex Park's, 1994
WS350	H350PNO	Leyland Swift LBM6T/2RS	Wadham Stringer Vanguard	B39F	1991	Ex West's, Woodford Green, 1997

Ancillary:-

BD357t	OJN357P	Bedford YRQ	Duple Dominant	C32F	1976	Ex Welwyn & Hatfield, 1990
BP504t	DDX741T	Bedford YLQ	Plaxton Supreme III	C45F	1978	Ex Davian, Enfield, 1991
BP507t	SGS497W	Bedford YMT	Plaxton Supreme IV	C53F	1981	Ex Davian, Enfield, 1991
TL30 t	WPH130Y	Leyland Tiger TRCTL11/2R	Eastern Coach Works B51	C49F	1982	Ex Luton & District, 1991

Previous registrations:

70CLT	CUL69V	H350PNO	H550AMT, A19BUS, H20BUS
124CLT	G661WMD	J64BJN	J9BUS
185CLT	E892KYW	J65BJN	J6BUS
205CLT	E893KYW	JIW3696	E908UOH
361CLT	G662WMD	K760JVX	K5BUS
453CLT	From new	K761JVX	K2BUS
464CLT	From new	K762JVX	J12BUS
530MUY	E118KFV	VLT12	C437BUV
BAZ7384	C210PPE	VLT88	C379BUV
G621YMG	G259EHD, A10BUS		

Opposite:- **Two examples of the recent investment in low floor vehicles are DPP424, R424COO, and PDL202, R202VPU. LRT route 34 was awarded to County Bus having previously been operated by sister company Cowie Leaside which used double deck Metrobuses. DPP424 is seen when new outside Arnos Grove underground station. A new vehicle type for the Arriva-owned Green Line network was introduced in 1997 when the then County Bus company commenced running the long 724 route linking Harlow with Heathrow Airport using a batch of nine Plaxton Prestige-bodied DAF buses with high back seating. PDL202 was seen at Heathrow when new.** *Colin Lloyd/Malcolm King*

Allocations & Liveries:

Livery:- Arriva turquoise and stone displacing; cream and green (lea Valley, Thameside, Townlink) blue and cream, ♣ (Sampsons); two-tone green and red ♠ (Green Line); red ✪ (LRT); maroon, white and blue ⓐ (Leaside Travel).

Edmonton (Edmonton Wharf, Lea Valley) - Lea Valley - Leaside Travel - Sampsons

Type								
Bedford	BP504♣	BP507♣						
Iveco	MB722	MB723	MBT713✪	MBT714✪	MBT715✪	MBT716✪		
Mercedes-Benz	MB918	MB919	MB927	MB928	MB929	MB930	MB931	MD601
	MD603	MD604	MD605	MD606	MD607	MD608	MD609	MD610
	MD611	MD612						
Vario	MBV951							
Dart	DP301	DP302	DP303	DP304	DP305	DP306	DP307	DP308
	DP309	DP310	DP311	DP312	DP313	DW314	DW315	
Coaches	DI753ⓐ	DI754ⓐ	DPL551ⓐ	DPL552ⓐ	TPL1ⓐ	TPL2ⓐ	TPL8ⓐ	VPL3ⓐ
	VPL4ⓐ							
Metrobus	M170ⓐ	M175ⓐ	M266	M491	M537ⓐ	M544	M573ⓐ	M625ⓐ
	M649ⓐ	M1248ⓐ	M1367ⓐ	M1379ⓐ	M1398ⓐ	M1437ⓐ		

Grays (Europa Park, London Road) - Thameside

Type								
Dart	DP321	DP323	DP324	DP325	DP326	DP327	DP328	DP329
	DP330	DP331	DP332	DP333	DP334	DP951	DW316	DW317
	SLF419	SLF420	SLF421	SLF422	SLF423	SLF424	SLF425	SLF426
	SLF427	SLF428	SLF429	SLF430	SLF431			
Metrobus	M80	M366	M367	M372	M782			
Iveco	MB725	MB726	MB727					
Mercedes-Benz	MB724	MB728	MB729	MB741	MB742	MB743	MB744	

Harlow (Fourth Avenue) - Townlink

Outstation - Langston Road, Debden.

Type								
Tiger	TBD61	TBD62	TBD63	TDL60♠	TDL65♠	TL30		
Volvo	VP564	VP565						
Iveco	MB707	MB708	MB709	MB710	MB711	MB712	MB717	MB718
	MB719	MB720	MB721	MB730	MB731	MB732	MB733	MB734
	MB735	MB736	MB737	MB738				
Mercedes-Benz	MB924	MB925	MB926	MB932	MB933	MB934	MB935	MB936
	MB937	MB938	MD613	MD614				
MetroRider	MR367	MR667	MR713	MR714	MR715	MR718	MR719	
Peugeot-Talbot	MBT801	MBT802	MBT803	MBT804	MBT805			
LDV	MBT865							
Swift	WS350							
Dart	DP318	DP319	DP320	DP322	DP545	DP546	DPL406	DPL407
	DPL408	DPL409	DPL410	DPL411	DPL412	DPL413	DPL406	DPL414
	DW64	DW65	DW761	DW762				
Lynx	LX251	LX252	LX253	LX254	LX255	LX256	LX257	LX258
	LX888	LX889						
DAF SB220	OD621	OD760	PDL208 ♠	PDL209 ♠				
Lance	SLF266	SLF267	SLF268	SLF269				
Atlantean	AN268							
Olympian	LR1	LR2	LR9	LR17				

Five Peugeot-Talbot Freeway buses are based at the Arriva depot in Harlow and used to provide wheelchair accessibility on several minibus routes centred on the Waltham Abbey area. These have a specific role within the fleet and are also the only tri-axle examples. The type is represented by MBT805, L805DVX, in a picture taken at Waltham Cross. *Colin Lloyd*

Ware (Marsh Lane) - Lea Valley

Bova	BOV594♣	BOV595♣	BOV596♣					
DAF bus	DIB56	DIB124	DI926	DI927	DI928	PDL201♠	PDL202♠	PDL203♠
	PDL204♠	PDL205♠	PDL206♠	PDL207♠				
Dart	DPL405	DWL401	DWL402	DWL403	DWL404	DWL415		
	SLF165	SLF169	SLF170	SLF416	SLF417	SLF418		
Olympian	LR3	LR4	LR7	LR10	LR15	LR23		
Iveco	MB45	MB52	MB53	MB54	MB115	MB154	MB706	MB739
	MB740	MB748	MB795	MB796	MC540			
Mercedes-Benz	MB939	MBV940	MBV941	MBV942	MBV943	MBV944	MBV945	MBV946
	MBV947	MBV948	MBV949	MBV950	MBV952			
Tiger	STL10 ♣	TDL54♠	TDL55♠	TPL518♣				
Volvo B10M	VDL185	VDL205	VDL891	VPL501♣	VPL503♣			
Metrobus	M1	M4	M5	M8	M9			

DIB, DI, M classes and LR7 are route-branded for the 310/310A routes.

ARRIVA COLCHESTER

Arriva Colchester Ltd, Magdalen Street, Colchester, Essex, CO1 2LD

STL10	BAZ7384	Leyland Tiger TRCTL11/3RH	Plaxton Paramount 3500 II	C49FT	1985	Ex London & Country, 1992
41	C41HHJ	Leyland Olympian ONLXCT/1RH	Eastern Coach Works	H47/31F	1985	
43	D43RWC	Leyland Olympian ONLXCT/1RH	Eastern Coach Works	H47/31F	1985	
45	F245MTW	Leyland Olympian ONCL10/1RZ	Leyland	DPH43/29F	1988	
46	F246MTW	Leyland Olympian ONCL10/1RZ	Leyland	DPH43/29F	1988	Ex Southend, 1996
47	H47MJN	Leyland Olympian ON2R50C13Z4	Leyland	DPH43/29F	1991	Ex Southend, 1996
48	H48MJN	Leyland Olympian ON2R50C13Z4	Leyland	H47/31F	1991	
49	H49MJN	Leyland Olympian ON2R50C13Z4	Leyland	H47/31F	1991	

55-61		Volvo B10M-61		East Lancashire(1992)	B49F	1984-85 Ex County, 1997	
55	A855UYM	57	B857XYR	59	B859XYR	60	B860XYR	61	B861XYR
56	A856UYM	58	B858XRY				

68-90		Leyland Atlantean AN68A/1R		Eastern Coach Works	H43/31F	1977-80 69 Ex Midland, 1994
68	TPU68R	75	TPU75R	80	YNO80S	84	MEV84V	88	RVW88W
69	TPU69R	76	TPU86R	81	YNO81S	85	MEV85V	89	RVW89W
71	TPU71R	77	YNO77S	82	YNO82S	86	MEV86V	90	RVW90W
74	TPU74R	78	YNO78S	83	MEV83V	87	MEV87V		

95	JHK495N	Leyland Atlantean AN68/1R	Eastern Coach Works	O43/31F	1975	
100	A250SVW	Leyland Tiger TRCTL11/3RP	Duple Caribbean	C57F	1984	Ex Southend, 1995
103	OHE274X	Leyland Tiger TRCTL11/3R	Duple Dominant IV	C53F	1982	Ex West Riding, 1987
104	OHE280X	Leyland Tiger TRCTL11/3R	Duple Dominant IV	C53F	1982	Ex West Riding, 1987
123	H123WFM	Mercedes-Benz 814D	North West Coach Sales	C24F	1991	Ex London & Country (GWS), 1996
M220	BYX220V	MCW Metrobus DR101/12	MCW	H43/28F	1980	Ex Cowie Leaside, 1998
M299	BYX299V	MCW Metrobus DR101/12	MCW	H43/28F	1980	Ex Cowie Leaside, 1998
M301	BYX301V	MCW Metrobus DR101/12	MCW	H43/28F	1980	Ex Leaside, 1997
M336	EYE336V	MCW Metrobus DR101/12	MCW	H43/28F	1980	Ex Leaside, 1997
M353	GYE353W	MCW Metrobus DR101/12	MCW	H43/28F	1980	Ex Arriva London North, 1998
M389	GYE389V	MCW Metrobus DR101/12	MCW	H43/28F	1980	Ex Arriva London North, 1998
M419	GYE419V	MCW Metrobus DR101/12	MCW	H43/28F	1980	Ex Arriva London North, 1998
M493	GYE493V	MCW Metrobus DR101/12	MCW	H43/28F	1980	Ex Arriva London North, 1998
347	NIW6507	Leyland 1151/1R/2402(6HLXB)	East Lancs Greenway(1993)	B49F	1974	Ex London & Country, 1996
348	NIW6508	Leyland 11351/1R(6HLXB)	East Lancs Greenway(1993)	B49F	1974	Ex London & Country, 1996
349	NIW6509	Leyland 11351A/1R(6HLXB)	East Lancs Greenway(1993)	B49F	1977	Ex London & Country, 1996
350	NIW6510	Leyland NL116AL11/2R(6HLXB)	East Lancs Greenway(1993)	B49F	1982	Ex London & Country, 1996
351	NIW6511	Leyland 11351/1R(6HLXB)	East Lancs Greenway(1993)	B49F	1978	Ex London & Country, 1996
352	NIW6512	Leyland NL116AL11/2R(6HLXB)	East Lancs Greenway(1993)	B49F	1982	Ex London & Country, 1996
354	JIL2194	Leyland 11351A/1R(6HLXB)	East Lancs Greenway(1994)	B49F	1977	Ex London & Country, 1996
355	JIL2195	Leyland 11351/1R(6HLXB)	East Lancs Greenway(1994)	B49F	1975	Ex London & Country, 1996
BOV594	HDZ8354	Bova FHD12.280	Bova Futura	C49FT	1986	Ex Arriva East Herts & Essex, 1998

Previous registrations:

BAZ7384	C210PPE	NIW6507	NEL863M	NIW6510	FCA8X
HDZ8354	C904JOF, 245DOC, C566LOG	NIW6508	GUA821N	NIW6511	LPR938P
JIL2194	CBV779S	NIW6509	TEL491R	NIW6512	FCA6X
JIL2195	JOX477P				

Allocation & liveries:- Livery :Arriva turquoise and stone replacing cream and crimson.

Colchester (Magdalen Street)

Coach	STL10	100	103	104	BOV594	Mercedes-Benz		123
Metrobus	M220	M229	M301	M336	M353	M389	M419	M493
Greenway	347	348	349	350	351	352	354	355
Volvo	55	56	57	58	59	60	61	
Atlantean	68	69	71	74	75	76	77	78
	80	81	82	83	84	85	86	87
	88	89	90	95				
Olympian	41	43	45	46	47	48	49	

ARRIVA SOUTHEND

Arriva Southend Ltd, 87 London Road, Southend-on-Sea, Essex, SS1 1PP

LSL001	M761JPA	Dennis Lance SLF 11SDA3201	Wright Pathfinder	N39F	1995	
LSL002	M762JPA	Dennis Lance SLF 11SDA3201	Wright Pathfinder	N39F	1995	
LSL003	M763JPA	Dennis Lance SLF 11SDA3201	Wright Pathfinder	N39F	1995	
LSL004	M764JPA	Dennis Lance SLF 11SDA3201	Wright Pathfinder	N39F	1995	
12	BVP812V	Leyland National 2 NL116L11/1R		B49F	1980	Ex Colchester, 1997
25	EON825V	Leyland National 2 NL116L11/1R		B49F	1980	Ex Colchester, 1997

DSL056-57

	Dennis Dart SLF	Plaxton Pointer	N39F	1997

056	P256FPK	059	P259FPK	062	P262FPK	064	P264FPK	066	P266FPK
057	P257FPK	060	P260FPK	063	P263FPK	065	P265FPK	067	P267FPK
058	P258FPK	061	P261FPK						

AN110	MPJ210L	Leyland Atlantean PDR1A/1	MCW	043/29D	1972	Ex Leaside, 1997
212	JTD392P	Daimler Fleetline CRL6-33	Northern Counties	H49/31D	1975	

221-242

	Leyland Fleetline FE33ALR	Northern Counties	H49/31D	1979-81 *233/5/7/8/42 are H49/33F

221	XTE221V	226	XTE226V	231	MRJ231W	235	MRJ235W	239	MRJ239W
222	XTE222V	227	XTE227V	232	MRJ232W	236	MRJ236W	240	MRJ240W
223	XTE223V	228	XTE228V	233	MRJ233W	237	MRJ237W	241	MRJ241W
224	XTE224V	229	XTE229V	234	MRJ234W	238	MRJ238W	242	MRJ242W
225	XTE225V	230	XTE230V						

250	Q475MEV	Daimler Fleetline CRL6-33	Northern Counties(1984)	H49/31D	1972	
251	Q476MEV	Daimler Fleetline CRL6-33	Northern Counties(1984)	H49/31D	1972	
252	Q552MEV	Daimler Fleetline CRL6-33	Northern Counties(1985)	H49/31D	1972	
253	Q553MEV	Daimler Fleetline CRL6-33	Northern Counties(1985)	H49/31D	1972	
254	Q554MEV	Daimler Fleetline CRL6-33	Northern Counties(1984)	H49/31D	1972	
256	A110FDL	Leyland Olympian ONLXB/1R	Eastern Coach Works	DPH41/23F	1984	Ex Southern Vectis, 1991
257	B185BLG	Leyland Olympian ONLXB/1R	Eastern Coach Works	H45/32F	1984	Ex Crosville Cymru, 1991
258	B189BLG	Leyland Olympian ONLXB/1R	Eastern Coach Works	H45/32F	1984	Ex Crosville Cymru, 1991
259	B183BLG	Leyland Olympian ONLXB/1R	Eastern Coach Works	H45/32F	1984	Ex Crosville Cymru, 1990
260	B184BLG	Leyland Olympian ONLXB/1R	Eastern Coach Works	H45/32F	1984	Ex Crosville Cymru, 1990
262	H262GEV	Leyland Olympian ON2R50G13Z4 Leyland		H47/31F	1990	
263	H263GEV	Leyland Olympian ON2R50G13Z4 Leyland		H47/31F	1990	
264	H264GEV	Leyland Olympian ON2R50G13Z4 Leyland		DPH43/29F	1990	
265	H265GEV	Leyland Olympian ON2R50G13Z4 Leyland		DPH43/29F	1990	

281	MUH281X	Leyland Olympian ONLXB/1R	Eastern Coach Works	H45/32F	1982	Ex Rhondda, 1992
282	MUH285X	Leyland Olympian ONLXB/1R	Eastern Coach Works	H45/32F	1982	Ex Rhondda, 1992
283	MUH283X	Leyland Olympian ONLXB/1R	Eastern Coach Works	H45/32F	1982	Ex Rhondda, 1992
284	MUH286X	Leyland Olympian ONLXB/1R	Eastern Coach Works	H45/32F	1982	Ex Rhondda, 1992
MM478	P478DPE	Mercedes-Benz 711D	Plaxton Beaver 2	B27F	1997	
MM481	P481DPE	Mercedes-Benz 711D	Plaxton Beaver 2	B27F	1997	
MM482	P482DPE	Mercedes-Benz 711D	Plaxton Beaver 2	B27F	1997	

Overleaf:- **Arriva Colchester have announced their intention to replace the Leyland Atlantean fleet with refurbished MCW Metrobuses cascaded from the Arriva fleets of both London North and London South. The first example to arrive was EYE336V seen here at Lexden on its usual haunt, route 5. Colchester Transport operated from new nine Leyland Olympians. Of these, two spent brief periods at Southend while another pair later transferred to Midland Fox. One of the seven survivors is 48, H48MJN, one of the last batch of Cummins engined examples and one that is fitted with normal urban seats. This Leyland-bodied example is seen near Colchester bus station.** *Colin LloydPaul Goodison*

Opposite:- **Arriva Southend's express coach operation now forms part of the Green Line network. Seen loading passengers at Lakeside when heading for London Victoria is 572, F572UPB, one of the Plaxton Paramount bodied Volvo B10Ms. Only three minibuses are used by Arriva Southend in comparison with local First Group's Essex Buses who operate many, though both use similar models of vehicle. A legacy of the period when Southend Transport was under London & Country control is the MM prefix seen here on MM478, P478DPE pictured opposite the bus station.** *Philip Stephenson*

The East Anglia Bus Handbook

546	A246SVW	Leyland Tiger TRCTL11/3RP	Duple Caribbean	C57F	1984	
547	A247SVW	Leyland Tiger TRCTL11/3RP	Duple Caribbean	C57F	1984	
548	A248SVW	Leyland Tiger TRCTL11/3RP	Duple Caribbean	C57F	1984	
549	A249SVW	Leyland Tiger TRCTL11/3RP	Duple Caribbean	C57F	1984	
551	B100XTW	Leyland Tiger TRCTL11/3RP	Duple Caribbean	C57F	1984	
553	A141EPA	Leyland Tiger TRCTL11/2R	Plaxton Paramount 3200 E	C51F	1984	Ex London & Country, 1990
557	B83SWX	Leyland Tiger TRCTL11/3RH	Plaxton Paramount 3200 IIE	C53F	1985	Ex Yorkshire Voyager, 1990
558	B84SWX	Leyland Tiger TRCTL11/3RH	Plaxton Paramount 3200 IIE	C53F	1985	Ex Yorkshire Voyager, 1990
559	B85SWX	Leyland Tiger TRCTL11/3RH	Plaxton Paramount 3200 IIE	C53F	1985	Ex Yorkshire Voyager, 1991
563	A124EPA	Leyland Tiger TRCTL11/2R	Plaxton Paramount 3200 E	C51F	1984	Ex Kentish Bus, 1990

565	H845AHS	Volvo B10M-60	Plaxton Paramount 3500 III	C53F	1991	Ex Express Travel, 1995
566	H566MPD	Volvo B10M-60	Plaxton Paramount 3500 III	C53F	1991	Ex Express Travel, 1995
567	H567MPD	Volvo B10M-60	Plaxton Paramount 3500 III	C53F	1991	Ex Express Travel, 1995
568	H372PHK	Volvo B10M-60	Plaxton Paramount 3500 III	C53F	1991	Ex Express Travel, 1995
569	F425UVW	Volvo B10M-60	Plaxton Paramount 3200 III	C53F	1989	Ex Express Travel, 1995
570	F467UVW	Volvo B10M-60	Plaxton Paramount 3200 III	C53F	1989	Ex Express Travel, 1995
571	F523UVW	Volvo B10M-60	Plaxton Paramount 3200 III	C53F	1989	Ex Express Travel, 1995
572	F572UPB	Volvo B10M-60	Plaxton Paramount 3200 III	C53F	1989	Ex Express Travel, 1995

LR705-709   Volvo Olympian YN2RV18Z4   Northern Counties Palatine II H47/32F*   1996   *708/9 are DPH43/30F

705	N705TPK	**706**	N706TPK	**707**	N707TPK	**708**	N708TPK	**709**	N709TPK

745	PJI3745	Leyland National 10351A/1R (DAF)		B41F	1978	Ex Blackpool, 1991

902-909   Leyland Olympian ONLXB/1RZ   Alexander RL   H47/32F   1988   Ex London & Country (GWS), 1996

902	F572SMG	**904**	F574SMG	**905**	F575SMG	**906**	F576SMG	**909**	F579SMG
903	F573SMG								

MBV953	R953VPU	Mercedes-Benz Vario O810	Plaxton Beaver 2	B27F	1998
MBV954	R954VPU	Mercedes-Benz Vario O810	Plaxton Beaver 2	B27F	1998

Previous registrations:

A110FDL	A701DDL, WDL748	H567MPD	H842AHS, NXI9001
F425UVW	F449PSL, NXI9004	PJI3745	GGE170T
F467UVW	F450PSL, NXI9005	Q475MEV	GHJ377L
F523UVW	F451PSL, NXI9006	Q476MEV	GHJ374L
F572UPB	F452PSL, NXI9007	Q552MEV	GHJ379L
H372PHK	H844AHS, NXI9003	Q553MEV	GHJ375L
H566MPD	H843AHS, NXI9002	Q554MEV	GHJ376L

Allocations and liveries

Livery: Arriva corporate cream and blue (buses); two-tone green white and yellow (Green Line)

Southend (London Road)

Mercedes-Benz	MM478	MM481	MM482	MBV953	MBV954			
Tiger	546	547	548	549	551	553	557	558
	559	563						
Volvo B10M	565	566	567	568	569	570	571	572
National	12	25	745					
Lance	LSL001	LSL002	LSL003	LSL004				
Dart	DSL56	DSL57	DSL58	DSL59	DSL60	DSL61	DSL62	
	DSL63	DSL64	DSL65	DSL66	DSL67			
Fleetline	212	221	222	223	224	225	226	227
	228	229	230	231	232	233	234	235
	236	237	238	239	240	241	242	250
	251	252	253	254				
Atlantean	110							
Olympian	256	257	258	259	260	262	263	264
	265	281	282	283	284	LR705	LR706	LR707
	LR708	LR709	902	903	904	905	906	909

The East Anglia Bus Handbook

ASSOCIATED COACHWAYS

Associated Coachways Ltd, Unit F5 The Seedbed Centre, Coldharbour Road, Harlow, Essex, CM19 5AC

Depot:- River Way, Harlow.

TJI7519	AEC Reliance 6U3ZR	Plaxton Panorama Elite	C53F	1971	Ex Timms, Sawbridgeworth, 1995
LPB217P	Leyland National 10351/1R		B41F	1978	Ex Bonner, Ongar, 1992
DCA31S	Leyland Leopard PSU3E/4R	Plaxton Supreme III Express	C53F	1978	Ex Hudson, Downley, 1992
PIW4789	Ford R1114	Plaxton Supreme III	C53F	1979	Ex Lambkin, Queensborough, 1996
BYW391V	Leyland National 10351A/2R		B36D	1979	Ex London United, 1991
KNP1X	Volvo B10M-61	Plaxton Paramount 3500 III	C53F	1988	Ex Goldenstand, North Acton, 1997
E933GPV	Freight-Rover Sherpa	Dormobile	B16F	1988	Ex Norfolk CC, 1996
E954ANO	Ford Transit VE6	Ford	M14	1988	Ex Essex CC, 1997
F213NST	Freight-Rover Sherpa	Aitken	B20F	1988	Ex Lumley, Speke, 1992
F752SPU	Sanos S315.21	FAP Charisma	C53F	1989	Ex Smith, St Leonards, 1996

Livery: Red, white and Maroon

Previous registration:-

KNP1X	E575UHS, OFA590, E930CDS, OFA990, E578CGA
PIW4789	DWK416T
TJI7519	TDK688J

Associated Coachways retain two examples of the Leyland National. The single-doored example is LPB217P, seen at Harlow bus station. The vehicle was new to London Country. Keith Grimes

AVRO & ELM PARK COACHES

B Roomes, 198 Abbots Drive, Stanford-le-Hope, Essex, SS17 7GW

SFF160M	Bedford YRQ	Duple Dominant	C45F	1974	Ex Thurrock Golden Twirlers, 1996
WGE37S	Bedford YMT	Plaxton Supreme III	C53F	1977	Ex Windmill Coaches, Copford, 1996
HAL241V	Bedford YMT	Duple Dominant II	C53F	1979	Ex Inland Travel, Flimwell, 1997
RSU883	Bedford YNT	Duple Dominant IV Express	C53F	1982	Ex Woollon, Feltham, 1995
USU677	Bedford YNT	Duple Dominant IV Express	C53F	1982	Ex Woollon, Feltham, 1994

Previous registrations:-

RSU883	PNT832X		USU677	FGD400X

Livery:- Beige and brown.

BJS TRAVEL

B J Snow, 32 Shoebury Road, Great Wakering, Essex SS3 0BW

Depot:- 61 High Street, Great Wakering.

BJS327Y	Leyland Tiger TRCTL11/3R	Plaxton Paramount 3200	C57F	1983	Ex Reliance, Gravesend, 1990
A197RUR	Mercedes-Benz L608D	Plaxton Mini Supreme	C25F	1984	Ex Felix, Long Melford, 1996
D215YHK	DAF SBR3000DKSB570	Berkhof Eclipse 400	CH57/16CT	1987	Ex APT, Rayleigh, 1995
E518PWR	Volkswagen LT55	Optare City Pacer	C25F	1987	Ex M & E, Shoeburyness, 1997
E457BOO	Toyota Hiace	Toyota	M11	1988	Ex private owner, 1993
BJS98Y	Volvo B10M-60	Plaxton Paramount 3500 III	C53F	1989	Ex Park's, Hamilton, 1992
F697PAY	Toyota Coaster HB31R	Caetano Optimo	C21F	1989	Ex Hanmer, Wrexham, 1991

Previous registrations:-

BJS98Y	F983HGE	BJS327Y	A72NKE	D215YHK	D401SHJ, A20APT

Livery:- Red and white

Representing the end of the long line of Duple's Dominant family is the mark IV variant which features high set, shallow windows and less chrome trim than on earlier models. Avro of Stanford-le-Hope own a pair of IV Express-bodied Bedford YNTs represented here by RSU883 seen as it leaves Basildon bus station.
Trevor Brookes

BARKERBUS

P J & S D Barker, Barleycroft, Hamlet Hill, Roydon, Essex, CM19 5JY

SJI9334	Bedford YNT	Plaxton Supreme V	C53F	1982	Ex Southern Star, Harlow, 1995
SIB3277	Bova EL26-581	Bova Europa	C53F	1983	Ex Pamray, Littleport, 1993
RJI4577	Mercedes-Benz L307D	Reeve Burgess	M12	1983	Ex Scott, Hertford, 1993
SJI9333	MCW CR126/9	MCW Metroliner	C51F	1984	Ex K & T, Stratford, 1995
SIB3276	Bedford Venturer YNV	Duple Laser	C57F	1985	Ex Wright, Brandon, 1991
RJI4576	Mercedes-Benz L608D	PMT Hanbridge	C21F	1985	Ex Croxford, Farnham, 1997
C791PEM	Neoplan N122/3	Neoplan Skyliner	CH61/16CT	1986	Ex Barfordian, Great Barford, 1997
OIB3517	Kässbohrer Setra S228DT	Kässbohrer Imperial	CH54/20CT	1986	Ex Parnham, Ludgershall, 1997
SJI9335	Volkswagen LT55	Optare City Pacer	B25F	1987	Ex Constable, Long Melford, 1993
D683YTN	MCW DR130/33	MCW Metroliner	CH53/16CT	1987	Ex Northumbria, 1994
E705GNH	Fiat 79.14	Caetano Beja	C24F	1987	Ex Mullover, Bedford, 1996
L345MKU	Plaxton 425	Lorraine	C51FT	1994	Ex Bywaters, Rochdale, 1997
L347MKU	Plaxton 425	Lorraine	C51FT	1994	Ex Eurocars, Harpurhey, 1997

Previous registrations:-

D683YTN	D193ESC, WLT859	SIB3277	PWP667Y
OIB3517	C358KGG	SJI9333	B459WHJ
RJI4576	B333SDD	SJI9334	FVX825Y
RJI4577	A70NPP	SJI9335	D371JUM
SIB3276	B224DJU		

Barkerbus operate several unusual vehicles including MCW Metroliners with both double and single deck models represented in the fleet. This picture shows the latter style of the integral coach, a former Eastern National example which has passed through several operators since new. As with many coaches it now carries an index mark initially issued in Northern Ireland, in this case SJI 9333.
Colin Lloyd

BEESTONS / MULLEYS / CONSTABLE

Beeston's (Hadleigh) Ltd, 21 Long Bessels, Hadleigh Suffolk, IP7 5DB
Constable Coaches Ltd, Station Yard, Long Melford, Sudbury, Suffolk, CO10 9LQ
Combs Coaches Ltd, Mulleys Motorways Ltd, Stow Road, Ixworth,
Bury St.Edmunds, Suffolk, IP31 2HZ

Bu	ATV11B	Bedford SB5	Plaxton Embassy III	C41F	1964	Ex Mulley, Ixworth, 1981
M	NCF888	Bedford C5Z1	Duple	C29F	1959	Ex Mulley, Ixworth, 1983
M	RGV111	AEC Reliance 2MU3RV	Harrington Cavalier	C37F	1961	
B	CRO689L	Leyland Leopard PSU3B/4R	Plaxton Panorama Elite III	C51F	1973	Ex Capitol, Cwmbran, 1995
B	WUL261N	Leyland Leopard PSU4B/4R	Plaxton Panorama Elite III	C37F	1974	Ex British Airways, Manchester, 1995
C	MIL4681	Leyland National 1151/1R/0402 (Volvo)		B52F	1974	Ex Classic, Annfield Plain, 1996
M	LDV398P	Volvo B58-61	Duple Dominant	C57F	1975	Ex Wangford, Thurton, 1992
M	JJT436N	Bristol VRT/SL2/6LX	Eastern Coach Works	H43/31F	1975	Ex Wilts & Dorset, 1995
C	JJT445N	Bristol VRT/SL2/6LX	Eastern Coach Works	H43/31F	1975	Ex Wilts & Dorset, 1995
B	SJI4429	Bristol VRT/SL2/6LX	Eastern Coach Works	H43/31F	1975	Ex Wilts & Dorset, 1994
B	SJI4430	Bristol VRT/SL3/6LX	Eastern Coach Works	H43/31F	1976	Ex Wilts & Dorset, 1994
B	SJI4431	Bristol VRT/SL3/6LX	Eastern Coach Works	H43/31F	1976	Ex Wilts & Dorset, 1994
B	TPU67R	Leyland Atlantean AN68A/1R	Eastern Coach Works	H43/31F	1977	Ex Colchester, 1998
M	UWA93S	Leyland Leopard PSU5C/4R	Duple Dominant I	C53F	1978	Ex Puttick, Letchworth, 1995
M	PJI5526	Bristol VRT/SL3/501	Eastern Coach Works	H43/31F	1978	Ex Clarkson, S. Elmsall, 1994
C	WWY126S	Bristol VRT/SL3/6LXB	Eastern Coach Works	H43/31F	1978	Ex Sovereign, 1994
C	MIL4682	Leyland National 11351A/1R (Volvo)		B49F	1978	Ex Eastern National, 1996
B	LHG440T	Bristol VRT/SL3/501	Eastern Coach Works	H43/31F	1978	Ex Southend, 1996
B	DWY146T	Bristol VRT/SL3/6LXB	Eastern Coach Works	H43/31F	1979	Ex Stephenson, Rochford, 1997
M	EWR166T	Bristol VRT/SL3/6LXB	Eastern Coach Works	H43/31F	1979	Ex Millman, Buckfastleigh, 1991
M	FRP907T	Bristol VRT/SL3/6LXB	Eastern Coach Works	H43/31F	1979	Ex Rover Coaches, Horsley, 1994
C	SJI4425	AEC Reliance 6U2R	Duple Dominant II Express	C53F	1979	Ex Wilts & Dorset, 1994
C	SJI4424	AEC Reliance 6U2R	Duple Dominant II Express	C53F	1979	Ex Wilts & Dorset, 1994
C	271AKV	Volvo B58-61	Plaxton Supreme IV	C57F	1979	Ex Colchester Coaches, 1997
M	FIL4344	Bedford YMT	Plaxton Supreme III Express	C53F	1979	
M	FIL4743	Bedford YMT	Plaxton Supreme III Express	C53F	1979	
C	AEG984A	Leyland Leopard PSU3E/4R	Plaxton Supreme III	C49F	1979	Ex Hunter, Moortown, 1997
M	HGA637T	Leyland Leopard PSU3/4R	Plaxton Supreme IV	C53F	1979	Ex New Viscount, Holloway, 1988
B	LUA283V	Leyland Leopard PSU5C/4R	Plaxton Supreme IV	C57F	1980	Ex Ipswich Travel, 1989
C	RFS585V	Leyland National 2 NL116L11/1R (6G)		B52F	1980	Ex Westbus, Ashford, 1993
C	RFS586V	Leyland National 2 NL116L11/1R (6G)		B52F	1980	Ex Westbus, Ashford, 1993
C	RFS588V	Leyland National 2 NL116L11/1R (6G)		B52F	1980	Ex Westbus, Ashford, 1993
C	BVP821V	Leyland National 2 NL116L11/1R		B52F	1980	Ex Colchester, 1998
M	FIL4345	Bedford YMT	Duple Dominant IV Express	C53F	1981	
B	219GRA	Leyland Leopard PSU3F/4R	Duple Dominant IV	C53F	1981	Ex BFN, Gt.Blakenham, 1997
B	MIL4421	Leyland Leopard PSU3G/4R	Duple Dominant IV	C47F	1981	Ex Clayton, Bungay, 1996
M	RUT684W	Volvo B58-61	Duple Dominant IV	C53F	1981	Ex Crawley Luxury, 1993
M	TND134X	Volvo B58-61	Duple Dominant IV	C53F	1982	Ex Thorpe, N. Kensington, 1993
M	FIL4169	Leyland Leopard PSU5D/5R	Duple Dominant III	C57F	1982	Ex New Viscount, Holloway, 1989
M	FIL4741	Leyland Leopard PSU5D/5R	Duple Dominant III	C57F	1982	Ex New Viscount, Holloway, 1989
B	WGV861X	Leyland Leopard PSU5D/5R	Duple Dominant III	C57F	1982	
B	VKN836X	Leyland Leopard PSU3G/4R	Willowbrook	DP57F	1982	Ex
B	TXI8762	Volvo B58-61	Plaxton Supreme IV	C57F	1982	Ex Petlen, Stevenage, 1994
B	FHJ565	Volvo B10M-61	Van Hool Alizée	C57F	1983	Ex Barratt's, Nantwich, 1992
B	FIL8613	Volvo B10M-61	Van Hool Astral	CH47/11FT	1983	Ex Ellard, Princes Gate, 1989
B	MIL4420	Leyland Tiger TRCTL11/3R	Duple Caribbean	C49F	1983	Ex Beardon, Colchester, 1996
B	FIL4164	Leyland Tiger TRCTL11/3R	Van Hool Alizée	C57F	1984	Ex Travellers, Hounslow, 1988
C	FIL4165	Leyland Tiger TRCTL11/3R	Van Hool Alizée	C57F	1984	Ex Davie's, Rye, 1988
B	FIL4166	Leyland Tiger TRCTL11/3R	Van Hool Alizée	C57F	1984	Ex Travellers, Hounslow, 1988
M	A784YGL	Leyland Tiger TRCTL11/3R	Van Hool Alizée H	C57F	1984	Ex Ford, Gunnislake, 1996
B	530VPJ	Kässbohrer Setra S228DT	Kässbohrer Imperial	CH55/20CT	1984	Ex Nestor, Turloughmore, 1997
M	WSV555	Volvo B10M-61	Van Hool Astral	CH49/11FT	1984	Ex Berryhurst, Lambeth, 1986
C	B948ASU	Volvo B10M-56	Van Hool Alizée L	B51F	1984	Ex Black Prince, Morley, 1996

Opposite:- **Van Hool bus-bodied vehicles are still a rarity in England. However, the Beestons group operate three of the type each wearing the blue and white livery. B948ASU is the only one based on a Volvo B10M chassis and was one of a pair new in 1984 to Hutchison of Overtown. The eye-catching livery of orange, yellow and white, afforded to the majority of the Mulleys fleet, suits this Jonckheere Jubilee P50-bodied Scania K112 well. FIL4034 is seen at Hampton Court.** *Colin Lloyd/Glyn Matthews*

The East Anglia Bus Handbook

Several high quality Kässbohrer Setra integral coaches are operated by Beestons. Seen at Tower Hill, outside the famous Tower of London, is 226LRB, an S215HR Rational model new in 1989. The diversity of liveries is interesting, this vehicle carrying a cream base with brown and caramel relief. As well as operating a bus and coach company, Beestons of Hadleigh are also a dealer in used passenger vehicles. *Colin Lloyd*

M	B711EOF	Volvo B10M-53	Jonckheere Jubilee P95	CH54/13DT	1985	Ex Flights, Birmingham, 1990
M	FIL4034	Scania K112CRS	Jonckheere Jubilee P50	C57F	1985	Ex Henry Crawford, Neilston, 1988
M	B387UEX	Leyland Tiger TRCTL11/3R	Plaxton Paramount 3200	C57F	1985	Ex Rosemary, Terrington St.Clement, 1992
M	B42ECV	Leyland Tiger TRCTL11/3RZ	Van Hool Alizée H	C57F	1985	Ex Ford, Gunnislake, 1995
B	RJI7972	Kässbohrer Setra S215HD	Kässbohrer Tornado	C48FT	1985	Ex Landtourers, Farnham, 1995
B	RJI7973	Kässbohrer Setra S215HD	Kässbohrer Tornado	C49FT	1985	Ex Landtourers, Farnham, 1995
C	SJI4426	Scania K92CRB	Jonckheere TransCity	B47D	1986	Ex Your Bus, Alcester, 1994
B	FIL8614	Leyland Tiger TRCTL11/3RZ	Van Hool Alizée H	C57F	1987	Ex Travellers, Hounslow, 1989
B	FIL8615	Leyland Tiger TRCTL11/3ARZ	Van Hool Alizée H	C57F	1987	Ex Travellers, Hounslow, 1989
B	SJI8098	Leyland Tiger TRCTL11/3RZ	Van Hool Alizée H	C57F	1987	Ex Travellers, Hounslow, 1989
C	E212FLD	Scania N112DRB	Van Hool Alizée L	C49F	1987	Ex Holmeswood, Rufford, 1997
C	SJI4427	Scania N112DRB	Van Hool Alizée L	DP44F	1988	Ex Terminus, Crawley, 1994
B	SJI9321	Volvo B10M-61	Van Hool Alizée H	C49FT	1988	Ex Shearings, 1993
B	SJI9320	Volvo B10M-61	Van Hool Alizée H	C49FT	1988	Ex Shearings, 1993
B	SJI9319	Volvo B10M-61	Van Hool Alizée H	C51FT	1988	Ex Shearings, 1993
B	PJI4712	Toyota Coaster HB31R	Caetano Optimo	C18F	1988	Ex SSS, Euston, 1992
B	E221LER	Mercedes-Benz L207D	Felix	M8L	1988	Ex Felix, Long Melford, 1996
M	E874DTT	Kässbohrer Setra S215HRI	Kässbohrer Rational	C49FT	1988	Ex APT, Rayleigh, 1996
M	F310EVG	Volvo B10M-61	Van Hool Alizée H	C51FT	1988	Ex Simonds, Botesdale, 1997
M	KJI6029	Scania K112CRB	Van Hool Alizée H	C51FT	1988	Ex One plus two, Swaffham, 1995
M	F880TNH	Toyota Coaster HB31R	Caetano Optimo	C20F	1988	Ex The Kings Ferry, 1991
B	MIL3728	Mercedes-Benz 811D	Reeve Burgess Beaver	C33F	1989	Ex Neal's Travel, Isleham, 1996
B	222GRA	Kässbohrer Setra S215HDI	Kässbohrer Tornado	C49FT	1989	Ex Highliner Travel, Felixstowe, 1993
B	226LRB	Kässbohrer Setra S215HR	Kässbohrer Rational	C49FT	1989	Ex Eve's Coaches, Dunbar, 1994
M	F477OFJ	Kässbohrer Setra S215HRI	Kässbohrer Rational	C49FT	1989	Ex Tally Ho!, Kingsbridge, 1996
M	F476OFJ	Kässbohrer Setra S215HRI	Kässbohrer Rational	C49FT	1989	Ex Tally Ho!, Kingsbridge, 1996
M	TIB8573	Scania K113CRB	Jonckheere Deauville P599	C51FT	1989	Ex Scan Coaches, North Acton, 1998
M	TIB8574	Scania K113CRB	Jonckheere Deauville P599	C51FT	1989	Ex Scan Coaches, North Acton, 1998
M	F94CBD	Volvo B10M-60	Jonckheere Deauville P599	C50FT	1989	Ex Hill's, Tredegar, 1992
M	F995UME	Volvo B10M-60	Duple 340	C53F	1989	Ex Westbus, Hounslow, 1997
M	F996UME	Volvo B10M-60	Duple 340	C53F	1989	Ex Westbus, Hounslow, 1997
M	G468JNH	Volvo B10M-60	Jonckheere Deauville P599	C50FT	1989	Ex West Kingdown Coaches, 1992
M	G973LRP	Volvo B10M-60	Jonckheere Deauville P599	C51FT	1990	Ex Hilo, Sandy, 1993
B	524FN	Neoplan N122/3	Neoplan Skyliner	CH57/20CT	1991	Ex Trathens, Plymouth, 1996
B	PJI6391	Mercedes-Benz 811D	Reeve Burgess Beaver	C33F	1991	Ex Javelin, Wandsworth, 1997

The East Anglia Bus Handbook

J765ONK is one of the three Reeve Burgess Beavers mounted on the Mercedes-Benz 811D chassis currently operated, and was seen at Colchester bus station during February 1998. *Glyn Matthews*

M	J762ONK	Mercedes-Benz 811D	Reeve Burgess Beaver	C33F	1991	Ex Javelin, Wandsworth, 1996
C	M759PVM	Mercedes-Benz 811D	Mellor	B31F	1995	
M	P888MUL	Iveco Euro Rider 391.12.35	Beulas Stergo E35	C49FT	1997	

Previous registrations:-

219GRA	TKJ769X	FIL4741	WGV864X	SJI4424	YPL89T
222GRA	F668DDO	FIL4743	HDX666V	SJI4425	YPL86T
226LRB	G182VBB	FIL8613	A297RSU	SJI4426	C354SVV
271AKV	GGD667T	FIL8614	D229HMT	SJI4427	E303FWV
524FN	H699DOD, PJI6391	FIL8615	D283HMT	SJI4429	JJT443N
530VPJ	A698GEF, 530VPJ,	KJI6029	F380CHE	SJI4430	MEL558P
	84-G-186	MIL3728	G806HRN	SJI4431	MEL562P
A784YGL	A142RMJ, WUF955	MIL4420	ODM534Y, MIB513,	SJI8098	D284HMT, FIL8617
AEG984A	GWU560T		EGV673Y	SJI9319	E621UNE, WSV528,
B42ECV	B311UNB, 353TPF	MIL4421	XHK214X, 502GMB,		E489CDB, PJI6391
E874DTT	E29SBO, YSU923		BUA935X	SJI9320	E620UNE, SPR124,
F310EVG	F711SFS, LIB226	MIL4681	NFN70M		E683CDB, PJI6392,
F476OFJ	F55YBO, 312KTT	MIL4682	YEV313S		RJI7972
F477OFJ	F54YBO, WUO505	NCF888	From new	SJI9321	E619UNE, XTW359,
FHJ565	ODS464Y	PJI4712	E174KNH		E684CDB, PJI6393,
FIL4034	B510GBD	PJI5526	URF671S		RJI7973
FIL4164	A143RMJ	PJI6391	J765ONK	TIB8573	F943RNV
FIL4165	A144RMJ	RGV111	From new	TIB8574	F944RNV
FIL4166	A145RMJ	RJI7972	876OEL, B486OPJ,	TXI8762	XWK9X
FIL4169	WGV862X		876OEL	WGV861X	WGV861X, 219GRA
FIL4344	HRO444V	RJI7973	D599BPA, LSU256		
FIL4345	RRT111W	RUT684W	ODJ576W, VOI6874		

Named Vehicles:- PPG7R *1914 Mons 1918*; MIL4681 *Hurricane*.

Livery:- Cream, caramel and brown (Beeston); white and three tone blue (Constable); orange gold and silver (Mulleys coaches); orange (Mulleys buses and contract fleet).

BELLE COACHES

B R Shreeve & Sons Ltd, Belle Coachworks, Horn Hill, Lowestoft, Suffolk, NR33 0AH

Depots:- Nine Acres, Aldringham; Ravenmere, Beccles; Horn Hill, Lowestoft and Horseshoe Corner, Uggeshall.

PPG3R	Bedford YMT	Plaxton Supreme III	C53F	1977	Ex Towler, Brandon, 1982
EGV719T	Bedford YMT	Plaxton Supreme III	C53F	1979	Ex Classic, Lowestoft, 1989
YYL783T	Bedford YMT	Duple Dominant II	C53F	1979	Ex Grey-Green, 1983
YYL786T	Bedford YMT	Duple Dominant II	C53F	1979	Ex Grey-Green, 1983
YYL776T	Bedford YMT	Duple Dominant II	C53F	1979	Ex Grey-Green, 1983
YYL778T	Bedford YMT	Duple Dominant II	C53F	1979	Ex Grey-Green, 1984
YYL795T	Bedford YLQ	Duple Dominant II	C41F	1979	Ex Grey-Green, 1985
JFA450V	Bedford YMT	Plaxton Supreme IV	C53F	1979	Ex Cross Gates Coaches, 1987
CDO999V	Bedford YMT	Duple Dominant II	C53F	1980	Ex Wing, Sleaford, 1983
MDX668V	Bedford YMT	Duple Dominant IV	C53F	1980	Ex Classic, Lowestoft, 1989
NPV308W	Bedford YMT	Duple Dominant IV	C53F	1980	Ex Claremont, Worcester Park, 1987
NPV309W	Bedford YMT	Duple Dominant IV	C53F	1980	Ex Claremont, Worcester Park, 1987
PRT700W	Bedford YMT	Duple Dominant IV	C53F	1981	Ex Constable, Felixstowe, 1981
NJI9241	Bedford YNT	Plaxton Supreme VI Express	C53F	1982	Ex Taylor, York, 1986
OJI4627	Bedford YNT	Duple Dominant IV	C53F	1982	Ex Back, Witney, 1985
NJI9242	Bedford YNT	Plaxton Paramount 3200	C53F	1983	Ex Farnham Coaches, 1986
NJI9243	Bedford YNT	Plaxton Paramount 3200	C53F	1983	Ex Farnham Coaches, 1986
NJI9244	Bedford YMT	Plaxton Supreme IV	C53F	1983	Ex Classic, Lowestoft, 1992
OJI4754	DAF SB2300DHS585	Plaxton Paramount 3200	C53F	1985	Ex Holt, Swinefleet, 1994
NJI9245	Bedford YNT	Plaxton Paramount 3200	C53F	1985	Ex Classic, Lowestoft, 1992
OJI4756	Scania K112CRS	Berkhof Esprite 350	C45FT	1986	Ex Scania demonstrator, 1988
LIL9713	LAG G355Z	LAG Panoramic	C49FT	1986	Ex Crusader, Clacton, 1991
LIL9456	LAG G355Z	LAG Panoramic	C49FT	1986	Ex Crusader, Clacton, 1991

Although around half of the Belle Coaches fleet is still based on Bedford chassis, many of them are confined to local contracts running near to their operating bases. However, a pair of very late model Venturer examples with Duple 320 bodywork still manage longer forays typified by LIL9457 pictured here at Hyde Park Corner, London. *Colin Lloyd*

Six second-hand LAG Panoramics were acquired by Belle Coaches in the early nineteen-nineties and all have since received private index marks in the LIL sequence. One of the older examples is LIL9713 seen on a very sunny day in Lincoln. *Tony Wilson*

OJI4758	DAF SB2300DHS585	Plaxton Paramount 3500 II	C49FT	1987	Ex Farnham Coaches, 1988
LIL9717	DAF SB2300DHS585	Plaxton Paramount 3500 III	C53F	1987	Ex Classic, Lowestoft, 1992
E597WAH	Bedford Venturer YNV	Duple 320	C57F	1987	Ex Classic, Lowestoft, 1992
LIL9457	Bedford Venturer YNV	Duple 320	C57F	1987	
LIL9454	LAG G355Z	LAG Panoramic	C48FT	1987	Ex Jalna Coaches, Church Gresley, 1991
LIL9455	LAG G355Z	LAG Panoramic	C49FT	1988	Ex Silver Coach Lines, Edinburgh, 1992
LIL9716	DAF SB3000DKV601	Van Hool Alizée	C51FT	1988	Ex Wharfedale Coaches, Yeadon, 1993
LIL9453	Volvo B10M-60	Plaxton Paramount 3200 III	C57F	1989	Ex Capital, West Drayton, 1997
LIL9452	Scania K113CRB	Van Hool Alizée H	C51F	1989	Ex Barnard, Kirton-in-Lindsey, 1993
LIL9714	LAG G355Z	LAG Panoramic	C49FT	1989	Ex Coach Stop, Leigh-on-Sea, 1994
DAZ4303	Volvo B10M-60	Plaxton Paramount 3200 III	C53F	1989	Ex Kime, Folkingham, 1996
DAZ4304	Volvo B10M-60	Plaxton Paramount 3200 III	C53F	1989	Ex Kime, Folkingham, 1996
LIL9458	Dennis Javelin 12SDA1907	Caetano Algarve	C53F	1989	Ex Lloyd, Nuneaton, 1994
LIL9715	LAG G355Z	LAG Panoramic	C49FT	1990	Ex Coach Stop, Leigh-on-Sea, 1994
LIL9718	DAF SB2305DHTD585	Duple 340	C57DL	1990	
J20GSM	MAN 11.180HOCL	Berkhof Excell. 1000 Midi	C35F	1991	Ex Mayne, Buckie, 1993
K101VJU	Toyota Coaster HDB30R	Caetano Optimo II	C21F	1993	
M312VET	Scania K113CRB	Van Hool Alizée HE	C49FT	1995	Ex Silver Knight, Malmesbury, 1997

Previous registrations:-

DAZ4303	F881OTL	LIL9716	F218RJX
DAZ4304	F45TMU	LIL9717	D613YCX
E597WAH	E83DRY, LIL9453	LIL9718	G224HCP
LIL9452	F466TJV	NJI9241	TPM615X
LIL9453	F884SMU	NJI9242	BPJ673Y
LIL9454	E134KRP	NJI9243	BPJ674Y
LIL9455	E674NNV	NJI9244	FUR895Y
LIL9456	D22XPF	NJI9245	B44LUT
LIL9457	E84DRY	OJI4627	WRY77X
LIL9458	G839VAY	OJI4754	B233RRU
LIL9713	D21XPF	OJI4756	C112JTM
LIL9714	F24WNH	OJI4758	D992DPE, 543FCG
LIL9715	G488KBD		

Livery:- Two tone blue and cream.

BIRD'S COACH TRAVEL

Birds Coach Travel (Hunstanton) Ltd, Valentine Road, Hunstanton, Norfolk, PE36 5EU

NTU183L	Ford R1114	Plaxton Panorama Elite III	C53F	1973	Ex Everest, Swanley, 1978
XMA194M	Ford R1114	Plaxton Panorama Elite III	C53F	1974	Ex Galloway, Mendlesham, 1994
SAH379R	Ford R1114	Plaxton Supreme III	C53F	1977	
XUY402R	Ford R1014	Plaxton Supreme III	C45F	1977	Ex Paul James Coaches, Ratcliffe-on-the-Wreake
JDB932V	Ford R1114	Plaxton Supreme IV	C53F	1980	Ex Jacksons, Altrincham, 1984
JDB948V	Ford R1114	Plaxton Supreme IV	C53F	1980	Ex Salopia, Whitchurch, 1984
HMB672X	Ford R1114	Plaxton Supreme IV	C53F	1981	Ex Taylor, Dinnington, 1992
HSB906Y	DAF MB200DKFL600	Van Hool Alizée	C55F	1983	Ex Gilchrist, East Kilbride, 1996
A20BCT	Van Hool T815	Van Hool Alicron	C53F	1990	

Previous registrations:-

A20BCT	G516LPW	HSB906Y	OGE8Y, HIL6570, HSB549Y, GIL3573, GIL7364
HMB672X	CCA894X, OLG7		

Livery:- White, black, orange and red.

BISS BROTHERS / AIRPORT COACH COMPANY

Airport Coaches Ltd, Building 44 First Avenue, Stansted Airport, Essex, CM24 1RY
Biss Brothers, Building 44 First Avenue, Stansted Airport, Essex, CM24 1RY

A	XEH254M	Leyland National 1051/1R/0402		B41F	1973	Ex Citibus, Middleton, 1994
B	DSU733	Leyland Leopard PSU5A/4R	Duple 320 (1988)	C57F	1976	Ex West Midlands, 1996
B	KBH860V	Leyland Leopard PSU5C/4R	Plaxton Supreme IV	C57F	1980	
B	125LUP	Mercedes-Benz 0303/15R	Jonckheere Jubilee P50	C51FT	1984	
A	BAZ7349	Leyland Tiger TRCTL11/3RH	Berkhof Everest 370	C49FT	1986	Ex Speedlink, 1993
B	E290OMG	Mercedes-Benz 709D	Reeve Burgess Beaver	DP25F	1988	Ex West Midlands, 1997
A	E940CJN	Mercedes-Benz 609D	Reeve Burgess	DP18F	1988	
A	G441PWW	Bova FHD12.290	Bova Futura	C51F	1990	Ex Belle View, Wakefield, 1997
B	G643YVS	Mercedes-Benz 814D	Reeve Burgess Beaver	DP29F	1990	
B	PUU970	Van Hool T815	Van Hool Acron	C49FT	1990	
A	H370GRY	Toyota Coaster HDB30R	CaetanoOptimo II	C18F	1991	Ex County, 1997
B	J7BBC	Bova FHM12.290	Bova Futura	C49FT	1992	
B	J8BBC	Bova FHM12.290	Bova Futura	C49FT	1992	
A	L343RWF	Bova FHD12.340	Bova Futura	C49FT	1994	
A	M131SKY	Toyota Coaster HZB50R	Caetano Optimo III	C21F	1994	
B	M121SKY	Toyota Coaster HZB50R	Caetano Optimo III	C18F	1994	
B	M384WET	Bova FHD12.340	Bova Futura	C49FT	1995	
B	M61WER	Iveco TurboDaily 59.12	Marshall C31	DP27F	1995	
B	N210FWA	Bova FHD12.340	Bova Futura	C49FT	1996	
B	P437OVW	Mercedes-Benz	Crystals	C15F	1997	
B	P438OVW	Mercedes-Benz	Crystals	C15F	1997	
A	P750HTW	Fiat Ducato	Atlas	M14	1996	
A	P751HTW	Fiat Ducato	Atlas	M14	1996	
B	R252KWY	Bova FHD12.340	Bova Futura	C49FT	1998	

Previous registrations:-

125LUP	A113SNH	DSU733	PNK160R, DSU470	PUU970	G601VML
BAZ7349	C140SPB	G441PWW	G425WFP, IIL5133		

Livery:- Red, yellow, white and gold (Airport Coaches); blue, white and orange (Biss Brothers)

The East Anglia Bus Handbook

A recent arrival with Birds Coach Travel is a Van Hool T815 Alicron integral coach with Select index mark A20BCT. It is featured at a sunny Hampton Court Palace while attending the annual flower show in July 1997.   *Geoff Rixon*

For a period, Biss Brothers formed part of County Bus & coach. When regaining independence the Airport Coaches operation also linked with Biss Brothers. Stansted airport is the location for this picture of BAZ7349, a Mercedes-Benz 709 in the red-based livery of Airport Coach Company. *Glyn Matthews*

BLUE DIAMOND COACHES

J Robilliard, 76 Morningstons, Harlow, Essex, CM19 4QJ

Depots:- 76 Morningtons, Harlow and Horseshoe Farm, Latton Bush, Harlow.

BAJ998T	Leyland Leopard PSU3E/4R	Plaxton Supreme IV Express	DP55F	1979	Ex Southern Star, Harlow, 1996
JMJ144V	Ford Transit 190	Dormobile	B16F	1979	Ex Cunningham, Corringham, 1997
OEH930W	Leyland Leopard PSU5C/4R	Duple Dominant IV	C57F	1980	Ex Bernards Coaches, Ongar, 1997
C141LOO	Bedford YNT	Plaxton Paramount 3200 II	C53F	1986	Ex Red Car Coach Hire, Abridge, 1990
D531NDA	Freight-Rover Sherpa	Carlyle	B19F	1986	Ex Ruffle, Castle Hedingham, 1997
D532NDA	Freight-Rover Sherpa	Carlyle	B19F	1986	Ex Ruffle, Castle Hedingham, 1997

Livery:- Navy blue, white and red.

BOON'S

M D Boon, 29 Church Road, Boreham, Chelmsford, Essex, CM3 3BN

JSC883E	Leyland Atlantean PDR1/1	Alexander A	H43/31F	1967	Ex Lothian, 1980
SPW92N	Leyland Atlantean AN68/2R	Roe	H45/33F	1974	Ex Pegg, Caston, 1980
NNO66P	Leyland Atlantean AN68A/1R	Eastern Coach Works	H43/31F	1976	Ex Colchester, 1991
NNO63P	Leyland Atlantean AN68A/1R	Eastern Coach Works	H43/31F	1976	Ex Colchester, 1991
MVK538R	Leyland Atlantean AN68A/2R	Alexander AL	H48/34F	1976	Ex Colchester, 1990
TSU611	Kässbohrer Setra S215HD	Kässbohrer Tornado	C49FT	1990	Ex Tours Exclusive, West Kensington, 1991
H435GVL	Kässbohrer Setra S215HR	Kässbohrer Rational	C49FT	1991	Ex Travellers, Hounslow, 1996
KSU369	Kässbohrer Setra S215HD	Kässbohrer Tornado	C48FT	1993	
SSU331	Kässbohrer Setra S215HD	Kässbohrer Tornado	C36FT	1993	Ex Kässbohrer demonstrator, 1994
K129OCT	Kässbohrer Setra S215HD	Kässbohrer Tornado	C48FT	1993	
K11BOO	Scania K113TRB	Van Hool Alizée SHE	C48FT	1993	
WSU225	Kässbohrer Setra S250	Kässbohrer Jupiter	C48FT	1995	
M313VET	Scania K113CRB	Berkhof Excellence 1000 L	C53F	1995	
N820DKU	Scania K113TRB	Irizar Century 12.37	C51FT	1996	
N5HGB	Kässbohrer Setra S250	Kässbohrer Jupiter	C48FT	1996	

On order: One Setra S250

Named Vehicles:- K11BOO *Royale Class*; N5HGB *Hecmobile.*

Previous registrations:-

K129OCT	J75VTG		TSU611	From new
N5HGB	N653OFW		SSU331	K124OCT, H435GVL
KSU369	From new		WSU225	M858YVW

Livery:- Cream, maroon and red, some coaches carry individual liveries.

Opposite:- **Boon's of Boreham, near Chelmsford, employ a standard livery of cream, maroon and red. However, many of the exceptionally high specification coaches have received individual and attractive liveries using a variety of other colours. As shown here, tri-axle Scania K113, with index mark K11BOO, features a yellow, red and orange scheme on its Van Hool Alizée body while Kässbohrer Setra N5HGB, which was featured at the 1995 Bus and Coach show took advantage of a design developed by Setra at Ulm, in Germany for their 'Jupiter' range of coaches. The fleet contains several of the S215 model, though not all of this model carry the Spanish-built Rational body.** *Paul Stockwell\Colin Lloyd*

BRANDONS

B M Brandon, School Green, Blackmoor End, Braintree, Essex, CM7 4DT

Reg	Chassis	Body	Layout	Year	History
MLK677L	Daimler Fleetline CRL6	Park Royal	H45/33F	1973	Ex Wiffen, Finchingfield, 1987
THM707M	Daimler Fleetline CRL6	MCW	H44/32F	1974	Ex Cedric, Wivenhoe, 1984
GHV3N	Daimler Fleetline CRL6	Park Royal	H45/32F	1974	Ex London Transport, 1985
GHV13N	Daimler Fleetline CRL6	Park Royal	H45/32F	1974	Ex London Transport, 1985
GHV23N	Daimler Fleetline CRL6	Park Royal	H44/32F	1974	Ex London Transport, 1985
GHV97N	Daimler Fleetline CRL6	Park Royal	H45/32F	1975	Ex London Transport, 1985
KUC217P	Daimler Fleetline CRL6	Park Royal	H44/32F	1976	Ex Florida Taxis, Halstead, 1983
OEG289P	Bristol LHS6L	Plaxton Supreme III	C33F	1976	Ex Steed, Haverhill, 1994
WOI2658	Volvo B58-61	Plaxton Supreme IV	C57F	1980	Ex Leon, Stafford, 1994
PNH183	Volvo B10M-61	Plaxton Viewmaster IV	C53F	1981	Ex Ford, Gunnislake, 1987
LXR958	Van Hool TD824	Van Hool Astromega	CH53/22DT	1983	Ex Hilo, Sandy, 1991
HIL2922	Bova FHD 12.280	Bova Futura	C49FT	1984	Ex Coachcraft, Armthorpe, 1987
HIL2921	Bova FHD 12.280	Bova Futura	C49FT	1984	Ex Harris, West Thurrock, 1990
HIL2325	Bova FHD 12.280	Bova Futura	C49FT	1985	Ex Goodwin, Stockport, 1991
C638KDS	Fiat 79.14	Caetano Beja	C22F	1985	Ex Dines, Boreham, 1995
625DAO	Bova FHD 12.280	Bova Futura	C49FT	1986	Ex O'Toole, Southwark, 1992
D855OJA	Freight-Rover Sherpa	Made-to-Measure	M16	1987	
841BMB	Kässbohrer Setra S228DT	Kässbohrer Imperial	CH54/20CT	1987	Ex APT, Rayleigh, 1993
E364KKV	Peugeot-Talbot Freeway	Talbot	B16FL	1988	Ex H B Coaches, Wood Green, 1996
BMB20M	Bova FHD 12.290	Bova Futura	C49FT	1989	Ex Lyles R & N, Batley, 1992

Previous registrations:-

625DAO	From new	HIL2922	A251SBM
841BMB	D868FSX, APT42S, D782YEV	LXR958	MSU586Y
BMB20M	F573WHD	OEG289P	RGF230P, 896RHA
HIL2325	B555KRY, 2TRB, B640RJF	PNH183	CNS550X, 904DRH, YAD505X
HIL2921	A86RWC, 6330FH	WOI2658	RHP24W

Livery:- Yellow, white and red.

Brandons' HIL2921 is one of five Bova Futura FHD coaches currently in stock and shows-off the attractive yellow, white and red colour scheme at Pleasurewood Hills amusement park near Lowestoft. *Trevor Brookes*

BUCKLAND OMNIBUS COMPANY

A J Buckland, Wayside Cottage, The Street, Bredfield, Woodbridge, Suffolk, IP13 6AX

Depot:- Old School Yard, Cavendish Street, Ipswich

TE7870	Dennis E	Brush	B29D	1929	Ex Buckland, Hanley, 1989
GRP260D	Bristol MW6G	Eastern Coach Works	C39F	1966	Ex preservation, 1989
BBM34A	Ford R1114	Plaxton Panorama Elite III	C53F	1974	Ex Whincop, Peasenhall, 1998
LPV111P	Ford R1014	Plaxton Panorama Elite III	C45F	1975	Ex Soames, Otley, 1996
YBM930S	Ford R1114	Duple Dominant II	C53F	1978	Ex Richies, Stradbroke, 1997
ODX102W	Ford R1114	Plaxton Supreme IV	C53F	1980	Ex Soames, Otley, 1996

Named Vehicles:- GRP260D *Florence*; LPV111P *Dougal*; TE7870 *Ermintrude.*

Livery:- Red and cream

BURE VALLEY COACHES

R A Woodcock, Aylsham Road, Buxton, Norwich, Norfolk, NR10 5EZ

OAY153P	Bedford YMT	Plaxton Supreme III	C53F	1976	Ex Hazeldine, Bilston, 1980
UDW142S	Bedford YMT	Plaxton Supreme III	C49F	1978	Ex Torquay Travel, 1988
503EUC	Bedford YMT	Plaxton Supreme III	C53F	1978	Ex Day, Kilnhurst, 1994
LVS426V	Bedford YMT	Duple Dominant II	C53F	1980	Ex Cavalier, Hounslow, 1984
HIW1175	Volvo B10M-61	Van Hool Alizée H	C53FT	1983	Ex Smith, High Wycombe, 1996
KGS483Y	Leyland Tiger TRCTL11/3R	Duple Caribbean	C53F	1983	Ex Travellers, Hounslow, 1985
MIW5802	Leyland Tiger TRCTL11/3RZ	Jonckheere Jubilee P...	C51FT	1985	Ex Gunns, Arley, 1994
C840SSB	Volvo B10M-61	Plaxton Paramount 3500 II	C48FT	1986	Ex Smart & Howieson, Newburgh, 1993

Previous registrations:-

503EUC	URD31S	HIW1175	YVO35Y
C840SSB	C449CWR, 4502RU, C372MGB, OCO251	MIW5802	B609VUG, 23PTA, B539XWX

Livery:- White, blue, green and yellow.

Buckland Omnibus Company own this restored Dennis E type. The vehicle, TE7870, was new to Accrington Corporation in 1929 and has dual doorway Brush bodywork. It was initially restored in 1971 having previously been in the hands of a Showman. The bus sees regular use.
Trevor Brookes

BRENTWOOD COACHES

WHM (Brentwood) Ltd, Rolphs House, Blasford Hill, Little Waltham, Chelmsford, Essex, CM3 3PF

Depot:- Little Waltham and Wash Road, Hutton.

1	610KWC	Volvo B10M-62	Caetano Algarve II	C49FT	1995	Ex Osborne, Tollesbury, 1997
2	HIL2391	Volvo B10M-61	Plaxton Paramount 3500 III	C53F	1988	Ex Hill, Congleton, 1992
4	XCF447	Volvo B10M-61	Plaxton Paramount 3200 III	C53FT	1987	Ex Excelsior, Bournemouth, 1989
5	HWY701	Volvo B10M-61	Plaxton Paramount 3200 III	C59F	1988	Ex London Cityrama, Battersea, 1993
6	HIL2392	Volvo B10M-60	Plaxton Excalibur	C49FT	1992	Ex Excelsior, Bournemouth, 1997
8	HIL9275	Volvo B10M-61	Plaxton Paramount 3200	C57F	1984	Ex O'Connor, Hanwell, 1986
9	HIL9272	Volvo B10M-61	Plaxton Supreme IV	C57F	1981	Ex Silverdale, Ruddington, 1989
10	454EAN	Volvo B10M-61	Plaxton Paramount 3200 II	C55F	1985	Ex London Coaches, 1993
11	WXC732	Volvo B10M-61	Plaxton Paramount 3200 III	C59F	1988	Ex London Cityrama, SW8, 1993
12	LIL7230	Leyland Olympian ONTL11/2RSp	Eastern Coach Works	CH45/28F	1985	Ex Metrobus, Orpington, 1995
15	HIL8221	Volvo B10M-60	Jonckheere Deauville P599	C51FT	1990	Ex APT, Rayleigh, 1995
16	UNW928R	Bristol VRT/SL3/6LXB	Eastern Coach Works	H43/31F	1977	Ex Carter, Colchester, 1995
20	GGM106W	Bristol VRT/SL3/6LXB	Eastern Coach Works	H43/31F	1980	Ex Alder Valley, 1992
21	CJH121V	Bristol VRT/SL3/6LXB	Eastern Coach Works	DPH41/25F	1980	Ex Alder Valley, 1992
23	GGM104W	Bristol VRT/SL3/6LXB	Eastern Coach Works	H43/31F	1980	Ex Alder Valley, 1992
25	KKK887V	Bristol VRT/SL3/6LXB	Eastern Coach Works	H43/31F	1980	Ex Alder Valley, 1992
28	ULS675T	Leyland Fleetline FE30AGR	Eastern Coach Works	H43/32F	1979	Ex Kelvin Central, 1995
29	LMS151W	Leyland Fleetline FE30AGR	Alexander AD	H44/31F	1980	Ex Kelvin Central, 1995
30	LMS166W	Leyland Fleetline FE30AGR	Alexander AD	H44/31F	1980	Ex Kelvin Central, 1995
31	LMS155W	Leyland Fleetline FE30AGR	Alexander AD	H44/31F	1980	Ex Kelvin Central, 1995
32	LMS152W	Leyland Fleetline FE30AGR	Alexander AD	H44/31F	1980	Ex Kelvin Central, 1995

Jonckheere's mid-1980's Jubilee style of coachwork was supplied to meet requirements ranging from the midi-sized P35 through to the P99 double decker found on tri-axle chassis. Brentwood Coaches' 7, NJI3995 was a P99 model built on a Scania K112 chassis which has recently left the fleet. The P99 was also built for the UK market on the DAF SBR chassis. *David Heath*

In common with several operators in the East Anglia area, Brentwood Coaches operate vintage vehicles. Restored in Eastern Belle livery is this superb 1953 AEC Regal III which carries a Duple body. NXL847 is seen on display at the 1997 Showbus Rally at Duxford. *Keith Grimes*

Heritage vehicles:-

JA5515	Leyland TigerTS7	Windover	C32F	1936	Ex Burton, Alfreton, 1993
JYC855	Leyland Tiger PS1	Harrington	C33F	1948	Ex Toppings, Wavertree, 1995
KBJ831	Albion Victor FT39N	Thurgood	B31F	1950	Ex Jenkinson, Consett, 1994
KEL95	Bedford OB	Duple Vista	C29F	1950	Ex Superscale, Basildon, 1986
NXL847	AEC Regal III	Duple	C39F	1953	Ex Hutchings, Brixham, 1993
WKJ787	Beadle-Commer TS3	Beadle	C41C	1956	Ex Jones, Llandeilo, 1994
XUP692	Albion Aberdonian MR11	Plaxton	C41F	1958	Ex Sharpe & Ship, Colchester, 1994
CBV308S	Leyland Atlantean AN68A/2R	East Lancashire	H50/38F	1977	Ex Hedingham & District, 1996
ULS671T	Leyland Fleetline, FE30AGR	Eastern Coach Works	H43/32F	1979	Ex Kelvin Central, 1995

Previous registrations:-

454EAN	B127PEL	JYC855	From new
610KWC	M577JBC	KBJ831	From new
HIL2391	E571UHS	KEL95	From new
HIL2392	J73NJT, A6XEL	LIL7230	B688BPU
HIL8221	G654ONH, A10APT	NXL847	From new
HIL9272	TFP3X	WKJ787	From new
HIL9275	A822XMK, 801BWC	WXC732	E308OMG
HWY701	E303OMG	XCF447	D263HFX
JA5515	From new	XUP692	From new

Livery:- Brown, orange and yellow (coaches); cream and blue (buses)

BURTONS

Burton Coaches (Haverhill) Ltd, Duddery Hill, Haverhill, Suffolk, CB9 8DR

CWF738T	Leyland Atlantean AN68A/1R	Roe	H45/29D	1979	Ex Guide Friday, 1996
DWJ566V	Leyland Atlantean AN68A/1R	Roe	H45/29F	1979	Ex Guide Friday, 1996
DWJ567V	Leyland Atlantean AN68A/1R	Roe	H45/29F	1979	Ex Guide Friday, 1996
CWG769V	Leyland Atlantean AN68A/1R	Roe	H45/29F	1979	Ex Guide Friday, 1996
JKW277W	Leyland Atlantean AN68B/1R	Alexander AL	H45/29D	1981	Ex Mainline, 1996
XSU913	Volvo B10M-61	Plaxton Paramount 3500 II	C51FT	1986	Ex Rambler, St. Leonards, 1994
D781SGB	Volvo B10M-61	Plaxton Paramount 3500 III	C53F	1987	Ex Yorkshire Rider, 1995
D68VJC	Volvo B10M-61	Plaxton Paramount 3500 III	C53F	1987	Ex Caelloi, Pwllheli, 1994
D328UTU	Volvo B10M-61	Plaxton Paramount 3500 III	C51F	1987	Ex Vale of Llangollen, Cefn Mawr, 1996
F464SJD	Volvo B10M-61	Duple 340	C55F	1988	Ex Geoff Wiffen, Finchingfield, 1995
F102CCL	Volvo B10M-61	Plaxton Paramount 3500 II	C53F	1989	Ex Stainton, Kendal, 1996
H352MLJ	Volvo B10M-60	Plaxton Expressliner	C57F	1990	Ex Dorset Travel, 1998
L299KKW	Volvo B10M-62	Plaxton Première 350	C49FT	199	Ex ?, 1998
M40TGM	Dennis Javelin 12SDA2155	Plaxton Première 320	C49FT	1995	Ex Tellings-Golden Miller, 1998
P178NAK	Volvo B10M-62	Plaxton Première 350	C49FT	199	Ex ?, 1998
R60BCL	Volvo B10M-62	Plaxton Excalibur	C49FT	1998	
R70BCL	Volvo B10M-62	Plaxton Excalibur	C49FT	1998	
R80BCL	Volvo B10M-62	Plaxton Excalibur	C49FT	1998	
R90BCL	Volvo B10M-62	Plaxton Excalibur	C49FT	1998	

Previous registrations:-

D328UTU	D287UDM, VLT229, VLT149	XSU913	C588SJK, FDY83,C164CCD
F464SJD	248D359		

Livery:- Cream, red and beige; white (Sunrise Holidays) D781SGB, F102CCL; blue, white and yellow - new Volvo coaches.

Many of the coaches operated by Burtons of Haverhill carry Plaxton Paramount bodywork, though a variety of chassis types, including Volvo, Bedford and DAF are used. This view, taken at the South Mimms services, shows one of the Volvos, D781SGB, which carries Sunrise Holidays livery. The company has recently been purchased by Tellings-Golden Miller and a former manager of Harris Bus, the latest vehicle carrying a livery similar to that used by Tellings-Golden Miller. *Colin Lloyd*

BUZZ

Buzz Co-operative Ltd, Arctic House, Riverway, Harlow, Essex, CM20 2DP

AUK47K	Leyland Leopard PSU3B/4R	Plaxton Panorama Elite II	C53F	1972	Ex Storey, Littleport, 1995
KBH861V	Leyland Leopard PSU5C/4R	Plaxton Supreme IV	C57F	1980	Ex Biss Bros., Stansted, 1996
GWV926V	Leyland Leopard PSU3E/4R	Plaxton Supreme IV Express	C53F	1980	Ex Guide Friday, Stratford-upon-Avon, 1996
FIL7253	Leyland Tiger TRCTL11/3RZ	Plaxton Paramount 3500 II	C49FT	1986	Ex Ambassador, 1993
F678AWW	Mercedes-Benz 811D	Optare StarRider	B27F	1988	Ex Optare demonstrator, 1989
F72SMC	Mercedes-Benz 609D	Reeve Burgess	B20F	1988	
F73SMC	Mercedes-Benz 609D	Reeve Burgess	B20F	1988	
F76SMC	Mercedes-Benz 609D	Reeve Burgess	B20F	1988	
F77SMC	Mercedes-Benz 609D	Reeve Burgess	B20F	1988	
F78SMC	Mercedes-Benz 609D	Reeve Burgess	B20F	1988	
F79SMC	Mercedes-Benz 609D	Reeve Burgess	B20F	1988	
L768XLK	Mercedes-Benz 814D	Autobus Classique	C33F	1994	Ex MCH, Uxbridge, 1997
N907GHJ	Mercedes-Benz 709D	Plaxton Beaver	B23F	1996	
N68GPU	Mercedes-Benz 709D	Plaxton Beaver	B23F	1996	

Previous registrations:-

AUK47K	LCN834K, 617WHT	FIL7253	C913BNG	L768XLK	L964JFU, MCH252

Livery:- Yellow, white and grey.

Representing the Buzz fleet is Leyland Leopard GWV926V, fitted with Plaxton Supreme bodywork it was pictured at Chessington shortly after the school bus symbol was applied.
David Donati collection

C & G COACH SERVICE

C L Day & G Ellwood, Honeysome Lodge, Honeysome Road, Chatteris,
Cambridgeshire, PE16 6SB

GJF274N	Scania BR111DH	MCW Metropolitan	H45/31D	1975	Ex Boorman, Henlow, 1996
OUC100R	Scania BR111DH	MCW Metropolitan	H43/29D	1976	Ex Cook, Biggleswade, 1993
GHB86W	Bristol VRT/SL3/6LXB	East Lancashire	H44/32F	1981	Ex Beeston, Hadleigh, 1994
OSV517	Volvo B58-61	Irizar Urko	C49FT	1981	Ex Tracks, Brookland, 1994
LIB1745	Scania K112TRS	Plaxton Paramount 4000 II	CH55/20CT	1986	Ex Jans, Soham, 1995
LIW1933	Scania K112TRS	Berkhof Eclipse	C51FT	1987	Ex Dorset Travel, 1998
LIB1474	Scania K112CRB	Van Hool Alizée DH	C51FT	1988	
MIL1030	Scania K93CRB	Duple 320	C59F	1990	
MIL1032	Scania K113CRB	Duple 320	C59F	1991	Ex O'Sullivan, Huyton, 1997
LIB8340	Scania K113CRB	Van Hool Alizée H	C49FT	1991	Ex Shearings, 1994
M4CNG	Scania K113CRB	Irizar Century 12.35	C49FT	1994	Ex Scania demonstrator, 1995
N4CNG	Scania K113CRB	Irizar Century 12.35	C49FT	1996	
N14CNG	Scania K113CRB	Irizar Century 12.35	C49FT	1996	Ex Scania demonstrator, 1997
P4CNG	Scania K113CRB	Irizar Century 12.35	C49FT	1997	
R4CNG	Scania K113CRB	Irizar Century 12.35	C49FT	1998	

Previous registrations:-

LIB1474	F717CWG	N14CNG	N845DKU
LIB1745	C352DWR, VLT37, C861MGB, 299SAE, C953UEW	MIL1030	H793RWJ
LIB8340	H155DVM	MIL1031	-
LIW1933	D332MHB, BUI4646, D308LEL	MIL1032	H399HTJ
M4CNG	M245TAK	OSV517	ODC426W

Named Vehicle:-   LIB1745 *Graham*

Livery:- White with yellow and red relief

CI COACHLINES

I R Lodge, C J Ferrier & S A Lodge, Pools Lane, Highwood, Chelmsford, Essex, CM1 3QL

BEV542S	Ford R1114	Plaxton Supreme III	C53F	1978	Ex Webb, Highwood, 1996
DRT681T	Bedford YMT	Plaxton Supreme III	C53F	1979	Ex Tigerways, Harlow, 1996
RGV684W	Bedford YMT	Duple Dominant II Express	C53F	1981	Ex Embling, Guyhirn, 1997
KSU470	Volvo B10M-61	Jonckheere Bermuda	C49FT	1983	Ex Cantabrica, Watford, 1990
IUI3589	DAF SB2300DHS585	Plaxton Paramount 3500	C46FT	1984	Ex Adkins, Upper Boddington, 1997
IUI2734	Volvo B10M-61	Ikarus Blue Danube 358	C49FT	1988	Ex A1, Ardrossan, 1994
IUI2733	Volvo B10M-61	Ikarus Blue Danube 358	C53FT	1989	Ex Goode's Coachways, West Bromwich, 1994
IUI2735	Volvo B10M-60	Ikarus Blue Danube 358	C53FT	1989	Ex Goode's Coachways, West Bromwich, 1994

Previous registrations:-

BEV542S	UUX364S, 52GYY	IUI2734	F881VSJ	IUI3589	A803LEL, XEL4, A268NFX
IUI2733	F635FDH	IUI2735	G720ONX	KSU470	JBM17Y

CAROLINE SEAGULL

Cobholm Hire Services Ltd, 59 Marine Parade, Great Yarmouth, Norfolk, NR30 2EJ

Depots:- Mill Road, Cobholm and Queens Road, Great Yarmouth.

6539FN	AEC Reliance 2U3RA	Plaxton Elite III (1974)	C51F	1963	Ex East Kent, 1981
6546FN	AEC Reliance CHS 2U3RA	Plaxton Supreme IV (1979)	C53F	1965	Ex East Kent, 1979
6545FN	AEC Reliance CHS 2U3RA	Plaxton Supreme IV (1979)	C53F	1965	Ex East Kent, 1979
JSC890E	Leyland Atlantean PDR1/1	Alexander A	O43/31F	1967	Ex Partridge, Hadleigh, 1982
GNM235N	Bristol LHL6L	Plaxton Supreme III	C51F	1975	Ex H & M, Chasetown, 1991
ODL175R	Bedford YMT	Duple Dominant II	C51F	1977	Ex Southern Vectis, 1988
ODL176R	Bedford YMT	Duple Dominant II	C51F	1977	Ex Southern Vectis, 1988
531FN	AEC Reliance 6U3ZR	Plaxton Supreme III	C55F	1977	Ex Scutt, Owston Ferry, 1992
TDL127S	Bedford YMT	Duple Dominant II	C51F	1978	Ex Southern Vectis, 1988
TDL420S	Bedford YMT	Duple Dominant II	C51F	1978	Ex Southern Vectis, 1988
CFX319T	Ford R1014	Plaxton Supreme III	C41F	1979	Ex Butlin's, Bognor Regis, 1995
ODX608W	Bedford YMT	Plaxton Supreme IV Express	C53F	1980	Ex Suffolk CC, Ipswich, 1996
522FN	Ford R1114	Plaxton Supreme IV	C53F	1981	Ex Norfolk, Gt Yarmouth, 1984
523FN	Ford R1114	Plaxton Supreme IV	C53F	1981	Ex Norfolk, Gt Yarmouth, 1984
526FN	Ford R1114	Plaxton Supreme IV	C53F	1981	Ex Norfolk, Gt Yarmouth, 1984
536FN	Ford R1114	Plaxton Supreme IV	C53F	1981	Ex Norfolk, Gt Yarmouth, 1984
538FN	Ford R1114	Plaxton Supreme IV	C53F	1981	Ex Norfolk, Gt Yarmouth, 1984
NIW3646	DAF MB200DKFL600	Plaxton Supreme VI	C57F	1982	Ex W. Sussex CC, Chichester, 1997
USV802	Leyland Tiger TRCTL11/3R	Duple 320 (1985)	C55F	1983	Ex Day, Kilnhurst, 1996
EPW928Y	Mercedes-Benz L307D	Reeve Burgess	M12	1983	
6547FN	Bedford YNT	Plaxton Paramount 3200	C53F	1983	
6543FN	Bedford YNT	Plaxton Paramount 3200	C53F	1983	
6544FN	Scania K112CRS	Plaxton Paramount 3200 II	C51F	1985	Ex Rossendale, 1993
B97PLU	Bedford VAS 5	Plaxton Supreme IV	C29F	1985	Ex Capital, West Drayton, 1992

The local bus services operated by Caroline Seagull usually use one of the older coaches in the fleet. 526FN is a Ford R1114 featuring Plaxton Supreme IV coachwork and was photographed while working Service 1 at Great Yarmouth during May 1997. *Trevor Brookes*

Carters of Litcham's fleet inlcudes a GAZ3137, a Mercedes-Benz 609D with Reeve Burgess Beaver bus bodywork and high-back seating. *Trevor Brookes*

535FN	Bedford Venturer YNV	Duple 320	C55F	1986	Ex Dhanoia, Orsett, 1995
537FN	Bedford Venturer YNV	Duple 320	C49FT	1987	
6541FN	Van Hool T815	Van Hool Alicron	C49FT	1988	Ex Lodge, High Easter, 1997
F327COV	Dennis Javelin 12SDA1907	Duple 320	C57F	1989	Ex BT, 1987
G469LVG	Dennis Javelin 12SDA1912	Plaxton Paramount 3200 III	C53F	1990	
G470LVG	Dennis Javelin 12SDA1907	Plaxton Paramount 3200 III	C53F	1990	
J652DVG	Toyota Coaster HDB30R	Caetano Optimo II	C21F	1992	

Previous registrations:-

522FN	TWX331W		6541FN	E432KRT
523FN	TWX332W		6543FN	GEX632Y
526FN	TWX329W		6544FN	B547CHJ, NSU181, B162SEC
531FN	OKY66R		6545FN	DJG631C, FEX818T
535FN	C445LGN		6546FN	DJG628C, FEX817T
536FN	SVF511W		6547FN	GEX631Y
537FN	D329LEX		NIW3646	OWA24X, YSV648, OUH238X,
538FN	SVF512W			1560KX, NTH128X
6539FN	From new		USV802	BDF201Y

Livery:- White, blue and orange

CARTER'S COACHES

K T & G P Carter, The Vernons, Tittleshall Road, Litcham, Norfolk, PE32 2PB

Depots:- Litcham and Hale Road Ashill.

TJE996S	Bedford YMT	Plaxton Supreme III	C53F	1978	Ex Rose, Holbeach St. John's, 1987
YPB829T	Bedford YMT	Duple Dominant II	DP57F	1979	Ex Easton, Brandiston, 1989
WIB1160	Bedford YMT	Duple Dominant II	C53F	1979	Ex Freestones, Beetley, 1997
XPP282X	Bedford YNT	Duple Dominant IV	C53F	1982	Ex Parker, Hindolveston, 1993
YPD111Y	Leyland Tiger TRCTL11/2R	Duple Dominant IV Express	C53F	1983	Ex Stonebridge, Biggleswade, 1996
JIL2146	DAF MB200DKFL600	Van Hool Alizée	C48FT	1984	Ex Euroview, E. Dereham, 1996
FSU826	Volvo B10M-61	Plaxton Paramount 3200 II	C53F	1985	Ex Empress, Bethnal Green, 1997
TJI4268	Bedford YNT	Plaxton Paramount 3200 II	C53F	1985	Ex Wainfleet, Nuneaton, 1989
TJI4267	Bedford YNT	Duple Laser 2	C53F	1985	Ex Garratt, Leicester, 1988
RIW4037	Bedford YNT	Plaxton Paramount 3200 III	C53F	1987	Ex Sanders, Holt, 1991
GAZ3137	Mercedes-Benz 609D	Reeve Burgess Beaver	DP25F	1987	Ex Bridges, Saham Toney, 1993
RIW4038	Bedford YNT	Duple 320	C53F	1988	Ex Kiddle, St. Ives, 1984
F771DKW	Ford Transit VE6	Advanced	M11	1989	Ex Kenning, 1991

Previous registrations:-

FSU826	B915SPR	RIW4038	E50JJU
GAZ3137	E815BMJ	TJI4267	C890SJF
JIL2146	A482PWW, A3GJL, A419AHB	TJI4268	B631OFP
RIW4037	E430MSE	WIB1160	CUT808T, 8844WF

Livery:- Two tone green.

Photographed while operating Carter's Coaches Norwich-bound school service, TJE996S is a Bedford YMT with Plaxton Supreme bodywork. The other Bedford coaches in the fleet all carry Duple coachwork including YPB829T which has been re-seated for service work. *Trevor Brookes*

CARTER'S COACH SERVICES ESSEXBUS

Mrs V J Carter, 100 The Willows, Colchester, Essex, CO2 8DE

Depot:- Heath Road, East Bergholt, Suffolk.

SVW274K	Bristol RELL6G	Eastern Coach Works	B53F	1972	Ex Essex CC, 1993
NNO61P	Leyland Atlantean AN68A/1R	Eastern Coach Works	H43/31F	1976	Ex Colchester, 1991
DWU293T	Bristol VRT/SL3/6LXB	Eastern Coach Works	H43/31F	1978	Ex Fowler, Holbeach Drove, 1997
GTX758W	Bristol LHS6L	Eastern Coach Works	DP29F	1980	Ex Guernseybus, 1996
GTX759W	Bristol LHS6L	Eastern Coach Works	DP29F	1980	Ex Meehan, Newton Ferrers, 1997
E107JPL	Renault-Dodge S56	Northern Counties	B25F	1988	Ex London & Country, 1997
F342VEF	Renault-Dodge S56	Northern Counties	B23F	1989	Ex Carter, Ipswich, 1997

Previous registrations:-

GTX758W	GTX758W, 19660	GTX759W	GTX759W, 19663

Named Vehicle:- F342VEF *Valerie*

Livery:- Red and white or green and cream.

During the minibus boom of the mid nineteen-eighties, several coach builders adopted designs which replaced the original cowl supplied by the chassis manufacturers. The Northern Counties style employed on the Renault-Dodge S56 is shown on Carter's Coach Services' 342, F342VEF, here arriving at Colchester. *Paul Stockwell*

CEDRIC'S

Cedric Garages (Wivenhoe) Ltd, The Avenue, Wivenhoe, Essex, CO7 9AH

3	L3CED	Bova FHD12.340	Bova Futura	C51FT	1994	
5	MXI8204	Volvo B10M-50	Jonckheere Deauville	C51FT	1991	Ex Harry Shaw, Coventry, 1994
6	HIL6244	Volvo B10M-61	Ikarus Blue Danube 358	C53FT	1988	Ex Direct, Birmingham, 1990
8	M8CED	Bova FLD12.340	Bova Futura Club	C49FT	1995	
9	PWR446W	Bristol VRT/SL3/6LXB	Eastern Coach Works	H43/31F	1981	Ex Yorkshire Rider, 1994
11	NIL2266	Neoplan N122/3	Neoplan Skyliner	CH57/18CT	1987	Ex Trathens, Plymouth, 1997
12	H881AVK	Neoplan N122/3	Neoplan Skyliner	CH57/22CT	1990	Ex Durham Travel Service, 1997
14	MIL2886	Bova FHD12.290	Bova Futura	C57F	1989	Ex Yorkshire Travel, Dewsbury, 1995
17	B694BPU	Leyland Olympian ONTL11/2R	Eastern Coach Works	H45/32F	1984	Ex MTL (Liverbus), 1998
18	TJI6306	Bova FHD12.290	Bova Futura	C53F	1990	Ex Bennetts Silverline, Chieveley, 1998
19	7463RU	Volvo B10M-61	Jonckheere Bermuda	C57F	1981	Ex Ayres, Dalkeith, 1986
21	K908RGE	Volvo B10M-60	Jonckheere Deauville 45	C49FT	1993	Ex Park's, Hamilton, 1994
22	HWJ934W	Bristol VRT/SL3/501	Eastern Coach Works	H43/31F	1981	Ex Lincolnshire, 1984
23	B162AKH	Leyland Olympian ONTL11/2RSp	Eastern Coach Works	CH45/24F	1985	Ex Northern Bus, Anston, 1998
24	B109LPH	Leyland Olympian ONTL11/2RSp	Eastern Coach Works	CH45/24F	1985	Ex Northern Bus, Anston, 1998
..	BKE835T	Bristol VRT/SL3/6LXB	Eastern Coach Works	H43/31F	1979	Ex Stephenson, Rochford, 1997
..	ACM708X	Leyland Olympian ONTL11/1R	Eastern Coach Works	H46/31F	1981	Ex Merseyside, 1997
..	R...CED	Volvo B10M-62	Plaxton Première 350	C53F	1998	
..	R...CED	Volvo B10M-62	Jonckheere Mistral 50	C49FT	On order	
..	R...CED	Volvo B10M-62	Jonckheere Mistral 50	C49FT	On order	
..	S...CED	Setra S300..	Setra Millenium	C32FT	On order	

Previous registrations:-

7463RU	XNV142W	HIL6244	E499UOP	NIL2266	E600WDV
B162AKH	B110LPH	MIL2886	G97VFP	TJI6306	G419WFP
H881AVK	H881AVK, H4DTS	MXI8204	H15URE		

Livery:- Red and yellow (buses); white and green (coaches); blue and white (Travelsphere) K908RGE

Cedric's of Wivenhoe suffered a serious fire at their depot in early 1998. One of the vehicles that escaped the inferno was this Volvo B10M number 5, MXI8204, which carries an unusual Jonckheere Deauville body. It was seen at Hampton Court Palace coach park.
Geoff Rixon

CHARIOTS

Chariots of Essex Ltd, The Coach House, One Tree Hill, Stanford-le-Hope, Essex, SS17 9NH

ADC836A	AEC Reliance 6U2R	Duple Dominant	C53F	1976	Ex , 1995
RDC113R	Bristol VRT/SL3/6LXB	Northern Counties	H43/31F	1977	Ex Jones, Llanfaethlu, 1997
RDC114R	Bristol VRT/SL3/6LXB	Northern Counties	H43/31F	1977	Ex Jones, Llanfaethlu, 1997
CXI8635	Bedford YMT	Van Hool McArdle 300	C53F	1978	Ex Ementon, Cranfield, 1991
DEL192T	Bedford YMT	Duple Dominant II	C53F	1979	Ex Hants & Dorset, 1995
8603PH	Kässbohrer Setra S215HD	Kässbohrer Tornado	C49FT	1982	Ex Reed's Travel, Kinsley, 1997
ADC366A	DAF MB200DKTL600	Van Hool Aragon	C49FT	1982	Ex Mulley, Ixworth, 1994
A600NWC	Ford R1115	Duple Laser	C51DL	1983	Ex Ford demonstrator, 1990
A209YSF	Mercedes-Benz L608D	Devon Conversions	C19F	1983	Ex Commandery Coaches, Worcester, 1996
A221PBM	Ford Transit 190	Chassis Developments	C16F	1984	Ex Chalkwell, Sittingbourne, 1992
JBZ3250	Volvo B10M-61	LAG Galaxy	C53F	1984	Ex Mycock, Monyash, 1997
C782BWY	Renault Master T35	Renault	M10L	1986	Ex Essex Ambulance Service, 1997
D408XEV	Toyota Hiace	Fosters	M14	1987	Ex private owner, 1993
E205EPB	Hestair-Duple SDA1510	Duple 425	C57F	1987	Ex D&G, Stevenage, 1997
E417MOU	Toyota Coaster HB31R	Caetano Optimo	C18F	1988	Ex Z-Cars, Bristol, 1993
G105APC	Toyota Coaster HB31R	Caetano Optimo	C21F	1989	Ex Horseman, Reading, 1997
G163TNM	Peugeot-Talbot Express	Chassis Developments	M14	1989	
G432SNN	Volvo B10M-60	Ikarus Blue Danube 358	C49FT	1990	Ex Reed's Travel, Kinsley, 1997
H170DVM	Volvo B10M-60	Van Hool Alizée H	C49FT	1991	Ex Shearings, 1997
H172DVM	Volvo B10M-60	Van Hool Alizée H	C49FT	1991	Ex Shearings, 1997
H176DVM	Volvo B10M-60	Van Hool Alizée H	C49FT	1991	Ex Hallmark, Luton, 1997
H177DVM	Volvo B10M-60	Van Hool Alizée H	C49FT	1991	Ex Hallmark, Luton, 1997

Previous registrations:-

8603PH	VPA109X	CXI8635	YUU253T
ADC366A	AGV260Y	JBZ3250	A61GRY
ADC836A	NDF153P		

Livery:- White, purple and turquoise.

Named Vehicles:- A600NWC *Annie*; E417MOU *Zoe*.

Belgian coachbuilder LAG started selling coaches to the UK market in 1982 with their Galaxy style body. Two variants were offered, low and high floors. Representing the low floor style mounted on a Volvo B10M is Chariots of Stanford-le-Hope's JBZ3250. It is seen at the Chessington World of Adventures.
David Heath

CHAMBERS

H C Chambers & Son Ltd, Knowles House, Bures, Suffolk, CO8 5AB

CCF669	Bedford OB	Duple Vista	C29F	1950	Ex preservation, 1984
D211LWX	Volvo B10M-61	Duple 340	C53FL	1987	Ex Wallace Arnold, 1992
D212LWX	Volvo B10M-61	Duple 340	C53FL	1987	Ex Wallace Arnold, 1992
JAZ9860	MCW Metrorider MF158/1	MCW	B30F	1988	Ex Stagecoach East London, 1996
JAZ9861	MCW Metrorider MF158/1	MCW	B30F	1988	Ex Stagecoach East London, 1996
E633SEL	Volvo B10M-61	Van Hool Alizée H	C49FT	1988	Ex Excelsior, Bournemouth, 1993
F246HNE	Peugeot-Talbot Pullman	Talbot	C22F	1988	Ex McCarthy, Stalybridge, 1992
F243RRT	Leyland Olympian ONCL10/1RZ	Alexander RL	H47/32F	1989	
MIL5015	Volvo B10M-60	Van Hool Alizée H	C....DTL	1989	Ex Dick, Slough, 1996
F50ACL	Volvo Citybus B10M-50	Alexander RV	H47/35F	1989	Ex Rhondda, 1997
F51ACL	Volvo Citybus B10M-50	Alexander RV	H47/35F	1989	Ex Rhondda, 1997
F779LNB	Peugeot-Talbot Pullman	Talbot	C22F	1989	Ex McCarthy, Stalybridge, 1992
G760VRT	Leyland Olympian ONCL10/1RZ	Alexander RL	H47/32F	1989	
G855KKY	Mercedes-Benz 609D	Whittaker	C24F	1989	Ex Brown, Edenbridge, 1993
G864XDX	Leyland Olympian ONCL10/1RZ	Alexander RL	H47/32F	1989	
H204DVM	Van Hool T815	Van Hool Alizée H	C53F	1991	Ex Shearings, 1995
K816HUM	Volvo B10M-60	Van Hool Alizée HE	C48FT	1993	Ex Wallace Arnold, 1996
K103VJT	Volvo B10M-60	Van Hool Alizée HE	C49FT	1993	Ex Excelsior, Bournemouth, 1998
K936GWR	Mercedes-Benz 814D	Optare StarRider	C27F	1993	Ex Ralphs, Langley, 1998
N952KBJ	Volvo Olympian YN2RC16Z4	Northern Counties Palatine	H47/30F	1995	

Previous registrations:-

CCF669	From new	JAZ9861	E642KYW
E633SEL	E305OPR, XEL158	K103VJT	K103VJT, A4XCL
JAZ9860	E641KYW	MIL5015	F801TMD

Livery:- Red

The Chambers of Bures fleet contains four new double deck buses purchased new for their trunk route into Colchester. The latest of these is Volvo Olympian N952KBJ with Northern Counties Palatine bodywork. New Olympians are supplemented by two Volvo Citybuses bought from Rhondda.
Richard Godfrey

CHELMSFORD TAXI BUS

Chelmsford Cab Company Ltd, Unit 4 Rivermead Industrial Estate, Bishophall Lane, Chelmsford, Essex, CM1 1RD

Depot:- Bishophall Lane and Railway Station Yard, New Street, Chelmsford and Terminal Road North, Stansted Airport.

Omni 1	G622EDC	CVE Omni	CVE	B8F	1990	Ex Kent CC, 1997
Omni 2	H228BKM	CVE Omni	CVE	B4F	1991	Ex Kent CC, 1995
Omni 3	H743LHN	CVE Omni	CVE	B23F	1990	Ex Gem Fairtax, Crawley, 1995
Omni 4	H744LHN	CVE Omni	CVE	B21F	1990	Ex Gem Fairtax, Crawley, 1995
Omni 5	H745LHN	CVE Omni	CVE	B21F	1990	Ex Gem Fairtax, Crawley, 1995
Omni 6	F385XVN	CVE Omni	CVE	B24F	1989	Ex Kent CC, 1995
Omni 7	H225BKM	CVE Omni	CVE	B6F	1991	Ex Kent CC, 1995
Omni 8	H210BKM	CVE Omni	CVE	B7F	1991	Ex Kent CC, 1996
Omni 9	H227BKM	CVE Omni	CVE	B8F	1991	Ex Kent CC, 1996
Omni 10	J110LKO	OCC Omni	Omni	B15F	1991	Ex Easton, Ramsgate, 1997
Omni 11	H224BKM	CVE Omni	CVE	B17F	1991	Ex Kent CC, 1996
Omni 12	H994DKL	CVE Omni	CVE	B.....	1991	Ex Kent CC, 1997
Omni 14	J998MKL	OBC Omni	OBC	B.....	1992	Ex Kent CC, 1997
C05	B405DWG	Volkswagen Caravelle	Volkswagen	M6	1984	Ex private owner, 1993
C20	F884PYM	Ford Transit VE6	Ford	M8	1988	Ex private owner, 1993
C28	G801VJU	Leyland-DAF 200	Leyland-DAF	M8L	1989	Ex private owner, 1993
C30	R271EVW	Ford Transit VE6	Ford	M8	1998	
C31	R272EVW	Ford Transit VE6	Ford	M8	1998	
C32	R273EVW	Ford Transit VE6	Ford	M8	1998	

Ford Transits are the mainstay of the Chelmsford Taxi Bus fleet although other types of minibuses are employed. Much of the stock is used on local contracts that require wheelchair access vehicles as well as local taxi bus work. G807SKP is numbered Charlie 78 in the fleet and was seen near Chelmsford Station. *Colin Lloyd*

C33	R289EVW	Ford Transit VE6	Ford	M8	1998	
C34	R290EVW	Ford Transit VE6	Ford	M8	1998	
C35	R291EVW	Ford Transit VE6	Ford	M8	1998	
C36	R270EVW	Ford Transit VE6	Ford	M8	1998	
C37	R292EVW	Ford Transit VE6	Ford	M8	1998	
C38	R293EVW	Ford Transit VE6	Ford	M8	1998	
C39	R269EVW	Ford Transit VE6	Ford	M8	1998	
C40	K341EYT	Ford Transit VE6	Ford	M8	1993	Ex private owner, 1996
C43	H933GFA	Ford Transit VE6	Ford	M8	1990	Ex private owner, 1994
C44	G855VGS	Ford Transit VE6	Ford	M8	1989	Ex private owner, 1993
C45	H356HPA	Ford Transit VE6	Ford	M8	1990	Ex private owner, 1993
C46	H836EKL	Ford Transit VE6	Ford	M8	1990	Ex private owner, 1995
C47	H846OHB	Ford Transit VE6	Ford	M8	1991	Ex private owner, 1994
C48	H862VCL	Ford Transit VE6	Ford	M8	1990	Ex Norwich Union, 1994
C49	G533BRK	Ford Transit VE6	Ford	M8	1990	Ex private owner, 1996
C52	H984XYH	Ford Transit VE6	Ford	M11	1990	Ex private owner, 1995
C53	G569YJF	Ford Transit VE6	Ford	M8	1990	Ex Eurohire, 1994
C54	F882FWJ	Volkswagen Caravelle	Volkswagen	M8	1989	Ex private owner, 1993
C55	H91YNL	Ford Transit VE6	Ford	M8	1990	Ex private owner, 1994
C56	H714MKV	Ford Transit VE6	Ford	M8	1990	Ex Van & Truck Rentals, Cwmbran, 1994
C57	H692HLC	Ford Transit VE6	Ford	M8	1991	Ex private owner, 1995
C58	K45DFA	Ford Transit VE6	Ford	M8	1993	Ex private owner, 1996
C59	J282GMF	Ford Transit VE6	Ford	M8	1992	Ex private owner, 1996
C67	N375EHJ	Ford Transit VE6	Ford	M8	1996	Ex private owner, 1997
C71	F118OGS	Mercedes-Benz 811D	Robin Hood	C29F	1989	Ex Harris, High Wycombe, 1997
C71	H259LNR	LDV 400	LDV	M16	1995	
C72	H258LNR	LDV 400	LDV	M16	1995	
C73	G801VJU	Leyland-DAF 400	Leyland-DAF	M16	1990	
C74	J996XKU	Ford Transit VE6	Advanced	M13	1992	Ex Kenning, 1994
C75	H709UKY	Ford Transit VE6	Advanced	M13	1990	Ex Kenning, 1994
C76	H729UKY	Ford Transit VE6	Advanced	M13	1991	Ex Kenning, 1994
C77	G651PKO	Ford Transit VE6	Crystals	M10L	1990	Ex Kent CC, 1996
C78	G807SKP	Ford Transit VE6	Crystals	M10L	1990	Ex Kent CC, 1996
C79	G124UKJ	Ford Transit VE6	Crystals	M8L	1990	Ex East Sussex CC, 1997
C80	G342PKR	Ford Transit VE6	Crystals	M10L	1990	Ex Kent CC, 1997
C88	J992AKY	Ford Transit VE6	Advanced	M8	1992	Ex Kenning, 1994
C90	R956RFP	LDV Convoy	LDV	M16	1997	
C91	R957RFP	LDV Convoy	LDV	M16	1997	
C92	R958RFP	LDV Convoy	LDV	M16	1997	
C93	R959RFP	LDV Convoy	LDV	M16	1997	
C99	J97BWG	Ford Transit VE6	Advanced	M13	1991	Ex Kenning, 1994
...	M257LNR	LDV 400	LDV	M16	1995	
...	N105BPU	Ford Transit	Ford	M8	1996	Ex private owner, 1996

Note:- The C prefix to vehicles replaces "Charlie".

Livery:- White with two tone blue, red and grey.

Chambers' coaching fleet is represented by K816HUM, a Volvo B10M-60 with Van Hool Alizée bodywork to the higher HE model. The vehicle was new to Wallace Arnold and is seen in Aldwych heading for the BBC's *Good Food* show.
Colin Lloyd

R W CHENERY

P G & G Chenery, The Garage, Dickleborough, Diss, Norfolk, IP21 4NJ

Depots:- Dickleborough and Finchingfield, Essex.

EGS158T	Bedford YLQ	Duple Dominant II	C45F	1979	Ex Unique, Brighton, 1984
MCL555V	Bedford YMT	Duple Dominant II	C53F	1980	
BNG444Y	Bedford YNT	Duple Dominant IV	C53F	1982	
HIL7618	Kässbohrer Setra S215HD	Kässbohrer Tornado	C49FT	1982	Ex Gale, Haslemere, 1996
MSU916	Volvo B10M-61	Plaxton Paramount 3200	C57F	1984	Ex Modern Super, Enfield, 1991
MSU917	Volvo B10M-61	Plaxton Paramount 3200	C57F	1984	Ex Lee, Barnet, 1991
XBL333	Kässbohrer Setra S215HD	Kässbohrer Tornado	C49FT	1984	
2508EL	Kässbohrer Setra S215HD	Kässbohrer Tornado	C48FT	1985	Ex Cooper, Killamarsh, 1990
SPV555	Kässbohrer Setra S215HD	Kässbohrer Tornado	C53F	1985	
C120SRB	Kässbohrer Setra S215HR	Kässbohrer Rational	C49FT	1987	Ex Paul James Coaches, Ratcliffe, 1997
NBU707	Kässbohrer Setra S215HD	Kässbohrer Tornado	C49F	1986	Ex Manorpond, Horley, 1990
5092EL	Kässbohrer Setra S215HR	Kässbohrer Rational	C53F	1987	Ex Davie's, Rye, 1989
UPV337	Kässbohrer Setra S215HR	Kässbohrer Rational	C49FT	1987	Ex Bebb, Llantwit Fardre, 1989
D411OSJ	Mercedes-Benz 0303/15RHS	Mercedes-Benz	C53F	1987	Ex Park's, Hamilton, 1992
D408OSJ	Mercedes-Benz 0303/15RHS	Mercedes-Benz	C53F	1987	Ex Park's, Hamilton, 1992
PPY238	Mercedes-Benz 0303	Mercedes-Benz	C49FT	1988	Ex Turner, Broxburn, 1994
TIA5599	Mercedes-Benz 811D	Whittaker	C19F	1989	Ex Field, Cranford, 1990
H62PDW	Kässbohrer Setra S215HD	Kässbohrer Tornado	C49FT	1991	Ex Bebb, Llantwit Fardre, 1993
H63PDW	Kässbohrer Setra S215HD	Kässbohrer Tornado	C49FT	1991	Ex Bebb, Llantwit Fardre, 1993
920ACH	Kässbohrer Setra S215HD	Kässbohrer Tornado	C49FT	1991	Ex Bebb, Llantwit Fardre, 1993
RYG684	Kässbohrer Setra S215HD	Kässbohrer Tornado	C49FT	1994	
N999RWC	Kässbohrer Setra S250	Kässbohrer Special	C48FT	1995	

Previous registrations:-

920ACH	H64PDW	MSU917	A379XMC
2508EL	from new	NBU707	C555PPM
5092EL	D398BPE	PPY238	F381MUT
C120SRB	5579MW, C385XLL, PJI7754	RYG684	From new
D408OSJ	D354CBC, GIL1685	SPV555	B634NPD
D411OSJ	D351CBC, GIL1682	TIA5599	F671GET
HIL7618	RAX19Y	UPV337	D704NUH
MSU916	A378XMC	XBL333	From new

Named Vehicles:- XBL333 *Norfolk Princess*; BNG444Y *Prince William*; EGS158T *Lady Diana*.

Livery:- Silver and two tone blue; white, red and blue (National Express) UPV337, H62-63PDW, RYG684.

The integral Mercedes-Benz 0303 coach was imported in small numbers when the GB Pound was stong a decade ago. Since then the cost of the Mercedes-Benz has reduced sales considerably. Chenery now have three of the integral coaches with PPY238, seen parked along the Embankment, London. *Colin Lloyd*

CLINTONA

R & B J. Staines, Little Warley Hall Lane, Brentwood, Essex, CM13 3AA

E125AAL	Ford Transit	Mellor	B10ML	1988	Ex Nottingham CC, 1995
E190YWE	Mercedes-Benz 609D	Whittaker	C24F	1988	
F173CKW	Mercedes-Benz 811D	Reeve Burgess Beaver	C33F	1988	
F239PAC	Peugeot-Talbot-Freeway	Talbot	DP18FL	1988	Ex Coventry Education Committee, 1984
F289PAC	Ford Transit VE6	Dormobile	M8L	1989	Ex Coventry MBC, 1995
G731PGA	Ford Transit VE6	Dormobile	C16F	1989	Ex Wright, Brandon, 1991
G716WDU	Ford Transit VE6	Dormobile	B16FL	1990	Ex Coventry MBC, 1995
G994JKY	Ford Transit VE6	Coachcraft	C16F	1990	
G922DVX	Ford Transit VE6	Dormobile	M16	1990	
G996DVX	Ford Transit VE6	Dormobile	C20F	1990	
H63BKM	Ford Transit VE6	Crystals	C20F	1990	Ex Graham & Wisbey, Rainham, 1992
H239ANE	Ford Transit VE6	Deansgate	DP16F	1990	Ex Deansgate, Manchester, 1991
H120KWC	Ford Transit VE6	Steedrive	B....	1991	Ex private owner, 1995
K317EJV	Mercedes-Benz 814D	Autobus Classique 2	C33F	1992	
L471DOA	Peugeot-Talbot Freeway	TBP	DP20FL	1993	
L472DOA	Peugeot-Talbot Freeway	TBP	DP20FL	1993	
L469DOA	Peugeot-Talbot Freeway	TBP	DP20FL	1993	
L470DOA	Peugeot-Talbot Freeway	TBP	DP20FL	1993	
M738OKK	Iveco Turbo Daily 49.10	Iveco	C19F	1994	
M365UML	Iveco Turbo Daily 49.10	Iveco	C19F	1995	
N420WJL	Mercedes-Benz 814D	Autobus Classique Nouvelle	C33F	1995	
N783OGA	Mercedes-Benz 814D	Mellor	C33F	1996	Ex Rennie, Dunfirmline, 1997
N157CMM	Iveco Turbo Daily 49.10	Iveco	C19F	1996	
P585HME	Iveco Turbo Daily 49.10	Mellor	C18F	1996	
P586HME	Iveco Turbo Daily 49.10	Mellor	C15F	1996	
P675LWA	LDV Convoy	Crystals	M16	1997	
P676LWA	LDV Convoy	Crystals	M16	1997	

Livery:- Blue, white and red.

Clintona operate a fleet consisting of both mini and midi sized vehicles. One of the larger vehicles is N420WJL, an Autobus Classique Nouvelle midi coach on a Mercedes-Benz 814D chassis. Wembley Stadium coach park provides the backdrop on a private hire duty during the summer of 1997.
Kevin Vincent

COACH SERVICES

Coach Services Ltd, 22 Croxton Road, Thetford, Norfolk, IP24 1AG

GRT520V	Bedford YMT	Plaxton Supreme IV Express	C53F	1979	Ex Squirrell, Gt. Finborough, 1992
MUD535W	Bedford YMT	Plaxton Supreme IV	C53F	1981	Ex Motts, Stoke Mandeville, 1993
WOD142X	Bedford YNT	Duple Dominant IV Express	C53F	1982	Ex Petch, Hopton, 1991
BGS304X	Bedford YNT	Plaxton Supreme IV	C53F	1982	Ex Crutwell, Ramsey, 1995
NLH288	DAF MB200DKFL600	Van Hool Alizée H	C53F	1984	Ex Bowen, Birmingham, 1996
B345RVF	Bedford YNT	Duple Laser 2	C53F	1984	Ex Petch, Hopton, 1991
PBB760	Leyland Tiger TRCTL11/3R	Van Hool Alizée H	C53F	1984	Ex HH Coaches, Settle, 1997
B23XKK	Bedford YNT	Plaxton Paramount 3200 II	C53F	1985	Ex Premier-Albanian, Watford, 1987
C815FMC	Bedford Venturer YNV	Duple Laser 2	C53F	1986	
D272HFX	Bedford Venturer YNV	Plaxton Paramount 3200 III	C53F	1987	Ex Excelsior, Bournemouth, 1988
E832EUT	Bedford Venturer YNV	Plaxton Paramount 3200 III	C57F	1987	Ex Wainfleet, Nuneaton, 1991
JIL2015	Bova FHD12.290	Bova Futura	C53F	1988	Ex West Row, Mildenhall, 1997
JIL3968	Leyland Tiger TRCL10/3ARZM	Plaxton Paramount 3500 III	C53F	1988	Ex HH Coaches, Settle, 1997
F708ENE	Leyland Tiger TRCL10/3ARZM	Plaxton Paramount 3200 III	C53F	1989	Ex Shearings, 1992
F709ENE	Leyland Tiger TRCL10/3ARZM	Plaxton Paramount 3200 III	C53F	1989	Ex Shearings, 1992
100BGO	Bova FHD12.290	Bova Futura	C53F	1989	Ex Petch, Hopton, 1991
F551TMH	Volvo B10M-60	Van Hool Alizée	C53F	1989	Ex Owen, Chapelhall, 1997
G501VRV	Leyland Tiger TRCL10/3ARZM	Plaxton Paramount 3200 III	C53F	1989	Ex Thamesdown, 1996
1273LJ	DAF SB3000DKV601	Jonckheere Deauville P599	C49FT	1990	Ex Dunn-Line, Nottingham, 1994
K861NST	Volvo B10M-60	Jonckheere Deauville P599	C51FT	1992	Ex Classic, Annfield Plain, 1997
L185PRF	Volvo B10M-60	Jonckheere Deauville P599	C49FT	1993	Ex Happy Days, Woodseaves, 1997
L531XUT	Volvo B10M-60	Jonckheere Deauville P599	C51F	1994	Ex Bruce, Shotts, 1997

Previous registrations:-

100BGO	F900RDX	K861NST	K148LAS, ESK985
1273LJ	G140MNH	L185PRF	L1HDC
BGS304X	BGS304X, PBB760	NLH288	A849UGB
JIL2015	E123UWW	PBB760	B297AMG
JIL3968	F315RMH		

Livery:- White, maroon and red.

Coach Services of Thetford have a mixed and varied fleet of coaches employed on school contracts, local authority tenders, private hire and tours. One of a pair of Bova Futura coaches, JIL2015 was acquired in 1997 from West Row of Mildenhall and was photographed in Norwich.
Colin Lloyd

COLCHESTER COACHES

M A & S Stevens, 15 Sydney Street, Colchester, Essex, CO2 8UP

Depot:- Fir Tree Cafe, Tenpenny Hill, Thorrington, Colchester.

KPJ268W	Leyland Atlantean AN68B/1R	Roe	H43/30F	1981	Ex Londonlinks, 1997
KPJ289W	Leyland Atlantean AN68B/1R	Roe	H43/30F	1981	Ex Londonlinks, 1997
C130PPE	Leyland Tiger TRCTL11/3RH	Berkhof Everest 370	C49FT	1985	Ex Stephenson, Rochford, 1995
G95VFP	Bova FHD12.290	Bova Futura	C57F	1989	Ex Priory, Gosport, 1997

Livery:- White

COLLINS

C R & R T Collins, Unit 4 Cambridge Road, Industrial Estate,
Milton, Cambridgeshire, CB4 4AZ

ECU772W	Bedford YMT	Duple Dominant IV	C53F	1981	Ex Matthews Blue, Shouldham, 1989
NAU924W	Ford Transit 190	Dormobile	B12FL	1981	Ex Nottinghamshire CC, 1990
MIL7165	Mercedes-Benz L508D	Reeve Burgess	C19F	1981	Ex Thomas, Clydach Vale, 1986
BFL497Y	Mercedes-Benz L508D	Bedford Coachworks	M16	1982	Ex Loyne, Peterlee, 1989
A926TEG	Ford Transit 190	Mellor	B16F	1984	Ex Cambridgeshire CC, 1994
B895YAV	Ford Transit 190	Mellor	B8FL	1984	Ex Cambridgeshire CC, 1992
MIL7163	Bedford YNT	Plaxton Paramount 3200 II	C53F	1985	Ex Robin Hood, Rudyard, 1992
B910YAV	Ford Transit 150	Ford	M8	1985	Ex Cambridgeshire CC, 1995
B122UAH	Freight-Rover Sherpa	Dixon Lomas	M14	1985	Ex Bonner, Ongar, 1990
C42LEW	Ford Transit 190	Mellor	B11FL	1985	Ex Cambridgeshire CC, 1994
NIB4968	Bedford Venturer YNV	Plaxton Paramount 3200 II	C53F	1986	Ex Woods, Goole, 1995
C247OFE	Mercedes-Benz L608D	Reeve Burgess	B20F	1986	Ex Waylands, Worlingham, 1996
D753JUB	Freight-Rover Sherpa	Dormobile	B20F	1986	Ex Black Prince, Morley, 1995
D774PTU	Freight-Rover Sherpa	Dormobile	B16F	1986	Ex Talbot, Huntingdon, 1994
MIL7164	Bedford Venturer YNV	Duple 320	C55F	1987	Ex Sanders, Holt, 1993
D267OOJ	Freight-Rover Sherpa	Carlyle	B18F	1987	Ex Coach Services, Thetford, 1991
D654DFL	Freight-Rover Sherpa	Freight-Rover	M15	1987	Ex private owner, 1991
D797KWR	Freight-Rover Sherpa	Dormobile	B20F	1987	Ex Talbot, Huntingdon, 1995
E48YDO	Mercedes-Benz 609D	Advanced Vehicle Builders	C26F	1988	Ex Spratts, Wreningham, 1995

Previous registrations:-

MIL7163	B630RRE	MIL7165	MAX332X
MIL7164	D446PGH	NIB4968	C167OCH

Livery:- White and orange

1996 saw the arrival of two Dennis Javelins in the Coach Stop fleet and these are fitted with Aüwaerter Transliner bodywork. Each vehicle in the fleet has an individually designed livery and internal finish, and several have won awards for their stunning appearance. Each is appropriately names, such as P969HWF is *Mischief*, seen here in Blackpool. *Colin Lloyd*

Bova integral coaches are favoured in the Cooks of Southend fleet. One of a pair bought new, K651EEV passes along Millbank, near Lambeth Bridge, and shows the distinctive style of the Futura bodywork. *Colin Lloyd*

COACH STOP

G E Hopes, 30 Rectory Grove, Leigh-on-Sea, Essex, SS9 3SQ

H302FSK	Dennis Javelin	Plaxton Paramount 3200 III	C53F	1990	Ex Reliance, Belfast, 1998
N581BDT	Bova FHD12.340	Bova Futura	C49FT	1995	
P969HWF	Dennis Javelin	Neoplan Transliner	C49FT	1996	
P970HWF	Dennis Javelin	Neoplan Transliner	C49FT	1996	
P466JWB	Bova FHD12.340	Bova Futura	C49FT	1996	
P692XVL	Kässbohrer Setra S250	Kässbohrer Special	C32FT	1997	
R877SDT	Scania K113TRB	Irizar Century 12.37	C49FT	1997	
R980GUB	Bova FHD12.340	Bova Futura	C49FT	1997	

Named Vehicles:- N581BDT *Masquerade*; P969HWF *Mischief*; P970HWF *Solar Polar*; P466JWB *Carousel*; P692XVL *Secrets*; R877SDT *Rajah;* R980GUB *Jazz.*

Livery :- various high lydistinctive schemes are adopted.

COOKS of SOUTHEND

W E Cook, 607 London Road, Westcliff-on-Sea, Southend, Essex, SS0 9PE

Depots:- Cottis Yard, Sutton Road, Rochford; Southview Drive, Westcliffe and London Road, Westcliff.

RAY742R	Ford R1114	Duple Dominant	C53F	1976	Ex Beeline, Southborough, 1987
RYL710R	Bedford YMT	Duple Dominant	C53F	1977	Ex Grey-Green, 1979
MBT674T	Ford R1114	Plaxton Supreme III	C53F	1978	Ex Whitwell, Southend, 1993
YNJ214	Bova EL28/581	Duple Calypso	C53F	1984	Ex Pugsley, Atherington, 1988
WWC820	Bova EL28/581	Duple Calypso	C53F	1984	
556EHN	Bova FHM12.290	Bova Futura	C49FT	1985	Ex Biss Bros, Stansted, 1996
NHJ714	Bova FLD12.250	Bova Futura	C53F	1986	Ex Burton, Fellbeck, 1994
799XWC	DAF MB2000DKVL600	Plaxton Paramount 3500 II	C53F	1986	Ex Stansted Coaches, Bishops Stortford, 1991
E377FVX	Freight-Rover Sherpa	Freight-Rover	M12	1988	
F258NUT	Bova FHD12.290	Bova Futura	C49FT	1988	Ex Hedingham & District, 1992
K651EEV	Bova FHD12.290	Bova Futura	C49FT	1992	
N75WSB	Bova FHD12.340	Bova Futura	C53FT	1996	Ex Silver Choice, East Kilbride, 1997

Previous registrations:-

556EHN	B558KRY	NHJ714	C516DWY	YNJ214	A806JAY
799XWC	D822SJX	WWC820	From new		

Livery:- Red and white.

COUNTY COACHES

County Coaches (Brentwood) Ltd, 1 Victoria Road, Brentwood, Essex, CM14 5DR

Depot:- Wash Road, Hutton Industrial Estate, Hutton.

EDR793	Bedford OB	Duple Vista	C29F	1949	Ex Bruce & Roberts, Lewdown, 1985
2786RU	Bristol VRT/SL3/6LX	Eastern Coach Works	H43/31F	1976	Ex Brentwood Coaches, Little Waltham, 1995
5189RU	Bristol VRT/SL3/6LXB	Eastern Coach Works	H43/31F	1978	Ex Brentwood Coaches, Little Waltham, 1995
NIW1639	Bedford YMT	Plaxton Supreme IV Express	C53F	1979	Ex Ingatestone Coaches, 1997
2629RU	Bedford YMT	Plaxton Supreme III	C53F	1979	Ex Heal & Howard, Settle, 1985
JTM106V	Bedford YMT	Plaxton Supreme IV	C53F	1979	Ex Cuttings, Brockley, 1997
UJN159V	DAF MB2000DKL600	Plaxton Supreme IV	C57F	1979	Ex Brentwood Coaches, Little Waltham, 1993
5281RU	Volvo B10M-61	Plaxton Paramount 3200	C53F	1983	Ex Wallace Arnold, 1987
PJI7727	Volvo B10M-61	Van Hool Alizée H	C49FT	1984	Ex Dawson & Cowley, Chesterfield, 1995
5919RU	Bedford Venturer YNV	Plaxton Paramount 3200 II	C55F	1987	Ex York Pullman, Elvington, 1993
D71HRU	Bedford Venturer YNV	Plaxton Paramount 3200 II	C57F	1987	Ex Burton, Haverhill, 1997
E710JJN	DAF MB230DKFL615	Caetano Algarve	C49FT	1987	Ex Grangeburn, Motherwell, 1992
2328RU	Volvo B10M-61	Ikarus Blue Danube 358	C57F	1988	Ex Star Cars, Witney, 1994
7947RU	Scania K113CRB	Jonckheere Deauville P599	C53F	1989	Ex Scancoaches, North Acton, 1996
3169RU	Volvo B10M-55	Van Hool Alizée	C53F	1989	Ex North Mymms, Potters Bar, 1993
9803RU	Toyota Coaster HZB50R	Caetano Optimo III	C21F	1994	
N245NNR	Volvo B10M-62	Caetano Algarve II	C..FT	1995	

Named Vehicles:- 1023RU *Norfolk*; 2328RU *Cornwall*; 2629RU *Wiltshire*; 3169RU *Berkshire*; 5281RU *Yorkshire*; 5919RU *Shropshire*; 7947RU *Somerset*; 9803RU *Kent*; E710JJN *Hampshire*; EDR793 *Devon*; N245NNR *Cumbria*; PJI7727 *Lancashire*.

Previous registrations:-

2328RU	E608YJO	7947RU	F947RNV
2629RU	FDU2T, 2629RU, EJN270T	9803RU	From new
2786RU	MEL561P	E710JJN	E712GNH, 2851RU
3169RU	F993UME	EDR793	From new
5189RU	VRP281S, HIL8221, BHJ370S	NIW1639	BJU13T
5281RU	FUA391Y	PJI7727	A198MNE, LAW829W
5919RU	D130HML	UJN159V	LKX280V, ACH973A, UJN51V, 2786RU

Livery:- White, green and red.

Volvos, DAFs and a Scania form the front line coaching fleet of County Coaches of Brentwood. One of the Volvo B10Ms is 2328RU, and features Ikarus Blue Danube style coachwork. It was photographed in the heart of London's theatreland, Haymarket.
Capital Transport

COUNTRY TRAVEL

D J & J Geater, Moores Yard, Bigsbys Corner, Benhall,
Saxmundham, Suffolk, IP17 2AF

MJA749W	Mercedes-Benz L508D	Williams Deansgate	C18F	1980	Ex Tuck, Chaldon, 1990
XCM495W	Mercedes-Benz L508D	Reeve Burgess	C19F	1981	Ex Evans, Pensby, 1989
ULR923X	Mercedes-Benz L308	Devon Conversions	M13	1982	Ex private owner, 1989
KCJ677Y	Bedford YMP	Duple Dominant IV	C35F	1982	Ex Globe Coaches, Aberdare, 1991
RIB8031	Mercedes-Benz 0303	Jonckheere Jubilee P50	C51FT	1983	Ex Vision International, Ipswich, 1997
THE383Y	Mercedes-Benz L207D	Whittaker	M12	1983	Ex Poulsom, Copford, 1995
C738CUC	Leyland Cub CU335	Wadham Stringer Vanguard	B23FL	1986	Ex Crystals, Dartford, 1994
E85AVO	Mercedes-Benz 814D	Coachcraft	C19F	1987	Ex Wickson, Walsall Wood, 1997
N75JDX	Mercedes-Benz 811D	Marshall C16	B29F	1995	

Previous registration:-

RIB8031   UJN488Y, 114UPH, GHJ569Y

Livery:- White and three tone blue.

The newest vehicle in Country Travel's fleet is N75JDX, a Marshall C16-bodied Mercedes-Benz 811D minibus. It was employed on private hire duties when photographed at South Mimms services near Potters Bar. *Colin Lloyd*

CROWN

Crown Coaches Ltd, 10/12 Gaywood, Laindon, Basildon, Essex, SS15 6GX

C504DYM	Iveco Daily 49.10	Robin Hood City Nippy	B21F	1986	Ex The Shires, 1996
D345JUM	Volkswagen LT55	Optare Citypacer	B25F	1986	Ex BJS, Great Wakering, 1996
D202NON	Freight-Rover Sherpa	Carlyle	B18F	1987	Ex BJS, Great Wakering, 1996
D420HPO	Bova FHD12.290	Bova Futura	C49FT	1987	Ex Lucketts, Fareham, 1997
E964EHK	Volvo B10M-61	Ikarus Blue Danube 358	C53F	1988	
F700OPA	Iveco Daily 49.10	Carlyle Dailybus 2	B16F	1988	Ex The Bee Line, 1997
F677BBD	LAG G355Z	LAG Panoramic	C49FT	1989	Ex Coach Stop, Leigh-on-Sea, 1994
F470BOH	Ford Transit VE6	Ford	M8	1989	Ex private owner, 1995
G442WLL	Iveco Daily 49.10	Carlyle Dailybus 2	C21F	1989	Ex British Airways, 1997

Named Vehicles:- E964EHK *Silver Lady*; F677BBD *Pure Gold*

Previous registration:-
D420HPO   D131CJF, SJI5028

Livery:- Silver, grey, red and orange or white, red, maroon and black.

CRUSADER HOLIDAYS

Staines Crusader Coaches Ltd, Crusader Business Park, Stephenson Road West,
Clacton-on-Sea, Essex, CO15 4HP

E245RBE	Mercedes-Benz 609D	Coachcraft	C19F	1988	Ex Hailstone, Basildon, 1997
R101HEV	Setra S250	Setra Special	C48FT	1998	
R102HEV	Setra S250	Setra Special	C48FT	1998	
R103HEV	Setra S250	Setra Special	C48FT	1998	
R104HEV	Setra S250	Setra Special	C48FT	1998	
E105GOO	Van Hool T815	Van Hool Acron	C48FT	1988	
E106GOO	Van Hool T815	Van Hool Acron	C48FT	1988	
E107GOO	Van Hool T815	Van Hool Acron	C48FT	1988	
E108GOO	Van Hool T815	Van Hool Acron	C48FT	1988	
L109PVW	EOS E180Z	EOS 90	C48FT	1994	
L110PVW	EOS E180Z	EOS 90	C48FT	1994	
L111PVW	EOS E180Z	EOS 90	C48FT	1994	
L112PVW	EOS E180Z	EOS 90	C48FT	1994	
LSU113	Iveco EuroRider 391.12.35	Beulas Stergo E	C48FT	1997	
114RVX	Iveco EuroRider 391.12.35	Beulas Stergo E	C48FT	1997	
N115FHK	Kässbohrer Setra S250	Kässbohrer Special	C48FT	1996	
N116FHK	Kässbohrer Setra S250	Kässbohrer Special	C48FT	1996	
N117FHK	Kässbohrer Setra S250	Kässbohrer Special	C48FT	1996	
N118FHK	Kässbohrer Setra S250	Kässbohrer Special	C48FT	1996	
N119FHK	Kässbohrer Setra S250	Kässbohrer Special	C48FT	1996	
P120KNO	Iveco EuroRider 391.12.35	Beulas Stergo E	C48FT	1997	
R121HEV	Setra S250	Setra Special	C48FT	1998	
R122HEV	Setra S250	Setra Special	C48FT	1998	
R123HEV	Setra S250	Setra Special	C48FT	1998	
R124HEV	Setra S250	Setra Special	C48FT	1998	

Previous registrations:-

114RVX	From new		E107GOO	E107GOO, DSU107
E105GOO	E105GOO,UDX105		LSU113	From new

Livery:-Silver, blue, red, orange and yellow

D202NON, pictured here at Basildon, is one of the cream and red minibuses operated in the area by Crown Coaches. The Freight-Rover Sherpa was new to the Bee Line Buzz in Greater Manchester, though the vehicle was latterly with BJS. *Richard Godfrey*

Among recent arrivals in the Crusader Holidays fleet are two Iveco EuroRider coaches. This model is bodied by Iveco subsidiary Beulas to their Stergo E design. LSU 113 shows the smart silver based livery, as well as the air-conditioning pod on the roof. All vehicles in the fleet except the minibus are fitted with air-conditioning. *Glyn Matthews*

CUNNINGHAM CARRIAGE COMPANY

P E J Cunningham, Fobbing Road, Corringham, Essex, SS17 9BG

HKG65N	Bristol LHS6L	Plaxton Supreme III	C33F	1975	Ex Cherry, Aintree, 1994
572XAE	Kässbohrer Setra S215HD	Kässbohrer Tornado	C49FT	1982	Ex Turner, Bristol, 1991
B885WNB	Mercedes-Benz L608D	Imperial	M16	1985	
N844DKU	Scania K113TRB	Irizar Century 12.37	C49FT	1996	
P112GHE	Scania K113TRB	Irizar Century 12.37	C49FT	1996	Ex Scania demonstrator, 1998
R447YDT	Scania K113TRB	Irizar Century 12.37	C49FT	1998	

Previous registrations:-
572XAE   KEU572X

Named   Vehicles:- 572XAE *Stephanie*; B885WNB *Sarah Jane*; HKG65N *Sylvia*.N844DKU, *Sea Horse*; P112GHE *Sea Lion*, R447YDT, *Optopus*.

Livery:- White with various graphics

Included in the range of Irizar Century coachwork is the 12.37 design exclusively mounted, for the UK market, on the Scania K113TRB underframe.   Cunningham Carriage Company's N844DKU displays a white based livery embellished with sea horses and swordfish when seen at Hampton Court coach park. R447YDT, which joined the fleet in 1998, was the last of the model before the results of a re-styling exercise became available. *Geoff Rixon*

The East Anglia Bus Handbook

CUTTINGS

G E & J N Cutting & R D & W J Stittle, Hawks Farm, Brockley, Bury St Edmunds, Suffolk, IP29 4AQ

ATH777V	Volvo B58-56	Plaxton Supreme IV	C53F	1979	Ex K & T, Stratford, 1995
WNP332V	Ford R1114	Plaxton Supreme IV	C53F	1980	Ex Royal, Redditch, 1984
SIB7517	DAF MB200DKFL600	Berkhof Esprite 350	C53F	1984	Ex Gatwick Flyer, Romford, 1997
A203RUR	Leyland Tiger TRCTL11/3R	Plaxton Paramount 3200	C53F	1984	Ex Safeguard, Guildford, 1990
RAZ2228	Leyland Tiger TRCTL11/3RZ	Plaxton Paramount 3500	IIC53F	1985	Ex Mitcham Belle, 1990
C413DUM	Bedford Venturer YNV	Plaxton Paramount 3200 II	C53F	1986	Ex Yorkshire European, Harrogate, 1994
D832DPF	Bedford YMP	Plaxton Paramount 3200 III	C35F	1987	Ex Oakley Coaches, 1995
F799NPP	Ford Transit VE6	Chassis Developments	C16F	1988	
H175DJF	Toyota Coaster HB31R	Caetano Optimo	C21F	1990	Ex Cheney, Banbury, 1996

Previous registrations:-

C413DUM	C531KFV, A4YET	H175DJF	H175DJF, YSU975.	SIB7517	B593XNO
D832DPF	9489PH	RAZ2228	B492UNB		

Livery:- Red and cream.

D-WAY TRAVEL

D T Thompson, 4 The Street, Earsham, Bungay, Norfolk, NR35 2TZ

YBT849	Leyland Leopard PSU5/4R	Plaxton Panorama Elite	C57F	1971	Ex Gemini, Bishops Stortford, 1992
HDW873N	Ford R1114	Plaxton Panorama Elite III	C53F	1975	Ex Dalby, Beccles, 1989
VRU204S	Ford R1114	Plaxton Supreme III	C53F	1978	Ex Mikes, Basildon, 1997
WED984S	AEC Reliance 6U3ZR	Duple Dominant II	C53F	1978	Ex ?,1997
MHX49X	MAN SR280	MAN	C48FT	1982	Ex Dalby, Beccles, 1989
B529GNV	MAN SR280	MAN	C49FT	1985	Ex PR Coaches, Southall, 1993
B531GNV	MAN SR280	MAN	C49FT	1985	Ex Drewcrete, Hampstead, 1991
M140AVG	Ford Transit VE6	Ford	M14	1995	

Previous registration:-

YBT849	KGJ476K

Livery:- White, orange, yellow and brown.

The MAN SR280 integral coach was imported into Britain during the nineteen-eighties coach boom. Available in two heights, the majority are of the standard low height type like B529GNV of D-Way Travel pictured here near Victoria Coach Station.
Colin Lloyd

DEREHAM COACHWAYS

Dereham Coachways Ltd, 20 Rash's Green Industrial Estate,
East Dereham, Norfolk, NR19 1JG

Depots:- Rashes Green Industrial Estate, East Dereham and, Cowper Road, East Dereham.

APR855T	Bedford YMT	Plaxton Supreme IV	C53F	1979	Ex Meale, Reepham, 1995
GBH506T	Bedford YMT	Plaxton Supreme IV	C53F	1979	Ex Meale, Reepham, 1995
FUJ903V	Bedford YMT	Duple Dominant II	C53F	1980	Ex Reynolds, Caister, 1994
A431ESO	Volvo B10M-56	Plaxton Paramount 3200	C53F	1983	Ex Cadger, Balmedie, 1993
B650JSS	Volvo B10M-61	Plaxton Paramount 3200	C53F	1984	Ex Meek, Cheltenham, 1993
C176EMU	Volvo B10M-61	Plaxton Paramount 3200 II	C32FT	1986	Ex Euroline, Radford, 1997
D256HFX	Volvo B10M-61	Plaxton Paramount 3200 III	C53F	1987	Ex Essex Coachways, Bow, 1997
E278YPS	Volvo B9M-46	Plaxton Paramount 3200 III	C26FTL	1987	Ex Shetland Islands Council, 1997
E838NHP	Volvo B10M-61	Jonckheere Jubilee	C49FT	1988	Ex Eniway, Saham Toney, 1997
FAZ3942	Volvo B10M-61	Van Hool Alizée H	C53D	1988	Ex Travellers, Hounslow, 1995
G167RBD	Volvo B10M-60	Jonckheere Deauville P599	C51FT	1990	Ex Harkins, Glasgow, 1994
H935DRJ	Volvo B10M-60	Plaxton Paramount 3500 III	C53F	1991	Ex Shearings, 1998
H277DPS	Dennis Javelin 8.5SDA1915	Duple 320	C..FTL	1990	Ex Shetland Islands Council, 1997
K15FTG	Volvo B10M-60	Plaxton Excalibur	C49FT	1993	Ex Flights, Birmingham, 1994
L659ADS	Volvo B10M-60	Van Hool Alizée HE	C53F	1993	Ex Park's, Hamilton, 1996
M440AVG	Optare MetroRider MR11	Optare	B33F	1994	
N275DWY	Optare MetroRider MR11	Optare	B27F	1996	
P413TNG	Volvo B10M-62	Jonckheere Mistral 50	C53F	1997	

Previous registrations:-

E838NHP	E32MKV, 9840RU	FAZ3942	E264OMT
L659ADS	HSK645		

Livery:- Grey or silver and blue.

Two Optare-built MetroRiders were introduced on local town services by Dereham Coachways and marketed as Dereham Nipper. The newer of these, N275DWY, is the 1996 example and here shows its attractive silver and blue colour scheme. *Richard Godfrey*

DEWS

Ron W Dew & Son Ltd, Parkhall Road, Somersham, Huntingdon, Cambridgeshire, PE17 3ER

CUT465	Bedford OWB	Duple Vista (1953)	C29F	1944	Ex Potter, Leicester, 1973
ABC330K	Bedford J2SZ10	Plaxton Embassy	C20F	1971	Ex preservation, 1992
UFX360L	Bedford VAL70	Plaxton Panorama	C53F	1973	Ex Driver, Rainham, 1988
OSM95M	Bedford YRT	Plaxton Derwent	B60F	1973	Ex Sworder, Walkern, 1995
TBD619N	Bedford YRT	Willowbrook 001	B53F	1974	Ex Sworder, Walkern, 1996
JPV221N	Bedford YRT	Duple Dominant	B66F	1975	Ex Sworder, Walkern, 1991
NBJ462P	Bedford YRT	Willowbrook 001	B60F	1976	Ex Sworder, Walkern, 1996
WCE95T	Bedford YRT	Plaxton Supreme IV Express	C53F	1979	Ex Cambridgeshire Constabulary, 1989
DWK410T	Bedford YRT	Plaxton Supreme III	C53F	1979	Ex Lambkin, Queensborough, 1996
GSC660X	Leyland Atlantean AN68C/1R	Alexander AL	PO45/31F	1981	On loan from Lothian, 1997
GSC661X	Leyland Atlantean AN68C/1R	Alexander AL	PO45/31F	1981	On loan from Lothian, 1997
GSC662X	Leyland Atlantean AN68C/1R	Alexander AL	PO45/31F	1981	On loan from Lothian, 1997
GSC664X	Leyland Atlantean AN68C/1R	Alexander AL	PO45/31F	1981	On loan from Lothian, 1997
GSC665X	Leyland Atlantean AN68C/1R	Alexander AL	PO45/31F	1981	On loan from Lothian, 1997
34DEW	Scania K113CRB	Van Hool Alizée HE	C49FT	1992	Ex Scania demonstrator, 1993
687DEW	Volvo B10M-62	Van Hool Alizée HE	C53FT	1995	
N10DEW	Scania K113CRB	Van Hool Alizée HE	C53FT	1996	
DEW130Y	Volvo B10M-62	Jonckheere Mistral 50	C51F	1997	
R268TEG	Dennis Javelin	Berkhof Axial	C51FT	1997	

Named Vehicles:- GSC660X *Granta Star,* GSC661X *Fenland Star,* GSC662X *Cambridge Star,* GSC664X *Anglian Star,* GSC665X *Eastern Star,*

Previous registrations:-

34DEW	K525EHE	CUT465	From new
687DEW	M51HEW	DEW130Y	From new

Livery:- Green with grey, white and red relief; white, blue and black (The Cambridge Classic Tour) GSC660-2/4/5X.

Most of the front line coaches with Dews of Somersham have Van Hool Alizée coachwork albeit with a mixture of Scania and Volvo chassis. N10DEW is based on a Scania K113 and is seen parked in Cardiff. Dews operate the Cambridge Classic Tour in conjunction with Lothian Regional Transport.
Richard Eversden

DMA MINI COACHES

D M & B Adams, 240 Hatch Road, Pilgrims Hatch, Brentwood, Essex, CM15 9QR

OCN902R	Bedford YMT	Plaxton Supreme III	C53F	1977	Ex Beeston, Hadleigh, 1995
PJI6079	Bedford YMT	Duple Dominant II	C53F	1978	Ex Steed, Haverhill, 1997
LVY520T	Ford R1114	Plaxton Supreme III	C53F	1978	Ex Owen, Oswestry, 1994
XUX540T	Bedford VAS 5	Duple Dominant	C29F	1978	Ex Robinson, Kimbolton, 1988
SJI4423	Bedford YMT	Plaxton Supreme III Express	C53F	1979	Ex Constable, Long Melford, 1995
ABV881V	Ford R1114	Duple Dominant II	C53F	1980	Ex Stephensons, Rochford, 1995
XUN344V	Ford R1114	Plaxton Supreme IV	C53F	1980	Ex Tiffin, Brentwood, 1991
PJT518W	Ford R1114	Plaxton Supreme IV	C53F	1981	Ex Sanders, Holt, 1994
WNT377Y	Ford R1114	Duple Dominant IV	C53F	1983	Ex Tiffin, Brentwood, 1991
HIL3087	Volvo B10M-61	Jonckheere Jubilee P90	CH49/9FT	1983	Ex Maddren, Seaton Carew, 1997
D822LVS	Freight-Rover Sherpa	Chassis Developments	C16F	1986	Ex Neighbour, Great Missenden, 1987
KIW7813	Volvo B10M-61	Ikarus Blue Danube 358	C49FT	1987	Ex Cedric, Wivenhoe, 1996
E502NMD	Peugeot-Talbot Express	TBP	M8	1988	Ex private owner, 1995
F770CKM	Ford Transit VE6	Ford	M8	1988	Ex private owner, 1995
E168FLK	Mercedes-Benz 307D	Pilcher-Greene	M2L	1988	Ex Hackney Dial & Ride, 1997
F313YOL	Peugeot-Talbot Express	Adams	M12	1988	
F661RVX	Ford Transit VE6	Ford	M8	1989	Ex private owner, 1995
F562KNM	Ford Transit VE6	Ford	M8	1989	Ex private owner, 1995
G396VMD	Leyland-DAF 400	Adams	M16	1989	
G901BLP	Ford Transit VE6	Adams	M14	1990	Ex private owner, 1993
G947PFD	Ford Transit VE6	Adams	M16	1990	Ex private owner, 1997

Previous registrations:-

KIW7813	D773WHJ	PJI6079	TPJ286S
HIL3087	A312EAJ, GIL3016, A779KAJ	SJI4423	FBJ3T

Livery:- White and black.

New to Cedric's of Wivenhoe in 1987, KIW7813 was acquired when nine years old by DMA Mini Coaches of Brentwood. It is currently the only single deck coach in the fleet with a heavyweight Volvo B10M chassis, all other coaches being based on lightweight Fords and Bedfords. *Trevor Brookes*

DOLPHIN

Dolphin Autos (Norwich) Ltd, 195, Nelson Street, Norwich, Norfolk, NR2 4DS

GVF777Y	Mercedes-Benz L207D	Whittaker	M6	1982	Ex Kitchen, Great Yarmouth, 1998
A483JEX	Ford Transit 190	Dormobile	C16F	1983	
A646LEX	Ford Transit 190	Dormobile	C16F	1984	
A647LEX	Ford Transit 190	Dormobile	C16F	1984	
B240RBA	Ford Transit 190	Dixon Lomas	M12	1984	
B156PPW	Ford Transit 190	Williams Deansgate	M12	1984	
B544PAH	Ford Transit 190	Dormobile	B..FL	1984	Ex Norfolk C C, 1991
B800TNE	Ford Transit 190	Dixon Lomas	M16	1985	
VG7	Mercedes-Benz L608D	Dixon Lomas	C27F	1986	
C318DRH	Ford Transit 190	Carlyle	B18F	1986	Ex East Yorksire, 1996
C319DRH	Ford Transit 190	Carlyle	B18F	1986	Ex East Yorksire, 1996
C348RPE	Ford Transit 190	Carlyle	B16F	1986	Ex Silk, Swaffield, 1998
C374WBF	Mercedes-Benz L608D	PMT Hanbridge	C25F	1986	
C381WBF	Mercedes-Benz L608D	PMT Hanbridge	C25F	1986	
C682VLJ	Ford Transit 190	Ford	M11	1986	Ex private owner, 1988
D628JPW	Ford Transit 190	Ford	M..	1986	Ex private owner, 1996
D952CDX	Ford Transit 190	Ford	M..	1986	Ex private owner, 1995
D174LNA	Mercedes-Benz 609D	Dixon Lomas	C27F	1987	
D849OJA	Mercedes-Benz 609D	Made-to-Measure	C27F	1987	
D967CVV	Ford Transit 190	Ray	M11	1987	Ex Ray, Chieveley, 1990
E703UND	Mercedes-Benz 609D	Made-to-Measure	C27F	1987	
E690UND	Mercedes-Benz 609D	Made-to-Measure	C27F	1988	
E158NEG	Renault Master T35D	Renault	M6L	1988	
E160NEG	Renault Master T35D	Renault	M6L	1988	
E935RWR	Freight Rover Sherpa	Carlyle	B20F	1987	Ex Four Coaches, Ringstead, 1998
E644UVG	Ford Transit VE6	Ford	M11	1988	Ex private owner, 1990
E206SVG	Mercedes-Benz 507D	Pilcher Green	M16	1988	Ex Sharrington Village Bus, 1997
E613UPW	Mercedes-Benz 811D	Made-to-Measure	C19F	1988	Ex Wells, Gt. Yarmouth, 1989
F448CAH	Citreon Relay C25D	Citroen	M6	1988	Ex Lodge Hotel, Old Hunstanton, 1996
F409CEW	Renault Master T35D	Renault	M7L	1989	Ex East Anglia Ambulance Trust, 1997
F399KKM	Renault Master T35D	Renault	M6L	1989	Ex Kent CC, 1997
KAC1	Volvo B10M-61	Plaxton Paramount 3500 III	C53F	1988	
F964XEW	Ford Transit VE6	Dormobile	B11FL	1988	Ex Norfolk CC, 1998
F967XEW	Ford Transit VE6	Dormobile	B11FL	1988	Ex Norfolk CC, 1998
F893CCL	Mercedes-Benz 811D	Made-to-Measure	C24F	1989	
F840BPW	Ford Transit VE6	Ford	M11	1989	Ex private owner, 1990
F533DVG	Ford Transit VE6	Ford	M11	1989	Ex private owner, 1990
G189HPW	Ford Transit VE6	Ford	M14	1989	
G391MAG	Mercedes-Benz 609D	....	M14	1989	Ex Colne Shipping, Lowestoft, 1994
G670RAV	Ford Transit VE6	Dormobile	B11FL	1990	Ex Norfolk CC, 1998
G965VBC	Toyota Coaster HB31R	Caetano Optimo	C19F	1989	Ex Easton, Stratton Strawless, 1995
G903KPW	Mazda E2200	Made-to-Measure	M14	1990	
G904KPW	Ford Transit VE6	Made-to-Measure	M12	1990	
G905KPW	Mazda E2200	Made-to-Measure	M14	1990	
G21KAH	Ford Transit VE6	Ford	M14	1990	
G40KAH	Ford Transit VE6	Ford	M14	1990	
G695LNV	Ford Transit VE6	Ford	M....	1990	Ex private owner, 1997
H487BND	Ford Transit VE6	Made-to-Measure	M16	1990	Ex City Centre, Cardiff, 1993
H425DVM	Mercedes-Benz ?	Made-to-Measure	M16	1991	
91KC	Mercedes-Benz ?	?	M16	199.	
M173YGF	Mercedes-Benz 308D	Devon Conversion	M14	1994	Ex Stevenston Transport, 1998
N473LCL	LDV Convoy	LDV	M16	1996	
N668YAV	LDV Convoy	LDV	M16	1996	Ex ?, 1997
P258NVG	LDV Convoy	LDV	M16	1996	

Previous registration:-

91KC	?	M173YGF	M957NCF, ?.
KAC1	from new	VG7	C134EBU

Livery:- White, red, yellow, green, pink and blue.

FIRST EASTERN COUNTIES
FIRST BLUE BUS

Eastern Counties Omnibus Co Ltd, 79 Thorpe Road, Norwich, NR1 1UA

1	A696OHJ	Leyland Tiger TRCTL11/2R	Alexander TE	C53F	1983	Ex Badgerline, 1995
2	HHJ372Y	Leyland Tiger TRCTL11/2R	Alexander TE	DP53F	1983	Ex Badgerline, 1995
3	HHJ381Y	Leyland Tiger TRCTL11/2R	Alexander TE	DP53F	1983	Ex Eastern National, 1996
4	HHJ382Y	Leyland Tiger TRCTL11/2R	Alexander TE	C53F	1983	Ex Eastern National, 1996
11	H691HRT	Toyota Coaster HB31R	Caetano Optimo	C21F	1990	Ex Waylands, Beccles, 1996
20	FEH1Y	Leyland Tiger TRCTL11/3R	Plaxton Paramount 3500	C50FT	1983	Ex Midland Red West, 1997
21	6149KP	Leyland Tiger TRCTL11/3R	Plaxton Paramount 3200 E	C53F	1983	Ex Vanguard, 1993
22	7694VC	Leyland Tiger TRCTL11/3R	Plaxton Paramount 3200 E	C53F	1983	Ex Vanguard, 1993
23	CSV992	Leyland Tiger TRCTL11/3R	Plaxton Paramount 3200 E	C53F	1983	Ex Badgerline, 1996
24	CSV303	Leyland Tiger TRCTL11/3R	Plaxton Paramount 3200 E	C53F	1983	Ex Badgerline, 1996
25	CSV524	Leyland Tiger TRCTL11/3R	Plaxton Paramount 3200 E	C53F	1983	Ex Badgerline, 1996
26	F613XWY	Leyland Tiger TRCTL11/3ARZA	Plaxton Paramount 3200 IIIE	C53F	1988	Ex Thamesway, 1996
27	F614XWY	Leyland Tiger TRCTL11/3ARZA	Plaxton Paramount 3200 IIIE	C53F	1988	Ex Thamesway, 1996
28	B104JAB	Leyland Tiger TRCTL11/3RH	Plaxton Paramount 3200 II	C50F	1985	Ex Midland Red West, 1997
29	B568BOK	Leyland Tiger TRCTL11/3RH	Duple Caribbean 2	C50FT	1984	Ex Western National, 1997
30	P330RVG	Volvo B10M-62	Plaxton Première 320	C53F	1997	
31	P731NVG	Volvo B10M-62	Plaxton Première 320	C53F	1996	
32	P732NVG	Volvo B10M-62	Plaxton Première 320	C53F	1996	
33	P733NVG	Volvo B10M-62	Plaxton Première 320	C53F	1996	
34	P734NVG	Volvo B10M-62	Plaxton Première 320	C53F	1996	
35	4750WY	Volvo B10M-61	Plaxton Paramount 3200 II	C53F	1986	Ex Blue Bus, 1996
36	6220WY	Volvo B10M-61	Plaxton Paramount 3200 III	C48FT	1989	Ex Blue Bus, 1996
38	HEX119Y	Volvo B10M-61	Plaxton Paramount 3200	C51F	1983	Ex Blue Bus, 1996
39	131ASV	Volvo B10M-60	Van Hool Alizée	C50FT	1990	Ex Grampian (Mairs), 1997
40	N619APU	Volvo B10M-62	Plaxton Première 320	C53F	1996	Ex Essex Buses (Thamesway), 1997

101	XHK235X	Leyland Olympian ONLXB/1R	Eastern Coach Works	H47/31F	1981	Ex Thamesway, 1996
102	XHK236X	Leyland Olympian ONLXB/1R	Eastern Coach Works	H47/31F	1981	Ex Thamesway, 1996
103	XHK237X	Leyland Olympian ONLXB/1R	Eastern Coach Works	H47/31F	1981	Ex Thamesway, 1996

104-108   Leyland Olympian ONLXB/1RZ   Northern Counties   H40/35F*   1989   *107/8 are DPH40/25F

104	F101AVG	**105**	F102AVG	**106**	F103AVG	**107**	F104AVG	**108**	F105AVG

109	H101KVX	Leyland Olympian ON2R50G13Z4 Leyland		H45/32F	1990	Ex Thamesway, 1996
110	H102KVX	Leyland Olympian ON2R50G13Z4 Leyland		H45/32F	1990	Ex Thamesway, 1996
111	H103KVX	Leyland Olympian ON2R50G13Z4 Leyland		H45/32F	1990	Ex Thamesway, 1996
112	H104KVX	Leyland Olympian ON2R50G13Z4 Leyland		H45/32F	1990	Ex Thamesway, 1996

113-117   Leyland Olympian ON2R50G13Z4 Leyland   H47/31F   1991-92

113	J621BVG	**114**	J622BVG	**115**	J623BVG	**116**	J624BVG	**117**	J625BVG

118	E40OAH	Volvo Citybus B10M-50	East Lancashire	DPH45/33F	1987	Ex Blue Bus, 1996
119	E41OAH	Volvo Citybus B10M-50	East Lancashire	DPH45/33F	1987	Ex Blue Bus, 1996

189-205   Bristol VRT/SL3/6LXB   Eastern Coach Works   H43/31F   1976-78

189	RPW189R	**192**	TEX402R	**199**	WPW199S	**203**	XNG203S	**205**	XNG205S

Opposite, top:- **Withdrawal of the MCW MetroRiders has commenced at First Eastern Counties though 788, E45OAH which is fitted with high-back seating was still very active when pictured in Great Yarmouth, though it was withdrawn while this editon was being prepared. Vehicles allocated to Great Yarmouth town services carry the Blue Bus name and the local livery is also blue.**
Phillip Stephenson
Opposite, bottom:- **Eastern Counties have benefitted from a large intake of low-floor Plaxton-bodied Dennis Darts, the latest examples of which have Pointer 2 body styling and carry the new corporate livery for the Group which is being applied to all low-floor single-deck buses and new Volvo Olympians that also feature the latest interior trim. Seen at Ipswich is 473, R473CAH.** *Colin Lloyd*

212	WWY122S	Bristol VRT/SL3/6LXB	Eastern Coach Works	H43/31F	1977	Ex Rider Group, 1996			
213	WWY123S	Bristol VRT/SL3/6LXB	Eastern Coach Works	H43/31F	1977	Ex Rider Group, 1996			
214	WWY118S	Bristol VRT/SL3/6LXB	Eastern Coach Works	H43/31F	1977	Ex Rider Group, 1996			

216-230   Bristol VRT/SL3/6LXB   Eastern Coach Works   H43/31F   1978-79

216	BCL216T	219	BVG219T	222	BVG222T	224	BVG224T	229	DEX229T
218	BVG218T	220	BVG220T	223	BVG223T	225	BVG225T	230	DEX230T

232	JWT762V	Bristol VRT/SL3/6LXB	Eastern Coach Works	H43/31F	1980	Ex Rider Group, 1996			
233	LUA718V	Bristol VRT/SL3/6LXB	Eastern Coach Works	H43/31F	1980	Ex Rider Group, 1996			
234	LUA719V	Bristol VRT/SL3/6LXB	Eastern Coach Works	H43/31F	1980	Ex Rider Group, 1996			
235	LWU472V	Bristol VRT/SL3/6LXB	Eastern Coach Works	H43/31F	1980	Ex Rider Group, 1996			
236	DNG236T	Bristol VRT/SL3/6LXB	Eastern Coach Works	H43/31F	1979				

238-243   Bristol VRT/SL3/6LXB   Eastern Coach Works   H43/31F   1979

238	HAH238V	240	HAH240V	241	JAH241V	242	JAH242V	243	JAH243V
239	HAH239V								

246-250   Bristol VRT/SL3/6LXB   Eastern Coach Works   H43/31F   1980   Ex Trent, 1991

246	GRA842V	247	GRA843V	248	GRA845V	249	GRA847V	250	GRA846V

251-259   Bristol VRT/SL3/6LXB   Eastern Coach Works   H43/31F   1980

251	PCL251W	253	PCL253W	255	PCL255W	258	RAH258W	259	RAH259W
252	PCL252W	254	PCL254W	257	PCL257W				

260	PWY42W	Bristol VRT/SL3/6LXB	Eastern Coach Works	H43/31F	1980	Ex Rider Group, 1995			
261	RAH261W	Bristol VRT/SL3/6LXB	Eastern Coach Works	H43/31F	1980				
262	RAH262W	Bristol VRT/SL3/6LXB	Eastern Coach Works	H43/31F	1980				
263	RAH263W	Bristol VRT/SL3/6LXB	Eastern Coach Works	H43/31F	1980				
264	GGM107W	Bristol VRT/SL3/6LXB	Eastern Coach Works	H43/31F	1980	Ex The Bee Line, 1997			
265	CJH144V	Bristol VRT/SL3/6LXB	Eastern Coach Works	H43/31F	1980	Ex The Bee Line, 1997			
266	RAH266W	Bristol VRT/SL3/6LXB	Eastern Coach Works	H43/31F	1980				
267	RAH267W	Bristol VRT/SL3/6LXB	Eastern Coach Works	H43/31F	1980				
268	PUM148W	Bristol VRT/SL3/6LXB	Eastern Coach Works	H43/31F	1980	Ex Rider Group, 1996			

269-282   Bristol VRT/SL3/6LXB   Eastern Coach Works   H43/31F   1980-81

269	RAH269W	271	TAH271W	273	TAH273W	276	TAH276W	281	VAH281X
270	RAH270W	272	TAH272W	275	TAH275W	277	VAH277X	282	VAH282X

283-302   Bristol VRT/SL3/6LXB   Eastern Coach Works   H43/31F*   1981-82 *284/5/7 are DPH41/25F

283	VEX283X	286	VEX286X	288	VEX288X	292	VEX292X	297	VEX297X
284	VEX284X	287	VEX287X	290	VEX290X	294	VEX294X	302	VEX302X
285	VEX285X								

303-310   Bristol VRT/SL3/6LXB   Eastern Coach Works   H43/31F*   1981   Ex Trent, 1991

303	PRC848X	305	PRC851X	307	PRC853X	309	PRC855X	310	PRC857X
304	PRC850X	306	PRC852X	308	PRC854X				

319	GGM90W	Bristol VRT/SL3/6LXB	Eastern Coach Works	H43/31F	1980	Ex First Bee Line, 1998			
320	CVF31T	Bristol VRT/SL3/6LXB	Eastern Coach Works	H43/31F	1979	Ex Blue Bus, 1996			
321w	OCK995K	Bristol VRT/SL2/6LX	Eastern Coach Works	O39/31F	1972	Ex Ribble, 1985			
322w	NCK980J	Bristol VRT/SL2/6LX	Eastern Coach Works	O39/31F	1971	Ex Ribble, 1985			

324-330   Bristol VRT/SL3/6LXB   Eastern Coach Works   H43/31F   1979-81 Ex Blue Bus, 1996

324	PVG24W	326	PVG26W	328	CVF28T	329	CVF29T	330	CVF30T
325	PVG25W	327	PVG27W						

335w	ABD71X	Bristol VRT/SL2/6LX	East Lancashire	H44/28D	1981	Ex Northampton, 1995			
336	ABD72X	Bristol VRT/SL2/6LX	East Lancashire	H44/28D	1982	Ex Northampton, 1995			
337	ABD73X	Bristol VRT/SL2/6LX	East Lancashire	H44/28D	1982	Ex Northampton, 1995			
338	ABD73X	Bristol VRT/SL2/6LX	East Lancashire	H44/28D	1982	Ex Northampton, 1995			
340	GGM89W	Bristol VRT/SL3/6LXB	Eastern Coach Works	H43/34F	1980	Ex The Bee Line, 1997			

During 1996 the former Great Yarmouth Transport fleet, which operated as Blue Bus, was acquired by FirstGroup and placed under Eastern Counties management. The adopted livery was a blue version of the Eastern Counties styling and Bristol VR 327, PVG27W, is seen in that scheme at the James Paget hospital. *Richard Godfrey*

344	OSG74V	Leyland Fleetline FE30AGR	Eastern Coach Works	H43/32F	1979	Ex SMT, 1995
345	OSG55V	Leyland Fleetline FE30AGR	Eastern Coach Works	H43/32F	1979	Ex SMT, 1995
346	GSC856T	Leyland Fleetline FE30AGR	Eastern Coach Works	H43/32F	1978	Ex SMT, 1995
351	OSG51V	Leyland Fleetline FE30AGR	Eastern Coach Works	H43/32F	1979	Ex Lowland, 1996

| 381 | M381KVR | Mercedes-Benz 709D | Alexander Sprint | B29F | 1995 | On extended loan. |

| **394-399** | | Volvo B6-9.9m | Alexander Dash | B40F | 1994 | Ex Rider Group (Kingfisher), 1998 |

| 394 | L101PWR | **369** | L103PWR | **397** | L104PWR | **398** | L105PWR | **399** | L106PWR |
| 395 | L102PWR | | | | | | | | |

| 400 | L601MWC | Volvo B6-9.9M | Northern Counties Paladin | B40F | 1993 | Ex Essex Buses (Thamesway), 1997 |

| **401-410** | | Volvo B6-9.9M | Plaxton Pointer | B40F | 1994 | |

| 401 | M584ANG | **403** | M586ANG | **405** | M588ANG | **407** | M590ANG | **409** | M592ANG |
| 402 | M585ANG | **404** | M587ANG | **406** | M589ANG | **408** | M591ANG | **410** | M593ANG |

411	L807OPU	Dennis Dart 9SDL3034	Plaxton Pointer	B34F	1994	Ex Essex Buses (Eastern National), 1997
412	M923TEV	Dennis Dart 9.8SDL3035	Plaxton Pointer	B39F	1994	Ex Essex Buses (Thamesway), 1997
413	N345CJA	Volvo B6-9.9m	Alexander Dash	B36F	1996	Ex Greater Manchester, 1997
414	N346CJA	Volvo B6-9.9m	Alexander Dash	B36F	1996	Ex Greater Manchester, 1997
415	L501VHU	Dennis Dart 9SDL3034	Plaxton Pointer	B35F	1994	Ex Bristol (City Line), 1997
416	G456KNG	Dennis Dart 9SDL3002	Duple Dartline	B39F	1990	Ex Blue Bus, 1996
417	G457KNG	Dennis Dart 9SDL3002	Duple Dartline	B39F	1990	Ex Blue Bus, 1996
418	G458KNG	Dennis Dart 9SDL3002	Duple Dartline	B39F	1990	Ex Blue Bus, 1996
419	K62KEX	Dennis Dart 9.8SDL3025	East Lancashire	DP43F	1993	Ex Blue Bus, 1996
420	K63KEX	Dennis Dart 9.8SDL3025	East Lancashire	DP43F	1993	Ex Blue Bus, 1996
421	K741JAH	Dennis Dart 9SDL3011	Plaxton Pointer	B33F	1993	
422	K742JAH	Dennis Dart 9SDL3011	Plaxton Pointer	B33F	1993	
423	K743JAH	Dennis Dart 9SDL3011	Plaxton Pointer	B33F	1993	

Ten Wright Axcess-ultralow bodies were supplied on Scania chassis to Eastern Counties in June 1997. They are branded and used on service 88 which operates from Ipswich to Bury St Edmunds. Photographed shortly after entering service, 543, P543RNG is seen in Ipswich Road, Stowmarket.

424	K744JAH	Dennis Dart 9SDL3011	Plaxton Pointer	B33F	1993			

425-430		Dennis Dart 9SDL3041	Plaxton Pointer	B35F	1994			
425	M375YEX	427	M377YEX	428	M378YEX	429	M379YEX	430	M380YEX
426	M376YEX							

431	N625GAH	Dennis Dart 9SDL3041	Plaxton Pointer	B34F	1995			
432	N626GAH	Dennis Dart 9SDL3041	Plaxton Pointer	B34F	1995			

433-450		Dennis Dart SLF	Plaxton Pointer	N35F	1996-97			
433	P433NEX	437	P437NEX	441	P441NEX	445	P445NEX	448	P448NEX
434	P434NEX	438	P438NEX	442	P442NEX	446	P446NEX	449	P449NEX
435	P435NEX	439	P439NEX	443	P443NEX	447	P447NEX	450	P450NEX
436	P436NEX	440	P440NEX	444	P844OAH				

451	P451RPW	Dennis Dart SLF	Plaxton Pointer	N40F	1997	
452	P452RPW	Dennis Dart SLF	Plaxton Pointer	N40F	1997	
453	P453RPW	Dennis Dart SLF	Plaxton Pointer	N40F	1997	
454	M201VWW	Dennis Dart 9.8SDL3054	Plaxton Pointer	B40F	1995	Ex Rider Group (Leeds City), 1997
455	M202VWW	Dennis Dart 9.8SDL3054	Plaxton Pointer	B40F	1995	Ex Rider Group (Kingfisher), 1997
456	M203VWW	Dennis Dart 9.8SDL3054	Plaxton Pointer	B40F	1995	Ex Rider Group (Kingfisher), 1997
457	M107RRJ	Dennis Dart 9.8SDL3054	Northern Counties Paladin	B40F	1995	Ex Rider Group (Rider York), 1997

458-478		Dennis Dart SLF	Plaxton Pointer 2	N37F	1997-98			
458	R458BNG	463	R463CAH	467	R467CAH	471	R471CAH	475	R475CAH
459	R459BNG	464	R464CAH	468	R468CAH	472	R472CAH	476	R476CAH
460	R460BNG	465	R465CAH	469	R469CAH	473	R473CAH	477	R477CAH
461	R461BNG	466	R466CAH	470	R470CAH	474	R474CAH	478	R478CAH

| 462 | R462BNG |

| 479 | L502VHU | Dennis Dart 9SDL3034 | Plaxton Pointer | B35F | 1994 | Ex Bristol (City Line), 1997 |

506-510
Dennis Javelin 11SDL1933 — Duple 300 — DP48F — 1989

| 506 | G706JAH | 507 | G707JAH | 508 | G708JAH | 509 | G709JAH | 510 | G710JAH |

511-520
Dennis Javelin 11SDL1924 — Plaxton Derwent II — DP51F — 1990

| 511 | H611RAH | 514 | H614RAH | 516 | H616RAH | 518 | H618RAH | 520 | H620RAH |
| 512 | H612RAH | 515 | H615RAH | 517 | H617RAH | 519 | H619RAH | | |

536-540
Dennis Lance 11SDA3101 — Northern Counties Paladin — B49F — 1993

| 536 | K736JAH | 537 | K737JAH | 538 | K738JAH | 539 | K739JAH | 540 | K740JAH |

541-550
Scania L113CRL — Wright Axcess-ultralow — N47F — 1997

| 541 | P541RNG | 543 | P543RNG | 545 | P545RNG | 547 | P547RNG | 549 | P549RNG |
| 542 | P542RNG | 544 | P544RNG | 546 | P546RNG | 548 | P548RNG | 550 | P550RNG |

| 592 | N592WND | Mercedes-Benz 709D | Alexander Sprint | B27F | 1996 | On extended loan. |

602-610
Leyland National 2 NL116L11/1R — B49F — 1980

| 602 | KVG602V | 604 | KVG604V | 607 | KVG607V | 609 | KVG609V | 610 | PEX610W |

611	AAE655V	Leyland National 2 NL116L11/1R		B52F	1980	Ex Badgerline, 1996
615	PEX615W	Leyland National 2 NL116L11/1R		B49F	1980	
617	PEX617W	Leyland National 2 NL116L11/1R		B49F	1980	
618w	MDS868V	Leyland National 2 NL116L11/1R		B52F	1980	Ex Kelvin Central, 1996
620w	MDS860V	Leyland National 2 NL116L11/1R		B52F	1980	Ex Kelvin Central, 1996
622	AST155W	Leyland National 2 NL116L11/1R		B52F	1981	Ex Kelvin Central, 1996
624	UVF624X	Leyland National 2 NL116AL11/1R		B49F	1981	
625	UVF625X	Leyland National 2 NL116AL11/1R		B49F	1981	
628	UVF628X	Leyland National 2 NL116AL11/1R		B49F	1981	
629	KEP829X	Leyland National 2 NL116AL11/1R		DP44F	1988	Ex Eastern National, 1995
630	MHJ731V	Leyland National 2 NL116L11/1R		B49F	1980	Ex Eastern National, 1996

641-645
Leyland National 2 NL116HLXCT/1R — B49F* — 1984 — Ex Badgerline, 1996
*642/4/5 are B52F

| 641 | A201YWP | 642w | A202YWP | 643 | A203YWP | 644 | A204YWP | 645 | A205YWP |

651	DPW781T	Leyland National 11351A/1R (6HLX)	E Lancs Greenway (1994)	B49F	1978	
652	NIL3952	Leyland National 11351A/1R	East Lancs Greenway (1995)	B52F	1976	
653	NIL3953	Leyland National 11351A/1R	East Lancs Greenway (1994)	B52F	1976	
654	NIL3954	Leyland National 11351A/1R	East Lancs Greenway (1996)	B52F	1976	
655	NIL3955	Leyland National 11351A/1R	East Lancs Greenway (1994)	B49F	1977	
656	NIL3956	Leyland National 11351A/1R	East Lancs Greenway (1995)	B49F	1977	
657	NIL3957	Leyland National 11351A/1R	East Lancs Greenway (1995)	B52F	1977	
658	NIL3958	Leyland National 11351A/1R	East Lancs Greenway (1995)	B52F	1977	
659	NIL3959	Leyland National 11351A/1R	East Lancs Greenway (1993)	B52F	1977	
660	NIL3960	Leyland National 11351A/1R	East Lancs Greenway (1993)	B52F	1978	
661	NIL3961	Leyland National 11351A/1R	East Lancs Greenway (1995)	B52F	1978	
662	NIL3962	Leyland National 11351A/1R	East Lancs Greenway (1995)	B52F	1978	
663	NIL3963	Leyland National 11351A/1R	East Lancs Greenway (1995)	B52F	1978	
664	NIL3964	Leyland National 11351A/1R	East Lancs Greenway (1995)	B49F	1978	
665	NIL3965	Leyland National 11351A/1R	East Lancs Greenway (1994)	B52F	1978	Ex Stagecoach South, 1993
666	NIL3966	Leyland National 11351A/1R	East Lancs Greenway (1994)	B52F	1978	Ex Stagecoach South, 1993
667	NIL3967	Leyland National 11351A/1R	East Lancs Greenway (1994)	B52F	1978	Ex Merseybus, 1993

694-705
Mercedes-Benz 811D — Alexander AM — B28F — 1989 — Ex CentreWest, 1997
*703-5 are DP28F

| 694 | F694XMS | 696 | F696XMS | 698 | F698XMS | 700 | F700XMS | 704 | F704XMS |
| 695 | F695XMS | 697 | F697XMS | 699 | F699XMS | 703 | F703XMS | 705 | F705XMS |

710	C212PCD	Mercedes-Benz L608D	Alexander AM	B20F	1985	Ex Midland Red West, 1996
711	C711BEX	Mercedes-Benz L608D	Alexander AM	B20F	1986	
717	C717BEX	Mercedes-Benz L608D	Alexander AM	B20F	1986	
732	D532FAE	Mercedes-Benz L608D	Dormobile	B20F	1986	Ex Rider Group, 1996
737	D537FAE	Mercedes-Benz L608D	Dormobile	B20F	1986	Ex Rider Group, 1996

758	D541FAE	Mercedes-Benz L608D	Dormobile	B20F	1986	Ex Rider Group, 1996
764	D544FAE	Mercedes-Benz L608D	Dormobile	B20F	1986	Ex SWT, 1996
783	D606AFR	MCW MetroRider MF151/4	MCW	B23F	1987	Ex Blue Bus, 1996
785	E42OAH	MCW MetroRider MF151/9	MCW	DP25F	1987	Ex Blue Bus, 1996
791	E48RVG	MCW MetroRider MF159/1	MCW	B33F	1988	Ex Blue Bus, 1996
792	E49RVG	MCW MetroRider MF159/1	MCW	B33F	1988	Ex Blue Bus, 1996
801	N627GAH	Mercedes-Benz 711D	Alexander Sprint	B25F	1995	
802	N628GAH	Mercedes-Benz 711D	Alexander Sprint	B25F	1995	
803	H411BVR	Mercedes-Benz 709D	Carlyle	B27F	1991	Ex Waylands, Beccles, 1996
804	M242AEX	Mercedes-Benz 711D	Marshall C19	B29F	1995	Ex Waylands, Beccles, 1996
805	N887FVF	Mercedes-Benz 709D	Marshall C19	B29F	1995	Ex Waylands, Beccles, 1996

806-822   Mercedes-Benz Vario O810   Plaxton Beaver 2   B27F   1997

806	P806REX	810	P810REX	814	P814REX	817	P817REX	820	P820SCL
807	P807REX	811	P811REX	815	P815REX	818	P818REX	821	P821SCL
808	P808REX	812	P812REX	816	P816REX	819	P819REX	822	P822SCL
809	P809REX	813	P813REX						

879	K379DBL	Mercedes-Benz 709D	Plaxton Beaver	B23F	1992	Ex The Bee Line, 1997
880	H335LAN	Mercedes-Benz 811D	Reeve Burgess Beaver	B33F	1991	Ex Porthcawl Omnibus Co, 1997
881	G52GEX	Mercedes-Benz 811D	Reeve Burgess Beaver	DP33F	1989	Ex Blue Bus, 1996
882	G53GEX	Mercedes-Benz 811D	Reeve Burgess Beaver	DP33F	1989	Ex Blue Bus, 1996
883	G54GEX	Mercedes-Benz 811D	Reeve Burgess Beaver	B33F	1989	Ex Blue Bus, 1996
884	G55GEX	Mercedes-Benz 811D	Reeve Burgess Beaver	B33F	1989	Ex Blue Bus, 1996
885	G833RDS	Mercedes-Benz 811D	Reeve Burgess Beaver	B31F	1990	Ex Blue Bus, 1996
886	G453SGB	Mercedes-Benz 811D	Reeve Burgess Beaver	B31F	1990	Ex Blue Bus, 1996
887	G834RDS	Mercedes-Benz 811D	Reeve Burgess Beaver	B33F	1990	Ex Blue Bus, 1996
888	G395OWB	Mercedes-Benz 811D	Whittaker Europa	B26F	1990	Ex Blue Bus, 1996
889	J404WDA	Mercedes-Benz 811D	Whittaker Europa	B31F	1992	Ex Blue Bus, 1996
890	M68XVF	Mercedes-Benz 811D	Marshall C16	B33F	1994	Ex Blue Bus, 1996
891	M69XVF	Mercedes-Benz 811D	Marshall C16	B33F	1994	Ex Blue Bus, 1996
892	E202PWY	Mercedes-Benz 811D	Optare StarRider	DP33F	1987	Ex Rider Group, 1996
893	E201PWY	Mercedes-Benz 811D	Optare StarRider	DP33F	1987	Ex Rider Group, 1996
894	G644YVS	Mercedes-Benz 709D	Reeve Burgess Beaver	B25F	1990	Ex The Bee Line, 1997
895	G645YVS	Mercedes-Benz 709D	Reeve Burgess Beaver	B25F	1990	Ex The Bee Line, 1997
896	G646YVS	Mercedes-Benz 709D	Reeve Burgess Beaver	B25F	1990	Ex The Bee Line, 1997
897	G647YVS	Mercedes-Benz 709D	Reeve Burgess Beaver	B25F	1990	Ex The Bee Line, 1997
898	J31KLR	Mercedes-Benz 811D	Plaxton Beaver	B28F	1991	Ex The Bee Line, 1997
899	J37KLR	Mercedes-Benz 811D	Plaxton Beaver	B28F	1991	Ex The Bee Line, 1997
901	D758LEX	Mercedes-Benz 609D	Reeve Burgess	B20F	1987	
903	E701TNG	Mercedes-Benz 609D	Robin Hood	B20F	1988	
904	E702TNG	Mercedes-Benz 609D	Robin Hood	B20F	1988	

905-914   Mercedes-Benz 609D   Dormobile   B20F   1992-93

| 905 | K26HCL | 907 | K28HCL | 909 | J530FCL | 911 | K732JAH | 913 | K734JAH |
| 906 | K27HCL | 908 | K29HCL | 910 | K731JAH | 912 | K733JAH | 914 | K735JAH |

915-944   Mercedes-Benz 609D   Frank Guy   B20F   1993-94

915	L245PAH	921	L251PAH	927	L257PAH	933	M363XEX	939	M369XEX
916	L246PAH	922	L252PAH	928	L258PAH	934	M364XEX	940	M370XEX
917	L247PAH	923	L253PAH	929	L259PAH	935	M365XEX	941	M371XEX
918	L248PAH	924	L254PAH	930	M360XEX	936	M366XEX	942	M372XEX
919	L249PAH	925	L255PAH	931	M361XEX	937	M367XEX	943	M373XEX
920	L250PAH	926	L256PAH	932	M362XEX	938	M368XEX	944	M374XEX

945-964   Mercedes-Benz 609D   Frank Guy   B20F   1995

945	N605GAH	949	N609GAH	953	N613GAH	957	N617GAH	961	N621GAH
946	N606GAH	950	N610GAH	954	N614GAH	958	N618GAH	962	N622GAH
947	N607GAH	951	N611GAH	955	N615GAH	959	N619GAH	963	N623GAH
948	N608GAH	952	N612GAH	956	N616GAH	960	N620GAH	964	N624GAH

965	F34TJN	Mercedes-Benz 609D	Reeve Burgess Beaver	B19F	1989	Ex Waylands, Beccles, 1996
966	M883XVG	Mercedes-Benz 609D	Cymric	B20F	1995	Ex Waylands, Beccles, 1996
967	M884XVG	Mercedes-Benz 609D	Cymric	B20F	1995	Ex Waylands, Beccles, 1996
970	E470CGM	Mercedes-Benz 609D	Robin Hood	B20F	1987	Ex The Bee Line, 1997
971	E465CGM	Mercedes-Benz 609D	Robin Hood	B20F	1987	Ex The Bee Line, 1997
972	E472CGM	Mercedes-Benz 609D	Robin Hood	B20F	1987	Ex The Bee Line, 1997
973	E473CGM	Mercedes-Benz 609D	Robin Hood	B20F	1987	Ex The Bee Line, 1997

In order to reduce the step height of the Mercedes-Benz minibus a new model, the Vario O814 was introduced into Britain in 1996, the main deliveries taking place from 1997. New bodywork for the model has been introduced by several of the suppliers, Plaxton's version being known as the Beaver 2 which is seen here on the first batch of the model for First Eastern Counties. Norwich is the base for 813, P813REX. *Colin Lloyd*

976	E476CGM	Mercedes-Benz 609D	Robin Hood	B20F	1987	Ex The Bee Line, 1997
1770	XNG770S	Leyland National 11351A/1R		B52F	1978	
1862	YEV320S	Leyland National 11351A/1R		B49F	1978	Ex Essex Bus (Eastern National), 1997

Ancilliary vehicles:-

37	HEX118Y	Volvo B10M-61	Plaxton Paramount 3200	C51F	1983	Ex Blue Bus, 1996
853	E853PEX	Ford Transit 190	Robin Hood	B16F	1987	
9024	XNM824S	Bedford YMT	Duple Dominant II	C53F	1978	Ex Go West, Kings Lynn, 1976
9039	JTY926P	Bedford YRT	Plaxton Supreme III	C53F	1975	Ex Rosemary Coaches, Terrington, 1993
9040	C891BEX	Ford Transit 190	Robin Hood	B16F	1986	
9042	EHE234V	Bedford YMT	Duple Dominant II	C41F	1980	Ex Rosemary Coaches, Terrington, 1993

Local livery: Stone, purple and magenta replacing (firstGroup corprate for low floor buses; cream and red (Eastern Counties); cream and blue (Blue Bus).

Previous Registrations:

131ASV	G260RNS	NIL3955	TVF620R
4750WY	C517DND	NIL3956	WAH587S
6149KP	WWA300Y, 9258VC, GAC98Y	NIL3957	WAH588S
6220WY	F486LHO, 1879RU, F947WFA	NIL3958	WAH590S
7694VC	FWH37Y	NIL3959	WAH593S
CSV303	A207SAE	NIL3960	WAH598S
CSV524	A208SAE	NIL3961	WAH599S
CSV992	A209SAE	NIL3962	XNG765S
H691HRT	H667ATN, SLK886, H667ATN	NIL3963	XNG768S
HEX119Y	FUA385Y, 4750WY	NIL3964	DPW782T
J404WDA	J11OPY	NIL3965	VFX981S
NIL3952	PVF367R	NIL3966	UFX854S
NIL3953	PVF368R	NIL3967	YFY7M
NIL3954	PVF369R		

A former Thamesway Eastern Coach Works-bodied Leyland Olympian, 103, XHK237X, is seen at Thetford bus station on a morning service from Sudbury to Hunstanton. Photographed in June 1996, this summer Sunday service did not operate in 1997. *Roger Harrison*

Allocations

Bury St Edmunds (Cotton Lane)

Mercedes-Benz	805	880	885	892	893	894	895	896
	897	898	899	922	923	926	932	934
	942	944						
Tiger	1	2	3	4				
National	641	643	645	655	656	657	658	660
	665	666						
Bristol VR	205	225	235	236	249	261	269	281
	304	307						
Volvo coach	38							

Great Yarmouth (Caister Road) - Blue Bus

Mercedes-Benz	879	881	882	883	884	886	887	888
	889	890	891	895				
MetroRider	783	785	791	792				
Volvo B10M Coach	35	36	39					
Dart	411	412	416	417	418	419	420	421
	422	423	424	451	452	453	479	
National	615	617						
Bristol VR	219	238	251	262	268	292	320	324
	325	326	327	328	329	330	338	
Volvo Citybus	118	119						
Olympian	104							

Ipswich (Foundation Street)

Mercedes-Benz	920	928					
Volvo B6	394	400	401	402	403	404	405	406
	407	408	409	410	413	414		
Dart	415	425	426	427	428	429	430	431
	432	458	459	460	461	462		
Javelin	514	517	519					
Lance	536	537	538	539	540			
Scania	541	542	543	544	545	546	547	548
	549	550						
Bristol VR	189	192	212	213	214	232	233	240
	242	243	250	258	260	264	265	270
	275	276	287	290	306	309		
Olympian	101	102	103	106				

Kings Lynn (Vancouver Avenue)

Mercedes-Benz	758	921	941	943	955	956	958	959
	960	961	964					
Tiger	26	27						
Volvo B10Mcoach	30	31	32	33	34	40		
National	604	651						
Javelin	512	518						
Bristol VR	224	229	239	255	283	285	302	303

Kings Lynn (St Michael's Road) - Rosemary Coaches

Mercedes-Benz	820	821	822					
Tiger	20	21	22	23	24	25	28	29
Dart	449							
National	1770							
Bristol VR	222	223	319	336	337	340		
Fleetline	344	345	346	351				

Lowestoft (Gas Works Road)

Mercedes-Benz	801	802	909	911	912	913	914	930
	931	951	952	954	957	970	972	973
	976							
National	609	628	630	1862				
Javelin	520							
Bristol VR	199	203	216	230	234	263	284	286
	294	310						
Olympian	107	108						

Norwich (Vulcan Road and Roundtree Way) - Park & Ride ♣

Mercedes-Benz	694	695	696	697	698	699	700	703
	704	705	710	711	717	732	737	764
	806	807	808	809	810	811	812	813
	814	815	816	817	818	819	901	903
	904	905	906	907	908	910	915	916
	917	918	919	924	925	927	929	933
	935	936	937	938	939	940	945	946
	947	948	949	950	953	962	963	
Dart	433	434	435	436	437	438	439	440
	441	442	443	444	445	446	447	448
	450	454	455	456	457	463♣	464♣	465♣
	466♣	467♣	468	469	470	471	472	473
	474	475	476	477	478			

Eastern Counties acquired five new Northern Counties Paladin-bodied Dennis Lances in 1993 and all are now allocated to Ipswich where 540, K740JAH the last of the batch, is seen. *Colin Lloyd*

Javelin	506	507	508	509	510	515	516	
National	602	607	610	611	622	624	629	644
	652	653	654	658	659	661	662	663
	664	667						
Bristol VR	218	220	241	246	247	248	252	253
	254	257	259	266	267	271	272	273
	277	282	288	297	305	308		
Olympian	105	109	110	111	112	113	114	115
	116	117						

Worlingham (College Lane) - Waylands

Toyota	11				
Javelin	511				
National	625				
Mercedes-Benz	803	804	966	967	971

Unallocated

Volvo B6	395	396	397	398	399	
National	618	620	642			
Scania L113	551	552	553	554	555	556
Bristol VR	321	322	335			

The East Anglia Bus Handbook

FIRST EASTERN NATIONAL
FIRST THAMESWAY

Essex Buses Ltd, Stapleford Close, New Writtle Street, Chelmsford CM2 0SD

230	D230PPU	Mercedes-Benz L608D	Reeve Burgess	B20F	1986
231	D231PPU	Mercedes-Benz L608D	Reeve Burgess	B20F	1986
233	D233PPU	Mercedes-Benz L608D	Reeve Burgess	B20F	1986
234	D234PPU	Mercedes-Benz L608D	Reeve Burgess	B20F	1986

245-260

Mercedes-Benz 709D   Reeve Burgess Beaver   B23F   1988-89

| 245 | F245MVW | 250 | F250NJN | 254 | F254RHK | 256 | F256RHK | 258 | F258RHK |
| 246 | F246MVW | 251 | F251NJN | 255 | F255RHK | 257 | F257RHK | 260 | F260RHK |

| 261 | D764KWT | Mercedes-Benz 609D | Robin Hood | B20F | 1987 | Ex SWT, 1994 |

301-356

Mercedes-Benz 709D   Reeve Burgess Beaver   B23F   1991

301	H301LPU	313	H314LJN	324	H331LJN	335	H344LJN	346	H356LJN
302	H302LPU	314	H315LJN	325	H332LJN	336	H345LJN	347	H357LJN
303	H303LPU	315	H317LJN	326	H334LJN	337	H346LJN	348	H358LJN
304	H304LPU	316	H319LJN	327	H335LJN	338	H347LJN	349	H359LJN
305	H305LPU	317	H321LJN	328	H336LJN	339	H348LJN	350	H361LJN
306	H306LPU	318	H322LJN	329	H337LJN	340	H349LJN	351	H362LJN
307	H307LJN	319	H324LJN	330	H338LJN	341	H351LJN	352	H363LJN
308	H308LJN	320	H326LJN	331	H339LJN	342	H352LJN	353	H364LJN
309	H310LJN	321	H327LJN	332	H341LJN	343	H353LJN	354	H365LJN
310	H311LJN	322	H329LJN	333	H342LJN	344	H354LJN	355	H366LJN
311	H312LJN	323	H330LJN	334	H343LJN	345	H355LJN	356	H367LJN
312	H313LJN								

357-387

Mercedes-Benz 709D   Reeve Burgess Beaver   B23F   1991

357	H368OHK	364	H375OHK	370	H381OHK	376	H387OHK	382	H393OHK
358	H369OHK	365	H376OHK	371	H382OHK	377	H388OHK	383	H394OHK
359	H370OHK	366	H377OHK	372	H383OHK	378	H389OHK	384	H395OHK
360	H371OHK	367	H378OHK	373	H384OHK	379	H390OHK	385	H396OHK
361	H372OHK	368	H379OHK	374	H385OHK	380	H391OHK	386	H397OHK
362	H373OHK	369	H380OHK	375	H386OHK	381	H392OHK	387	H398OHK
363	H374OHK								

Essex Buses operate under First Thamesway and First Eastern National trading names, the former concentrating on the area from London to the southern part of Essex. Pictured on London Transport duties is Mercedes-Benz minibus 406, P406HPU.
Colin Lloyd

388-395

		Mercedes-Benz 709D		Reeve Burgess Beaver	B23F	1991	
388	H388MAR	390	H390MAR	392	H392MAR	394	H394MAR	395	H395MAR
389	H389MAR	391	H391MAR	393	H393MAR		

396	K396KHJ	Mercedes-Benz 709D	Plaxton Beaver	B23F	1993
397	K397KHJ	Mercedes-Benz 709D	Plaxton Beaver	B23F	1993
398	K398KHJ	Mercedes-Benz 709D	Plaxton Beaver	B23F	1993

401-410

Mercedes-Benz 711D — Plaxton Beaver — B23F — 1996

401	P401HPU	403	P403HPU	405	P405HPU	407	P407HPU	409	P409HPU
402	P402HPU	404	P404HPU	406	P406HPU	408	P408HPU	410	P410HPU

411-419

Mercedes-Benz Vario O814 — Marshall Master — B27F — 1997

411	R411VPU	413	R413VPU	415	R415VPU	417	R417VPU	419	R419VPU
412	R412VPU	414	R414VPU	416	R416VPU	418	R418VPU		

421-428

Mercedes-Benz Vario O814 — Plaxton Beaver 2 — B27F — 1997

421	P701PWC	423	P703PWC	425	P705PWC	427	P707PWC	428	P708PWC
422	P702PWC	424	P704PWC	426	P706PWC				

601-618

Volvo B10M-62 — Plaxton Premiére 320 — C53F — 1995-96

601	N601APU	605	N605APU	609	N609APU	613	N613APU	616	N616APU
602	N602APU	606	N606APU	610	N610APU	614	N614APU	617	N617APU
603	N603APU	607	N607APU	611	N611APU	615	N615APU	618	N618APU
604	N604APU	608	N608APU	612	N612APU				

701	N701CPU	Dennis Dart SLF	Plaxton Pointer	N37F	1995

702-711

Dennis Dart — Plaxton Pointer — B37F — 1996

702	P702HPU	704	P704HPU	706	P706HPU	708	P708HPU	710	P710HPU
703	P703HPU	705	P705HPU	707	P707HPU	709	P709HPU	711	P711HPU

712-721

Dennis Dart SLF — Plaxton Pointer 2 — N37F — 1998

712	R712DJN	714	R714DJN	716	R716DJN	718	R718DJN	720	R720DJN
713	R713DJN	715	R715DJN	717	R717DJN	719	R719DJN	721	R721DJN

800-804

Mercedes-Benz 811D — Reeve Burgess Beaver — B31F — 1989

800	F800RHK	801	F801RHK	802	F802RHK	803	F803RHK	804	F804RHK

805-811

Mercedes-Benz 811D — Plaxton Beaver — B31F — 1992

805	K805DJN	807	K807DJN	809	K809DJN	810	K810DJN	811	K811DJN
806	K806DJN	808	K808DJN						

851	N851CPU	Dennis Dart 9SDL3040	Marshall C36	DP17FL	1995
852	N852CPU	Dennis Dart 9SDL3040	Marshall C36	DP17FL	1995
853	N853CPU	Dennis Dart 9SDL3040	Marshall C36	DP17FL	1995
854	N854CPU	Dennis Dart 9SDL3040	Marshall C36	DP17FL	1995

901-917

Dennis Dart 9SDL3016 — Plaxton Pointer — B35F — 1992 — On loan to MTL London.

901	K901CVW	905	K905CVW	909	K909CVW	912	K912CVW	915	K915CVW
902	K902CVW	906	K906CVW	910	K910CVW	913	K913CVW	916	K916CVW
903	K903CVW	907	K907CVW	911	K911CVW	914	K914CVW	917	K917CVW
904	K904CVW	908	K908CVW						

918-943

Dennis Dart 9.8SDL3035 — Plaxton Pointer — B39F — 1994

918	M918TEV	925	M925TEV	930	M930TEV	935	M935TEV	940	M940TEV
919	M919TEV	926	M926TEV	931	M931TEV	936	M936TEV	941	M941TEV
920	M920TEV	927	M927TEV	932	M932TEV	937	M937TEV	942	M942TEV
921	M921TEV	928	M928TEV	933	M933TEV	938	M938TEV	943	M943TEV
922	M922TEV	929	M929TEV	934	M934TEV	939	M939TEV		
924	M924TEV								

944-972

	Dennis Dart 9.8SDL3054		Plaxton Pointer		B39F*	1995	*959-72 are B37F	

944	N944CPU	950	N950CPU	956	N956CPU	962	N962CPU	968	N968CPU
945	N945CPU	951	N951CPU	957	N957CPU	963	N963CPU	969	N969CPU
946	N946CPU	952	N952CPU	958	N958CPU	964	N964CPU	970	N970CPU
947	N947CPU	953	N953CPU	959	N959CPU	965	N965CPU	971	N971CPU
948	N948CPU	954	N954CPU	960	N960CPU	966	N966CPU	972	N972CPU
949	N949CPU	955	N955CPU	961	N961CPU	967	N967CPU		

973-987

Dennis Dart — Plaxton Pointer — B40F — 1996

973	N973EHJ	976	N976EHJ	979	N979EHJ	982	N982EHJ	985	N985EHJ
974	N974EHJ	977	N977EHJ	980	N980EHJ	983	N983EHJ	986	N986EHJ
975	N975EHJ	978	N978EHJ	981	N981EHJ	984	N984EHJ	987	N987EHJ

1001-1006

Leyland Tiger TRBTL11/2R — Duple Dominant — DP47F — 1983-84 Ex Rider Group, 1995

1001	EWR651Y	1002	EWR652Y	1003	EWR653Y	1004	A660KUM	1006	A665KUM

1114w	HHJ375Y	Leyland Tiger TRCTL11/3R	Alexander TE	C53F	1983	
1115w	HHJ376Y	Leyland Tiger TRCTL11/3R	Alexander TE	C53F	1983	
1128	B696WAR	Leyland Tiger TRCTL11/3R	Plaxton Paramount 3500 II	C51F	1985	
1129	B697WAR	Leyland Tiger TRCTL11/3R	Plaxton Paramount 3500 II	C51F	1985	
1130	C130HJN	Leyland Tiger TRCTL11/3R	Plaxton Paramount 3200 II E	C53F	1986	
1131	EWW946Y	Leyland Tiger TRCTL11/3R	Plaxton Paramount 3200 E	C53F	1983	Ex Rider Group, 1995

1400-1429

Leyland Lynx LX112L10ZR/1R — Leyland Lynx — B49F* — 1988 — 1427-9 are B47F

1400	E400HWC	1406	F406LTW	1412	F412MNO	1418	F418MWC	1424	F424MJN
1401	E401HWC	1407	F407LTW	1413	F413MNO	1419	F419MWC	1425	F425MJN
1402	F402LTW	1408	F408LTW	1414	F414MNO	1420	F420MJN	1426	F426MJN
1403	F403LTW	1409	F409LTW	1415	F415MWC	1421	F421MJN	1427	F427MJN
1404	F404LTW	1410	F410MNO	1416	F416MWC	1422	F422MJN	1428	F428MJN
1405	F405LTW	1411	F411MNO	1417	F417MWC	1423	F423MJN	1429	F429MJN

1430	D755DLO	Leyland Lynx LX112TL11ZR1S	Leyland Lynx	B49F	1987	Ex CentreWest, 1997

1501-1513

Dennis Lance — Northern Counties Paladin — B49F — 1997

1501	P501MNO	1504	P504MNO	1507	P507MNO	1510	P510MNO	1512	P512MNO
1502	P502MNO	1505	P505MNO	1508	P508MNO	1511	P511MNO	1513	P513MNO
1503	P503MNO	1506	P506MNO	1509	P509MNO				

1803-1870

Leyland National 11351A/1R — B49F — 1977-78

1803	TJN502R	1833	VAR899S	1850	YEV308S	1863	YEV321S	1870	YEV328S
1830w	VNO732S	1845	WJN565S						

1882-1924

Leyland National 11351A/1R — B49F — 1978-79

1882w	BNO672T	1889w	BNO679T	1899	DAR121T	1916	JHJ142V	1924	JHJ150V
1886	BNO676T	1896w	DAR118T	1907w	DAR129T	1921	JHJ147V		

2217w	C217HJN	Mercedes-Benz L608D	Reeve Burgess	B20F	1986	
2230w	C485BHY	Mercedes-Benz L608D	Reeve Burgess	B20F	1986	Ex City Line, 1993
2231w	C486BHY	Mercedes-Benz L608D	Reeve Burgess	B20F	1986	Ex City Line, 1993
2232w	C489BHY	Mercedes-Benz L608D	Reeve Burgess	B20F	1986	Ex City Line, 1993
2233w	C493BHY	Mercedes-Benz L608D	Reeve Burgess	B20F	1986	Ex City Line, 1993
2237w	C678ECV	Mercedes-Benz L608D	Reeve Burgess	B20F	1986	Ex Western National, 1993
2242w	C695ECV	Mercedes-Benz L608D	Reeve Burgess	B19F	1986	Ex Western National, 1993
2244w	C698ECV	Mercedes-Benz L608D	Reeve Burgess	B19F	1986	Ex Western National, 1993
2247w	D534KGL	Mercedes-Benz L608D	Robin Hood	B20F	1986	Ex Western National, 1994
2248w	C107HGL	Mercedes-Benz L608D	Reeve Burgess	B20F	1986	Ex Western National, 1994
2252w	C230HCV	Mercedes-Benz L608D	Robin Hood	B20F	1986	Ex Western National, 1994

2601-2617 Mercedes-Benz 709D Reeve Burgess Beaver B23F 1991

2601	H601OVW	2605	H605OVW	2609	H609OVW	2612	J612UTW	2615	J615UTW
2602	H602OVW	2606	H606OVW	2610	J610UTW	2613	J613UTW	2616	J616UTW
2603	H603OVW	2607	H607OVW	2611	J611UTW	2614	J614UTW	2617	J617UTW
2604	H604OVW	2608	H608OVW						

2618-2630 Mercedes-Benz 709D Plaxton Beaver B23F 1991

2618	J618UTW	2621	J621UTW	2624	J624UTW	2627	J627UTW	2629	J629UTW
2619	J619UTW	2622	J622UTW	2625	J625UTW	2628	J628UTW	2630	J630UTW
2620	J620UTW	2623	J623UTW	2626	J626UTW				

2631-2656 Mercedes-Benz 709D Plaxton Beaver B23F 1993-94

2631	K631GVX	2637	K637GVX	2642	K642GVX	2647	L647MEV	2652	L652MEV
2632	K632GVX	2638	K638GVX	2643	K643GVX	2648	L648MEV	2653	L653MEV
2633	K633GVX	2639	K639GVX	2644	K644GVX	2649	L649MEV	2654	L654MEV
2634	K634GVX	2640	K640GVX	2645	K645GVX	2650	L650MEV	2655	L655MEV
2635	K635GVX	2641	K641GVX	2646	K646GVX	2651	L651MEV	2656	L656MEV
2636	K636GVX								

2657-2676 Mercedes-Benz 709D Plaxton Beaver B23F 1995

2657	M657VJN	2661	M661VJN	2665	M665VJN	2669	M669VJN	2673	M673VJN
2658	M658VJN	2662	M662VJN	2666	M166VJN	2670	M670VJN	2674	M674VJN
2659	M659VJN	2663	M663VJN	2667	M667VJN	2671	M671VJN	2675	M675VJN
2660	M660VJN	2664	M664VJN	2668	M668VJN	2672	M672VJN	2676	M676VJN

2677	L21AHA	Mercedes-Benz 709D	Plaxton Beaver	B23F	1993	Ex Frontline, 1995

2678-2682 Mercedes-Benz 709D Plaxton Beaver B23F 1996

2678	P678HPU	2679	P679HPU	2680	P680HPU	2681	P681HPU	2682	P682HPU

2801-2822 Dennis Dart 9SDL3034 Plaxton Pointer B34F 1993-94

2801	L801MEV	2806	L806OPU	2811	L811OPU	2815	L815OPU	2819	L819OPU
2802	L802MEV	2808	L808OPU	2812	L812OPU	2816	L816OPU	2820	L820OPU
2803	L803OPU	2809	L809OPU	2813	L813OPU	2817	L817OPU	2821	L821OPU
2804	L804OPU	2810	L810OPU	2814	L814OPU	2818	L818OPU	2822	L822OPU
2805	L805OPU								

2823-2830 Dennis Dart 9.8SDL3054 Plaxton Pointer B39F 1995

2823	N823APU	2825	N825APU	2827	N827APU	2829	N829APU	2830	N830APU
2824	N824APU	2826	N826APU	2828	N828APU				

3069-3094 Bristol VRT/SL3/6LXB Eastern Coach Works H43/31F* 1980-81 *3069/71/92 are H39/31F

3069	KOO787V	3076	KOO794V	3079	STW23W	3084	STW28W	3093	STW37W
3071	KOO789V	3077	STW21W	3083	STW27W	3092	STW36W	3094	STW38W
3072	KOO790V	3078	STW22W						

3101	UAR591W	Bristol VRT/SL3/6LXB	Eastern Coach Works	H43/31F	1981
3103	UAR593W	Bristol VRT/SL3/6LXB	Eastern Coach Works	H43/31F	1981
3106	UAR596W	Bristol VRT/SL3/6LXB	Eastern Coach Works	H43/34F	1981
3109	UAR599W	Bristol VRT/SL3/6LXB	Eastern Coach Works	H43/31F	1981
3110	XHK215X	Bristol VRT/SL3/6LXB	Eastern Coach Works	H43/31F	1981
3112	XHK217X	Bristol VRT/SL3/6LXB	Eastern Coach Works	H43/34F	1981
3113	XHK218X	Bristol VRT/SL3/6LXB	Eastern Coach Works	H43/31F	1981
3127	XHK232X	Bristol VRT/SL3/6LXB	Eastern Coach Works	H43/31F	1981

Opposite, top:- **Eight Mercedes-Benz Vario minibuses entered service at Chelmsford in June 1997. Pictured with its initial fleet number, P701PWC is now numbered 421 with Essex Buses. Later deliveries of the Vario carry bodywork by Marshalls of Cambridge.** *Phillip Stephenson*
Opposite, bottom:- **Thamesway's operations dominate south Essex and perform the London Transport workings if Essex Buses and there coaches now undertaking the City Saver express service between Southend and the capital. For this service a fleet of Plaxton Premiére 320s based on Volvo chassis are used. A modified version of the normal scheme is seen on 606, N606APU.** *Colin Lloyd*

3219	VTH941T	Bristol VRT/SL3/501	Eastern Coach Works	H43/31F	1978	Ex Brewers, 1990
3220	WTH949T	Bristol VRT/SL3/501	Eastern Coach Works	H43/31F	1979	Ex Brewers, 1990
3221	WTH958T	Bristol VRT/SL3/501	Eastern Coach Works	H43/31F	1979	Ex Brewers, 1990
3222	BEP963V	Bristol VRT/SL3/501(6LXB)	Eastern Coach Works	H43/31F	1980	Ex Brewers, 1990

3225-3234

		Bristol VRT/SL3/6LXB	Eastern Coach Works	H43/31F	1977-81	Ex Rider Group, 1994-96
						3226 was rebodied 1979

3225	AYG850S	3227	LUA716V	3229	PWY44W	3233	LUA717V	3234	NUM339V
3226	DWU298T	3228	LWU469V	3230	SUB789W				

4003	B698BPU	Leyland Olympian ONLXB/1R	Eastern Coach Works	H45/32F	1984
4004	B699BPU	Leyland Olympian ONLXB/1R	Eastern Coach Works	H45/32F	1984
4005	C711GEV	Leyland Olympian ONLXB/1R	Eastern Coach Works	H45/32F	1985

4007-4021

		Leyland Olympian ONLXB/1R	Eastern Coach Works	DPH42/30F	1986

4007	C407HJN	4010	C410HJN	4014	C414HJN	4017	C417HJN	4019	C419HJN
4008	C408HJN	4012	C412HJN	4015	C415HJN	4018	C418HJN	4021	C421HJN
4009	C409HJN	4013	C413HJN	4016	C416HJN				

4304	L304PWR	Volvo Olympian YN2RV18Z4	Northern Counties Palatine	H47/29F	1994	Ex Rider Group (Calderline), 1998
4501	B689BPU	Leyland Olympian ONTL11/2RHSp	Eastern Coach Works	CH45/28F	1985	
4503	B691BPU	Leyland Olympian ONTL11/2RHSp	Eastern Coach Works	CH45/28F	1985	
4510	D510PPU	Leyland Olympian ONTL11/2RHSp	Eastern Coach Works	CH45/28F	1986	
4511	D511PPU	Leyland Olympian ONTL11/2RHSp	Eastern Coach Works	CH41/24F	1986	
4512	D512PPU	Leyland Olympian ONTL11/2RHSp	Eastern Coach Works	CH45/24F	1986	

Heritage vehicles:-

2383	WNO479	Bristol KSW5G	Eastern Coach Works	O33/28R	1953	Ex Westcliffe-on-Sea, 1955
2384	WNO480	Bristol KSW5G	Eastern Coach Works	O33/28R	1953	Ex Westcliffe-on-Sea, 1955
9001	AJN825	Bristol K5G	Eastern Coach Works	L27/26R	1939	

Ancilliary vehicles:-

9014	CTN635V	Bedford YMQ	Duple Dominant II Express	C45F	1980	Ex County, 1994
9016	XYK761T	Bedford YLQ	Duple Dominant II	C41F	1978	
9017	YYL794T	Bedford YLQ	Duple Dominant II	C41F	1978	
9018	D228PPU	Mercedes-Benz L608D	Reeve Burgess	B20F	1986	
9717	C511BFB	Ford Transit 190	Dormobile	B16F	1986	

On order:- 10 Dart SLF and 5 Dart SPD.

Local livery: FirstGroup stone, purple and magenta (on low floor vehicles) replacing green and yellow (Eastern National); canary yellow and purple (Thamesway); yellow, orange and blue (City Saver); cream and green (traditional). **Note:** All vehicles were new to Eastern National or Thamesway except where shown.

Allocations

Basildon (Cherrydown) - Thamesway - City Saver ç

Mercedes-Benz	336	337	338	339	340	341	342	343
	344	345	346	347	348	356	358	359
	360	361	362	363	364	365	366	367
	368	369	370	371	372	373	374	375
	376	377	378	379	380	381	401	402
	403	404	405	406	407	408	409	410
	2660	2661	2662					
Dart	851	852	853	854	918	919	920	921
	922	924	925	926	927	928	929	930
	931	932	933	934	935	936	937	939
	940	941	942	943	944	959	960	961
	962	963	964	965	966	967	968	969
	970	971	972	2808	2817	2819	2821	2822
Volvo B10M Coach	601ç	602ç	603ç	604ç	605ç	606ç	607ç	608ç
	609ç	610ç	611ç	612ç	613ç	614ç	615ç	616ç
	617ç	618ç						
Olympian	4003	4004	4005					

Pictured heading for Southend and carrying the initial City Saver livery is Essex Bus 613, N613APU. For the time being the new corporate First livery is not being applied to vehicles other than low floor buses and Olympians that contain the new colour interior. Further details of the scheme can be found in the 1998 FirstGroup Bus Handbook. *David Heath*

Braintree (Fairfield Road) - Eastern National

Mercedes-Benz	382	383	384	385	386	387	2602	2621
	2625	2626	2627	2628	2629	2630	2661	2662
	2663	2664	2665	2666				
Dart	2812	2826						

Brentwood (Brentwood Station) - Thamesway

Mercedes-Benz	349	350	351	352	353	354	355	357
	2657	2658	2659					

Chelmsford (Duke Street) - Eastern National

Outstations: Bishops Stortford, Dunmow and Maldon.

Mercedes-Benz	421	422	423	424	425	426	427	428
	2603	2604	2605	2606	2607	2608	2609	2610
	2611	2612	2613	2614	2615	2616	2617	2618
	2619	2620	2622	2623	2624	2631	2632	2633
	2634	2635	2636	2637	2638	2639	2640	2641
	2642	2643	2644	2645	2646	2677		
Dart	712	713	714	715	716	2802	2813	2814
	2815	2816	2823	2824	2825			

Like many of the larger groups, FirstGroup order vehicles centrally for the whole group and these are then allocated to companies as each company's budget allows. During 1997 the Thamesway share included 704, P704HPU, seen here in Southend. This Dennis Dart is of the low floor version, though the bodywork remains to the original Pointer styling. FirstGroup were the only recipients of the Pointer 2 model during 1997. *Colin Brown*

Tiger	1001	1002	1003	1004	1006	1128	1129	1130
	1131							
Lynx	1401	1402	1403	1407	1408	1413	1414	1415
	1416	1425	1426	1427	1428	1429		
National	1833	1896						
Bristol VR	3069	3071	3077	3079	3083	3084	3092	3103
	3106	3110	3112	3230				
Olympian	4013	4014						

Clacton-on-Sea (Telford Road) - Eastern National

Mercedes-Benz	308	328	329	330	331	332	333	334
	335	2601	2647	2648	2649	2650	2651	2652
	2653	2654	2655	2668				
Dart	2827	2828	2829	2830				
Bristol VR	3072	3219	3220	3221	3222			
Olympian	4009							

Colchester (Queen Street & Haven Road) - Eastern National

Mercedes-Benz	2670	2671	2672	2673	2674	2675	2676	2678
	2679	2680	2681					
Dart	2801	2803	2804	2805	2806	2809	2810	2811
	2818	2820						
Lance	1501	1502	1503	1504	1505	1506	1507	1508
	1509	1510	1511					
National	1850	1899	1916	1921	1924			
Bristol VR	3093	3094	3101	3127	3226	3227	3228	3229
	3233							
Olympian	4010	4012	4015	4016	4017	4018	4021	4304
	4501	4503	4512					

Hadleigh (London Road) - Thamesway

Mercedes-Benz	309	310	311	312	313	314	315	316
	317	318	319	320	321	322	323	324
	325	326	327					
Dart	701	702	703	704	705	706	707	708
	709	710	711	717	718	719	720	721
	938	945	946	947	948	949	950	951
	952	953	954	955	956	957	958	987
National	1803	1845	1863	1870	1886			
Lynx	1400	1404	1405	1406	1409	1410	1411	1412
	1417	1418	1419	1420	1421	1422	1423	1424
	1430							
Bristol VR	3113	3225	3234					

Harwich (Station Road) - Eastern National

Mercedes-Benz	2656	2667	2669	2682
Lance	1512	1513		
Bristol VR	3076	3078	3109	
Olympian	4007	4008	4019	

Ponders End (Morson Road) - Thamesway

Mercedes-Benz	230	231	233	234	245	246	250	251
	254	255	256	257	258	260	261	301
	302	303	304	305	306	307	388	389
	390	391	392	393	394	395	396	397
	398	413	414	800	801	802	803	804
	805	806	807	808	809	810	811	
Dart	973	974	975	976	977	978	979	980
	981	982	983	984	985	986		

Unallocated

Mercedes-Benz	411	412	415	416	417	418	419	2217
	2230	2231	2232	2233	2237	2242	2244	2247
	2248	2252						
National	1830	1882	1889	1896	1907			
Tiger	1114	1115						
Olympian	4510	4511						
Open-top	2383	2384						
Dart	901-917 are on loan to MTL London.							

EASTONS

A W Easton Coaches Ltd, The Old Coach House, Stratton Strawless, Norwich, Norfolk, NR10 5LR

NFP110W	Bedford YMT	Plaxton Supreme IV	C49F	1980	Ex Kirby, High Wycombe, 1983
C932EWW	DAF MB200DKFL600	Plaxton Paramount 3500 II	C57F	1986	Ex AJC, Leeds, 1997
C667DVG	Bedford Venturer YNV(Volvo)	Plaxton Paramount 3200 II	C57F	1986	Ex Wright, Brandon, 1994
D468ALR	Bedford Venturer YNV(Volvo)	Plaxton Paramount 3200 II	C57F	1987	Ex Lewis, Greenwich, 1993
E174CDS	DAF MB230DKFL615	Plaxton Paramount 3500 III	C53F	1987	Ex Dewar, Falkirk, 1998
D866TFJ	Bedford YNT	Plaxton Paramount 3200 II	C53F	1987	Ex Heard, Hartland, 1995
A18AWE	Volvo B10M-61	Van Hool Alizée H	C53F	1988	Ex Park's, Hamilton, 1994
F356BWU	Mercedes-Benz 811D	Reeve Burgess Beaver	C25F	1988	Ex Stringer, Pontefract, 1997
H184CNS	Mercedes-Benz 609D	Made-to-Measure	B26F	1991	Ex Lofty, Bridge Trafford, 1997
A16AWE	DAF SB3000DKVF601	Van Hool Alizée HE	C49F	1992	Ex Invictaway (New Enterprise), 1998
A17AWE	DAF SB3000DKVF601	Van Hool Alizée HE	C49FT	1992	Ex Invictaway (Kentish Bus), 1998
A19AWE	DAF SB3000DKVF601	Van Hool Alizée HE	C51FT	1993	Ex Hallmark, Luton, 1998
P1AWE	Iveco EuroRider 391E.12.35	Beulas Stergo E35	C49FT	1997	
R3AWE	Iveco EuroRider 391E.12.35	Beulas Stergo E35	C49FT	1998	

Previous registrations:-

A16AWE	J17AMB	A19AWE	?
A18AWE	E627UNE, TDR725, E516CDS	C667DVG	C85VNR, 256JPA
A17AWE	K22AMB		

Livery:- Purple, replacing white, red, orange and yellow or white and red.

The majority of the Eastons fleet is made up of full size coaches that are mostly employed on local bus routes and contracts. Bedford YMT, NFP110W, has Plaxton Supreme IV coachwork and is seen in Norwich on service 37. The two Volvo-powered Bedfords in the fleet are unusual while the Cummins replacement has been used elsewhere most successfully. *Richard Godfrey*

EMBLING COACHES

J & B Embling, Bridge Garage, Guyhirn, Wisbech, Cambridgeshire, PE13 4ED

MEB626	Trojan 19	Trojan	C13F	1961	
UUF110J	Bristol VRT/SL2/6G	Eastern Coach Works	H39/31F	1971	Ex Brighton & Hove, 1987
LIL2816	Leyland Leopard PSU3B/4R	Plaxton Panorama Elite	C51F	1973	Ex Williamson, Catchcliffe, 1995
LVH481P	Ford R1114	Plaxton Supreme III	C53F	1978	Ex Fowler, Holbeach Drove, 1998
3196DD	Bristol VRT/SL2/6G	Eastern Coach Works	H43/34F	1974	Ex Rover, Horsley, 1990
HTU154N	Bristol VRT/SL2/6G	Eastern Coach Works	H43/31F	1975	Ex Crosville, 1988
JVE370P	AEC Reliance 6U3ZR	Plaxton Supreme III Express	C49F	1975	Ex Fowler, Holbeach Drove, 1994
PRE205R	Bedford VAS5	Plaxton Supreme III	C29F	1976	Ex Kirkpatricks of Deeside, 1994
XFC777R	Bedford YMT	Duple Dominant	C53F	1976	Ex Bonfield, Leyton, 1997
LIL2697	Bedford YMT	Duple Dominant	C53F	1977	Ex Soul, Olney, 1995
UTV221S	Leyland Fleetline FE30AGR	Northern Counties	H47/31D	1978	Ex Bugden, Swadlincote, 1996
CWU150T	Leyland Fleetline FE30AGR	Roe	H43/33F	1978	Ex Yorkshire Rider, 1995
BKE838T	Bristol VRT/SL3/6LXB	Eastern Coach Works	H43/31F	1979	Ex Maidstone & District, 1997
BEW49T	Bedford YMT	Duple Dominant II	C53F	1979	Ex Grey, Ely, 1997
YXI9255	Ford R1014	Plaxton Supreme IV	C35F	1980	Ex Hunter, Hucknall, 1993
HSD77V	Leyland Fleetline FE30AGR	Alexander AD	H44/31F	1980	Ex Clydeside, 1995
MIL5733	Bova FHD12.280	Bova Futura	C49FT	1984	Ex Brown, Darlington, 1996
GIL3244	Bova FHD12.280	Bova Futura	C49FT	1984	Ex Sanders, Holt, 1997
H271CEW	Scania K113CRB	Van Hool Alizée	C49FT	1990	
H430KOV	Ford Transit VE6	Ford	M14	1990	
J233XKY	Scania K93CRB	Van Hool Alizée H	C55F	1992	Ex Budden, Romsey, 1995
N770BWF	Leyland-DAF 400	Autobus Classique	M16	1995	
N2JWE	Scania K113CRB	Van Hool Alizée HE	C55F	1996	
R2JWE	Scania K113CRB	Van Hool Alizée HE	C49FT	1998	

Previous registrations:-

3196DD	GUD750N, YWD687, KAD397N	MEB626	From new
BEW49T	BWE195T, WSU463	MIL5733	3927TR, A630FRM, GIL2163
GIL3244	?	N2JWE	N807DKU
LIL2697	WNH283S	YXI9255	GJU854V
LIL2816	EFW964L, IXI7275, WWB943L		

Livery:- White, blue and red; white (Grand UK Tours) N2JWE

ENTERPRISE

Enterprise Safety Coaches Ltd, 1 Blackhorse Lane, High Street, Chatteris, Cambridgeshire, PE16 6RB

SHL882S	Bedford YMT	Plaxton Supreme III	C53F	1978	Ex Angel Motors, Tottenham, 1984
THX225S	Leyland National 10351A/2R		B48F	1978	Ex London Buses, 1991
YWF512T	Bedford YMT	Duple Dominant II	C53F	1978	Ex Vision, Ipswich, 1994
RJR869Y	Ford R1114	Duple Dominant IV	C53F	1982	Ex Melton Bus & Coach, Queniborough, 1994
YSK331	DAF MB200DKVL600	Plaxton Paramount 3500 II	C49FT	1984	Ex Earnside, Glenfarg, 1994
C333HHB	DAF SBR2305DHS570	Jonckheere Jubilee P99	CH55/16CT	1986	Ex Thomas, Tonypandy, 1989
D369JUM	Volkswagen LT55	Optare City Pacer	B25F	1987	Ex Goodlad, Chelmsford, 1994
E519PWR	Volkswagen LT55	Optare City Pacer	B25F	1987	Ex Morgan, Staplehurst, 1994
L3LWR	Bova FHD12-340	Bova Futura	C53FT	1994	

Previous registrations:-

L3LWR	L121OWF	YSK331	B367ECS, NHG550, B134YSL

Livery:- Three tone green and grey.

EUROSUN COACHES

North Quay Services Ltd, 100 Oulton Road, Lowestoft, Suffolk, NR32 4QR

Depot:- Norwich Road, North Walsham, Norfolk.

RRW900W	Bedford YNT	Duple Dominant IV	C53F	1981	Ex Underwood, N.Walsham, 1996
RHB234Y	Fiat 60.10	Caetano Beja	C18F	1982	Ex Underwood, N.Walsham, 1996
FIL6002	Bova FHD12.280	Bova Futura	C53F	1984	Ex Robinsons, Stewkley, 1996
NIJ2384	Bova FHD12.280	Bova Futura	C49FT	1986	Ex Underwood, N.Walsham, 1996
SJI8130	DAF MB230LT615	Plaxton Paramount 3500 III	C53F	1988	Ex Luckett, Fareham, 1997
OSU894	Bova FHD12.290	Bova Futura	C49FT	1988	Ex Underwood, N.Walsham, 1996

Previous registrations:-

FIL6002	354FTA, B841BDV, 2522VU	OSU894	E113GBB
NIJ2384	C30VJF	SJI8130	E334EVH, A10APT, E651JHJ

Livery:- White, blue and red.

EUROVIEW COACHING

D J Reeve, The Coach Depot, Dereham Road, Scarning, East Dereham, Norfolk

Depots:- Dereham Road, Scarning and Station Road Lorry Park, Swaffam.

KKV701V	Ford R1114	Plaxton Supreme IV	C53F	1980	Ex Lewis, Bury St.Edmunds, 1996
DIB3122	Bedford YMT	Duple Dominant II	C53F	1980	Ex Wood's, Wigston, 1995
YBK605	Bedford YNT	Duple Laser 2 Express	C53F	1984	Ex Wheelband, Weymouth, 1995
J222SJS	Scania K93CRB	Van Hool Alizée H	C49FT	1992	Ex Solid Entertainment, Grimsby, 1996
M244TAK	Scania K113CRB	Irizar Century 12.35	C49FT	1994	
P113GHE	Scania K113CRB	Irizar Century 12.35	C49FT	1997	

Previous registrations:-

DIB3122	KBC608V	YBK605	B836FTY

Livery:- Lilac and white.

FARGO COACHLINES

L J Smith, Allviews, School Road, Rayne, Braintree, Essex, CM7 8JJ

MFN45R	Bristol VRT/SL3/6LXB	Eastern Coach Works	H43/31F	1976	Ex Stephenson, Rochford, 1997
MBE616R	Leyland Atlantean FE30AGR	Roe	H45/29F	1977	Ex Stephenson, Rochford, 1994
TPE155S	Bristol VRT/SL3/6LXB	Eastern Coach Works	H43/31F	1977	Ex Stephenson, Rochford, 1997
YBF682S	Bristol VRT/SL3/6LXB	Eastern Coach Works	H43/31F	1977	Ex Stephenson, Rochford, 1997
FNJ993V	Bedford YLQ	Duple Dominant II	C45F	1980	Ex Brentwood coaches, 1988
KHB35W	Ford R1114	Plaxton Supreme IV Express	C53F	1981	Ex Bebb, Llantwit Fardre, 1986
GGD847X	Bova EL26/581	Bova Europa	C53F	1982	Ex Stallion Coaches, Boreham, 1998
HIJ6931	Mercedes-Benz 0303/15R	Mercedes-Benz	C49FT	1984	Ex Kinch, Barrow-on-Stour, 1990

The East Anglia Bus Handbook

Irizar's 1998 model range for Britain includes the InterCentury model seen here mounted on a Scania L94 IB underframe. One of the first to enter service was R449YDT operated by Fargo. It is seen in Temple Place, just off the Embankment, in London. *David Heath*

A862UDM	Mercedes-Benz L608D	Coachcraft	C21F	1984	Ex ?, 1997
B423CMC	Mercedes-Benz L608D	Reeve Burgess	C19F	1985	Ex Ellis, Kelvedon, 1995
C238HNO	Mercedes-Benz L508D	Fargo Coachlines	C19F	1986	
F82WBD	Freight-Rover Sherpa	Chassis Developments	C18F	1988	
F589HUS	Peugeot-Talbot Freeway	Talbot	B12FL	1989	Ex Bryans, Denny, 1997
G228PGU	Fiat Ducato	Jubilee	M11L	1990	Ex Graham's, Kelvedon, 1998
H144NVW	Ford Transit VE6	Ford	M8	1991	Ex private owner, 1994
H982KVX	Ford Transit VE6	Ford	M10	1991	
K555KGM	Scania K93CRB	Plaxton Paramount 3200 III	C57F	1993	Ex Mayne, Buckie, 1997
L668WFT	Leyland-DAF 400	Jubilee	M10L	1993	
L634ANX	Leyland-DAF 400	Jubilee	M16	1993	
L637ANX	Leyland-DAF 400	Jubilee	M8L	1993	
L399LHE	Scania K113TRB	Van Hool Alizée SH	C49FT	1993	Ex Wharfdale Team, Yeadon, 1998
M306VET	Scania K113TRB	Irizar Century 12.37	C49FT	1995	
M307VET	Scania K113TRB	Irizar Century 12.37	C49FT	1995	
M310VET	Scania K113CRB	Van Hool Alizée HE	C53F	1995	
P145GHE	Scania K113CRB	Van Hool Alizée HE	C49FT	1997	
R448YDT	Scania L94IB	Irizar InterCentury	C53F	1998	
R449YDT	Scania L94IB	Irizar InterCentury	C53F	1998	

Named Vehicles:- FNJ993V *Wisconsin*; KHB35W *Nevada*.

Livery:- Orange and yellow. A number of cars are also operated as PCV.

FELIX

P L, S T, M F, & C P Golynia & L T Warnack,
8 Windmill Hill, Long Melford, Sudbury, Suffolk, CO10 9AD

AJD959	Morris Commercial CV11/40	Stocker	C16	1945	Ex preservation, 1993
DBU889	Bedford OB	Duple Vista	C27F	1947	Ex preservation, 1988
RRT535R	Bedford VAS 5	Plaxton Supreme III	C29F	1977	Ex Banham, Hartest, 1996
FSU637	Van Hool T815H	Van Hool Alizée H	C53F	1984	Ex Lodge, High Easter, 1995
B873XFL	Mercedes-Benz L207D		M..	1985	Ex 1993
JXI6133	Leyland Cub CU435	Wright TT	DP35FL	1987	Ex Glenmachen, Church of God, Belfast, 1997
D352OAK	Mercedes-Benz L608D	Whittaker	C23F	1987	Ex Lewis, Coventry, 1993
E856GFV	Mercedes-Benz 609D	Elme Orion	C16F	1987	
E743OEW	Mercedes-Benz L207D	Felix	M11	1988	
F301RMH	Mercedes-Benz 709D	Reeve Burgess Beaver	B25F	1988	
F898KHJ	Mercedes-Benz 307D	Pilcher-Greene	M7L	1988	Ex Bexley Dial-a-ride, 1995
J764ONK	Mercedes-Benz 811D	Reeve Burgess Beaver	C33F	1991	Ex Javelin, Wimbledon, 1997
J220HDS	Mercedes-Benz 811D	Dormobile Routemaker	B33F	1992	
K142PLP	Mercedes-Benz 308D	Devon Conversions	M8	1992	Ex Alamo. West Drayton, 1995
K392BVS	Mercedes-Benz 711D	Plaxton Beaver	C25F	1993	
L198SCM	Mercedes-Benz 814D	North West Coach Sales	C35F	1994	
M391KVR	Mercedes-Benz 709D	Dormobile Routemaker	DP29F	1994	Ex Sanders, Holt, 1996
N783WEF	Mercedes-Benz 609D	Autobus Classique	C24F	1995	
N993JRT	Mercedes-Benz 711D	Autobus Classique	C24F	1995	

Previous registration:-

AJD959	From new		FSU637	A779VFM
DBU889	From new		JXI6133	From new

Livery:- White, black and red.

The majority of the fleet operated by Felix of Long Melford is based on Mercedes-Benz chassis. J220HDS is one such with coachbuilt bodywork for use on services centred on Sudbury. The vehicle is an 811D with Dormobile Routemaker bodywork. *Paul Goodison*

FENN HOLIDAYS

Fenn Holidays Ltd, Whittlesey Road, March, Cambridgeshire, PE15 0AG

JEV706N	Bedford YRT	Willowbrook 001	B55F	1975	Ex Sworder, Walkern, 1995
LVV124P	Bedford YRT	Willowbrook 001	B53F	1976	Ex Sworder, Walkern, 1995
B4FEN	Bova FHD12.290	Bova Futura	C55F	1989	
H4FEN	Ford Transit VE6	Ford	M8	1991	Ex Budget Rental, 1996
M4FEN	Bova FHD12.340	Bova Futura	C49FT	1995	
P5FEN	Scania K113CRB	Van Hool Alizée HE	C49FT	1996	
R4FEN	Bova FHD12.340	Bova Futura	C49FT	1998	

Previous registration:-

B4FEN	F877CFL		H4FEN	H379MBF

Livery:- Two tone blue and white

One of five coaches in the March-based Fenn Holidays fleet to carry appropriate, undated Select index marks is B4FEN. One of a pair of Bova Futuras in the fleet it was originally delivered with an F prefix plate when new. It is seen in the coach park in Portsmouth showing its two tone blue and white upswept livery. *Kevin Vincent*

FIRST CHOICE

First Choice Travel (Peterborough) Ltd, 9 Lythemere, Orton Malbourne,
Peterborough, Cambridgeshire, PE2 5NG
D H Ely, First Choice Travel, 9 Lythemere, Orton Malbourne, Peterborough, PE2 5NG

Depot:- Maxwell Road, Peterborough

E515MME	Renault-Dodge S56	Reeve Burgess	B25F	1987	Ex Aldermaston Coaches, 1993
D858CKV	Iveco Daily 49.10	Robin Hood City Nippy	B21F	1987	Ex Stagecoach Midland Red, 1997
E331LHN	Renault-Dodge S56	Northern Counties	B23F	1988	Ex Midland Fox, 1997
G21CSG	Renault-Dodge S56	Reeve Burgess Beaver	B25F	1989	Ex Red & White, 1996
G24CSG	Renault-Dodge S56	Reeve Burgess Beaver	B25F	1989	Ex Red & White, 1996
H909SKW	Renault-Dodge S75	Whittaker	B29F	1990	Ex Brighton & Hove, 1997

Livery:- Maroon, dark blue and grey

FLAGFINDERS

Flagfinders (CTB) Ltd, 267 Coggeshall Road, Braintree, Essex, CM7 6EF

MFN44R	Bristol VRT/SL3/6LXB	Eastern Coach Works	H43/31F	1976	Ex Brentwood Coaches, 1995
NJP35P	Bristol VRT/SL3/6LX	Eastern Coach Works	H43/31F	1976	Ex Brentwood Coaches, 1995
TXI8748	Ford R1014	Duple Dominant II	C33FT	1978	Ex King's, Stanway, 1991
NIL7951	Bedford YMT	Van Hool Argon	C53F	1980	Ex Yorkshire European, Boroughbridge, 1996
MIB1366	Bedford YMT	Duple Dominant IV	C53F	1981	Ex Porter, Great Totham, 1994
DPO567W	Mercedes-Benz L508DG	Robin Hood	C21F	1981	Ex Lucas, West Kingsdown, 1997
MAZ6740	Volvo B10M-61	Van Hool Alizée H	C52DT	1988	Ex Golden Tours, Shepherds Bush, 1996
D703NUH	Kässbohrer Setra S215HR	Kässbohrer Rational	C49FT	1987	Ex ?, 1998
F688KWC	Volkswagen Caravelle	Volkswagen	M8	1990	Ex private owner, 1994
L520CAY	Mazda E2200	Howletts	M13	1994	
N571AWJ	Dennis Javelin	Neoplan Transliner	C49FT	1996	Ex S J Carlton demonstrator, 1997
R267THL	Dennis Javelin	Neoplan Transliner	C49FT	1997	

Previous registration:-

MAZ6740	E35OFL	NIL7951	JGV319V, 447HWT, MGV645V
MIB1366	SGS507W	TXI8748	XPP421S

Livery:- Silver, white, yellow and blue.

FLYING BANANA

Halesworth Transit Ltd, Unit 12, Yarmouth Business Park, Suffolk Road, Great Yarmouth, Norfolk, NR31 0ER

B201GNL	Ford Transit 190	Alexander	B16F	1985	Ex Metro Taxis, 1991
B204GNL	Ford Transit 190	Alexander	B16F	1985	Ex Metro Taxis, 1991
B420NJF	Ford Transit 190	Rootes	B16F	1985	Ex Midland Fox, 1992
C430BHY	Ford Transit 190	Dormobile	B16F	1986	Ex City Line, 1989
C431BHY	Ford Transit 190	Dormobile	B16F	1986	Ex City Line, 1989
C315DRH	Ford Transit 190	Carlyle	B20F	1986	Ex East Yorkshire, 1996
D227OOJ	Freight-Rover Sherpa	Carlyle	O20F	1987	Ex Priory, Gosport, 1997
D70TLV	Freight-Rover Sherpa	Carlyle	O20F	1987	Ex Brian Isaac, Morriston, 1993
E237VOM	Freight-Rover Sherpa	Carlyle	B20F	1988	Ex Bebb, Llantwit Fardre, 1990
M384KVR	Mercedes-Benz 709D	Alexander Sprint	B27F	1995	
N589WND	Mercedes-Benz 709D	Alexander Sprint	B27F	1996	
P681HND	Mercedes-Benz 709D	Alexander Sprint	B27F	1996	
P682HND	Mercedes-Benz 709D	Alexander Sprint	B27F	1996	Ex Glossopdale, Hadfield, 1997
P692HND	Mercedes-Benz Vario O810	Plaxton Beaver 2	B31F	1997	
P693HND	Mercedes-Benz Vario O810	Plaxton Beaver 2	B31F	1997	

Livery:- Canary yellow and green.

1995 saw the arrival of the first new Mercedes-Benz 709Ds which Flying Banana chose to replace the initial fleet that was concentrated on acquired Ford Transits. The latest arrivals have been a pair of the Vario model and one of these, P692HND is seen in Great Yarmouth. As the book was being prepared, it was announced that First Eastern Counties had acquired the operation though it would retain a separate identity for the time being. *Richard Godfrey*

FORDS OF ALTHORNE

A A J Ford, Three Ways Garage, Fambridge Road, Althorne, Essex, CM3 6BZ

PRG124J	Daimler Fleetline CRG6LX	Alexander L	H48/35F	1971	Ex Moffat & Williamson, Gauldry, 1984
PRG127J	Daimler Fleetline CRG6LX	Alexander L	H48/35F	1971	Ex Moffat & Williamson, Gauldry, 1984
PRG134J	Daimler Fleetline CRG6LX	Alexander L	H48/35F	1971	Ex Partridge, Hadleigh, 1984
PRG138J	Daimler Fleetline CRG6LX	Alexander L	H48/32D	1971	Ex Maldon Majorettes, Maldon, 1991
PKE809M	Bristol VRT/SL2/6LX	Eastern Coach Works	H43/31F	1973	Ex Cedric, Wivenhoe, 1994
SRP816N	Bristol VRT/SL2/6LX	Eastern Coach Works	H39/31F	1974	Ex Lattimore, Markyate, 1991
820KPO	Bedford YRT	Plaxton Supreme III	C53F	1975	Ex Porter, Great Totham, 1988
AUD460R	Bristol VRT/SL3/6LXB	Eastern Coach Works	H43/31F	1977	Ex Carter, Colchester, 1990
RRP857R	Bristol VRT/SL3/6LXB	Eastern Coach Works	H43/31F	1977	Ex Thamesway, 1991
WGR66R	Bedford YRQ	Plaxton Supreme III	C45F	1977	Ex Weardale, Frosterley, 1981
TDT32S	Bedford YMT	Duple Dominant II	C53F	1977	Ex Morris, Borehamwood, 1978
XNV882S	Bristol VRT/SL3/6LXB	Eastern Coach Works	H43/31F	1978	Ex Thamesway, 1991
LJI477	Bedford YMT	Willowbrook Warrior(1986)	B55F	1978	Ex Cave, Shirley, 1992
CKX392T	Bedford YMT	Duple Dominant II	C53F	1978	Ex Morris, Borehamwood, 1980
EYH693V	Bedford YMT	Plaxton Supreme IV	C53F	1979	Ex Barnes, Clacton, 1987
CHK312X	Bedford YNT	Plaxton Supreme IV	C53F	1982	
SMW56Y	Dennis Dominator DDA164/590	Northern Counties	H43/31F	1983	Ex Stephenson, Rochford, 1996
JEV245Y	Van Hool TD824	Van Hool Astromega	CH57/27F	1983	Ex Southend, 1990
GEX790Y	Bova EL26/581	Bova Europa	C53F	1983	Ex Bird, Hunstanton, 1985
C141KFL	DAF SB2300DHS585	Jonckheere Jubilee	C53FT	1985	Ex Fenn, March, 1989
C995ERO	Bedford YNT	Plaxton Paramount 3200 II	C53F	1985	Ex Dinsey, Luton, 1988
C658KVW	Bedford Venturer YNV	Van Hool Alizée	C53F	1986	
D66ONS	Bedford Venturer YNV	Duple 320	C57F	1986	Ex Squirrell, Hitcham, 1990
DSK107	Van Hool TD824	Van Hool Astromega	CH55/16DT	1987	Ex Crusader, Clacton, 1997
G854VAY	Dennis Javelin 12SDA1907	Caetano Algarve	C53F	1989	Ex APT, Rayleigh, 1992
H411CJF	DAF MB230LB515	Caetano Algarve	C51FT	1990	Ex Welsh & Pollitt, Upton, 1995
H830YGA	Mercedes-Benz 609D	Scott	C20F	1990	Ex Earl, Stockton, 1992
M486HBC	Dennis Javelin 12SDA2136	Caetano Algarve II	C53F	1994	

Previous registrations:-

820KPO	LAY474P		DSK107	D228HMT, 114RVX	LJI477	XNM830S

Livery:- White, orange, red and brown

FOURWAYS COACHES

D J V & D C Merriday, 50 Laburnum Drive, Chelmsford, Essex, CM2 9NX

Depot:- Unit 8, Yard 2, Pooles Lane, Highwood.

KNG999L	Bedford YRT	Duple Dominant	C53F	1973	Ex Spratt, Wreningham, 1989
OTO547M	Leyland Atlantean AN68/1R	East Lancashire	H47/30D	1974	Ex Maun, Sutton-in-Ashfield, 1994
XJX795V	Ford R1114	Plaxton Supreme IV	C53F	1979	Ex O'Connor, Ilford, 1997
MBC39V	Volvo B58-61	Plaxton Supreme IV	C49FT	1980	Ex Colin's Coaches, Shepshed, 1990
MNK427V	Leyland Leopard PSU3E/4R	Duple Dominant II	C53F	1980	Ex Hedingham & District, 1997
MNK429V	Leyland Leopard PSU3E/4R	Duple Dominant II	C53F	1980	Ex Hedingham & District, 1997
DKE350Y	Leyland Leopard PSU5D/5R	Duple Dominant IV	C53F	1982	Ex Smith, Brenzett, 1992
WNU27Y	Volvo B58-61	Jonckheere Bermuda	C49FT	1982	Ex Go-Don, Dunmow, 1993
C979HOX	MCW Metroliner DR130/31	MCW	CH55/16DT	1986	Ex Stephenson, Rochford, 1997
E317OMG	Leyland Royal Tiger RTC	Leyland Doyen	C53F	1988	Ex Hopkins, East Dereham, 1997

Previous registration:-

MBC39V	NLC672V, ORJ701

Livery:- Yellow, maroon, green and black.

FREESTONES COACHES

R S Morant & B J Feeke, Green Lane, Beetley, East Dereham, Norfolk, NR20 4DL

GDZ9097	Leyland National 11351/1R (Volvo)		B52F	1976	Ex Badgerline, 1996
PKG735R	Leyland National 11351/1R (Volvo)		B52F	1976	Ex Berkeley, Paulton, 1998
GDZ571	Leyland Tiger TRCTL11/3R	Plaxton Supreme V	C57F	1981	Ex Copeland, Meir, 1997
KJN299	Volvo B10M-61	Van Hool Alizée H	C53F	1983	Ex Bowens, Birmingham, 1996
GDZ540	Leyland Tiger TRCTL11/2R	Van Hool Alizée	C53F	1984	Ex Travellers, Hounslow, 1992
GDZ967	Bedford YNT	Plaxton Paramount 3200	C53F	1984	Ex Ford, Althorne, 1993
GDZ435	Bedford YMT	Duple Dominant	B55F	1987	Ex Western Buses, 1997
GDZ481	Volvo B10M-62	Van Hool Alizée HE	C53F	1987	Ex Clarkes of London, 1998
GDZ541	Volvo B10M-62	Van Hool Alizée HE	C53F	1987	Ex Clarkes of London, 1998
GDZ760	Volvo B10M-60	Van Hool Alizée HE	C53F	1993	Ex Park's, Hamilton, 1997
GDZ623	Volvo B10M-62	Van Hool Alizée HE	C53F	1994	Ex Park's, Hamilton, 1997
R687ACL	Toyota Coaster BB50R	Caetano Optimo IV	C21F	1997	

Previous registrations:-

GDZ435	D799USB	GDZ760	HSK644, L648ADS
GDZ540	A146RMJ	GDZ967	A123MAC
GDZ541	D25CNR	GDZ9097	KHT125P
GDZ571	XGS765X, 5300RU, XEL913X, MIB536	KJN299	ODS465Y
GDZ623	KSK952, M436ECS		

Livery:- Grey, red and orange

Looking resplendent in Kings Lynn bus station is Leyland National GDZ9097. This vehicle was new in 1976 to the Bristol Omnibus Company, as their 3027 for use on country routes and the bus and routes later passed to Badgerline. The vehicle has been fully refurbished to Urban Bus specification and is now fitted with a Volvo engine. Because of the good entrance design and durable structure, the Leyland National continues to prove suitable for refurbishment. *Trevor Brookes*

GALLOWAY / REX

Galloway European Coachlines Ltd, Denter's Hill, Mendlesham,
Stowmarket, Suffolk, IP14 5RR

Depot:- Denter's Hill, Mendlesham and Rex Service Station, Thorndon, Eye.

GOI1294	Bedford YMT	Plaxton Supreme III	C53F	1978	Ex Bebb, Llantwit Fardre, 1982
WFO866T	Bedford YMT	Plaxton Supreme III	C53F	1979	Ex Burton, Haverhill, 1996
AFJ759T	Bristol VRT/SL3/6LXB	Eastern Coach Works	H43/31F	1979	Ex City of Nottingham, 1994
1754PP	DAF MB200DKL550	Plaxton Supreme IV	C53F	1979	Ex Bluebird of Weymouth, 1995
KHD832V	Bedford YMT	Plaxton Supreme IV	C53F	1979	Ex Squirrell, Hitcham, 1993
BBM53A	Bedford YMT	Plaxton Supreme IV	C53F	1980	Ex County, 1990
1440PP	DAF MB200DKL600	Plaxton Supreme IV	C57F	1980	Ex Majestic, Cheslyn Hay, 1985
TPA666X	Bedford YNT	Plaxton Supreme IV	C53F	1982	Ex Beckett, Horwood, 1988
6037PP	Leyland Tiger TRCTL11/3R	Plaxton Supreme V	C53F	1982	Ex Cuttings, Brockley, 1994
A504HUT	Bedford YNT	Duple Laser	C53F	1984	Ex Rex, Thorndon, 1990
C46DUR	Bedford YNT	Plaxton Paramount 3200 II	C53F	1985	Ex Dinsey, Luton, 1988
5048PP	DAF SB2305DHS585	Van Hool Alizée	C53F	1987	Ex Landtourers, Farnham, 1996
E233WKW	Mercedes-Benz 609D	Whittaker	C24F	1988	Ex Happy Days, Woodseaves, 1991
2513PP	DAF MB230LB615	Plaxton Paramount 3500 III	C53F	1988	Ex Eastbourne, 1996
5946PP	Mercedes-Benz 609D	Whittaker	C24F	1989	Ex Rex, Thorndon, 1990
F491DNY	Nissan Vanette	Galloway (1994)	M8	1989	
G434ART	Mercedes-Benz 609D	Whittaker	C24F	1990	Ex Albany, Norwich, 1992
4092PP	Scania K93CRB	Plaxton Premiére 320	C53F	1992	Ex Shearings, 1997
J276NNC	Scania K93CRB	Plaxton Premiére 320	C53F	1992	Ex Shearings, 1997
5611PP	Scania K93CRB	Plaxton Premiére 320	C53F	1992	Ex Shearings, 1997
1482PP	Scania K93CRB	Plaxton Premiére 320	C53F	1992	Ex Shearings, 1997
5516PP	DAF SB3000DKV601	Van Hool Alizée DH	C51FT	1992	Ex Amberline, 1994
2086PP	DAF SB3000DKVF601	Van Hool Alizée DH	C49FT	1993	
K919TBC	Vauxhall Midi	Vauxhall	M8	1993	Ex private owner, 1995
K329KVG	Vauxhall Midi	Vauxhall	M8	1993	Ex private owner, 1995
M830RCP	DAF DE33WSSB3000	Van Hool Alizée HE	C49FT	1995	
M3ERH	Dennis Javelin 12SDA2125	Plaxton Expressliner II	C46FT	1995	Ex Express Travel, Speke, 1997
N212KBJ	Mercedes-Benz 711D	Autobus Classique	C24F	1995	
N665JGV	DAF DE02LTSB220	Ikarus CitiBus	B51F	1995	
N991FWT	DAF DE33WSSB3000	Van Hool Alizée HE	C51FT	1996	
N992FWT	DAF DE33WSSB3000	Van Hool Alizée HE	C51FT	1996	
P309PBJ	Mercedes-Benz 711D	Autobus Classique	C24F	1996	
R255FBJ	DAF DE33WSSB3000	Van Hool Alizée HE	C49FT	1998	
R256FBJ	DAF DE33WSSB3000	Van Hool Alizée HE	C49FT	1998	

Previous registrations:-

1440PP	NRO229V, 7476PP	5516PP	J811KHD
1482PP	J283NNC	5611PP	J281NNC
1754PP	EPC906V	5946PP	F863FWB
2086PP	K110TCP	6037PP	OHE283X
2513PP	E328EVH	BBM53A	KBH850V
4092PP	J273NNC	GOI1294	YUE593S
5048PP	D863EFS, GSU371, ?		

Named Vehicle:- 1440PP *European Ranger*

Liveries:- White and gold or cream, yellow and orange; white (National Express), M3ERH, R255FBJ

GO-DONS

Don's Coaches (Dunmow) Ltd, Parsonage Downs, Great Dunmow, Essex, CM6 2AT

NKY161	Bedford SBG	Yeates Europa	C41F	1957	Ex Law & Jobson, Walthamstow, 1989
ETC760B	Bedford VAS2	Plaxton Panorama	C29F	1964	Ex Goodwin, Stockport, 1989
HDX907N	Leyland Atlantean AN68/1R	Roe	H43/29F	1975	Ex Ipswich, 1992
JGA189N	Leyland Atlantean AN68/1R	Alexander AL	H45/31F	1975	Ex Strathclyde, 1984
JUS774N	Leyland Atlantean AN68/1R	Alexander AL	H45/31F	1975	Ex Strathclyde, 1983
KSU850P	Leyland Atlantean AN68A/1R	Alexander AL	H45/31F	1975	Ex Strathclyde, 1983
TET748S	Leyland Fleetline FE30AGR	Roe	H43/33F	1977	Ex South Yorkshire, 1988
YDS650S	Leyland Atlantean AN68A/1R	Alexander AL	H45/31F	1977	Ex Grahams, Paisley, 1990
A62OJX	Leyland Leopard PSU5/2L	Plaxton Paramount 3200	C57F	1984	Ex Gobig, Mirfield, 1985
TXI8756	Dennis Lancet SDA519	Jonckheere Piccolo P35	C37FT	1985	Ex Ayres, Dalkeith, 1989
NIW4122	Dennis Javelin 12SDA1901	Duple 320	C57F	1987	Ex Nu-Venture, Aylesford, 1993
E256PEL	Toyota Coaster HB31R	Caetano Optimo	C21F	1988	Ex Clegg & Brooking, Middle Wallop, 1992
E41SBO	Dennis Javelin 12SDA1906	Duple 320	C53F	1988	Ex Waddon, Bedwas, 1995
E758JAY	Dennis Javelin SDA1907	Duple 320	C57F	1988	Ex Morris Travel, Pencoed, 1992
F337JTN	Toyota Coaster HB31R	Caetano Optimo	C21F	1988	Ex O'Toole, Eltham, 1995
F635SAY	Dennis Javelin 12SDA1907	Duple 320	C53F	1989	Ex Globe Coaches, Aberdare, 1996
H194TYC	Dennis Javelin 12SDA1907	Duple 320	C57F	1990	Ex Redwood, Hemyock, 1994
H633GUD	Iveco 315-8-17	Lorraine	C30F	1990	Ex Poynter, Duston, 1997
K17WEB	Dennis Javelin 12SDA2101	Caetano Algarve II	C53F	1993	Ex Swallow, Rainham, 1996
M707HBC	Dennis Javelin 12SDA2136	Marcopolo Explorer	C51F	1995	Ex Allied, Uxbridge, 1997

Previous registrations:-

K17WEB	K104UFP	NKY161	From new
NIW4122	E951EPD	TXI8756	B135AAV

Named Vehicles:- E256PEL *The Lady Beatrice*; ETC760B *Lady Beatrice*; NKY161 *Nicky*

Livery:- Orange, white and black or white, yellow, red and black.

The only single deck bus in the Galloway of Mendlesham fleet is N665JGV, a DAF SB220 with steel framed Ikarus CitiBus bodywork branded with 'easy access' and 'travel rural bus' lettering. It was caught on *County Connections* route 107 near Whatfield in May 1997. *Richard Godfrey*

GOLDEN BOY COACHES

Jetsie Ltd, Low Hill Garage, Meadgate Road, Sedge Green, Roydon, Essex CM19 5JT

402	YOI7757	Volvo B10M-61	Van Hool Alizée H	C53F	1986	Ex Smith Shearings, Wigan, 1992
403	YXI8897	Volvo B10M-61	Van Hool Alizée H	C53F	1989	Ex Shearings, 1996
404	YOI1214	Mercedes-Benz 811D	Reeve Burgess Beaver	C29F	1989	Ex NPT, Bilsthorpe, 1993
405	YXI3057	Volvo B10M-61	Van Hool Alizée H	C53F	1989	Ex Shearings, 1996
406	YOI8271	Mercedes-Benz 811D	Reeve Burgess Beaver	C33F	1989	Ex Neal's Travel, Isleham, 1994
407	YOI7374	Mercedes-Benz 811D	Reeve Burgess Beaver	C33F	1991	Ex Javelin, Battersea, 1996
409	YOI7353	Volvo B10M-61	Van Hool Alizée H	C53F	1985	Ex Shearings, 1991
410	YOI7725	Mercedes-Benz 811D	Reeve Burgess Beaver	C33F	1991	Ex Javelin, Battersea, 1996
412	YOI5475	Leyland Leopard PSU3E/4R	Plaxton Supreme IV Express	C53F	1979	Ex Alder Valley South, 1988
414	M635UCT	Mercedes-Benz 814D	Autobus Classique 2	C33F	1995	
415	K966GWR	Mercedes-Benz 410D	Mellor	M15	1992	Ex Cropper, Kirkstall, 1995
416	YOI7079	Mercedes-Benz L307D	Reeve Burgess	M12	1983	Ex Graves, Hertford, 1991
417	YXI3049	Volvo B10M-61	Van Hool Alizée H	C53F	1989	Ex Shearings, 1996
419	YOI5997	Volvo B10M-60	Van Hool Alizée H	C49FT	1990	Ex Shearings, 1995
420	YOI7744	Mercedes-Benz 811D	Reeve Burgess Beaver	C25F	1990	Ex Jones, Market Drayton, 1996
423	YOI2642	Mercedes-Benz 811D	Reeve Burgess Beaver	C33F	1991	Ex Javelin, Battersea, 1996
426	YOI2805	Leyland Tiger TRCTL11/3ARZ	Plaxton Paramount 3200 III	C53F	1989	Ex ABC, Ainsdale, 1997
429	YOI949	Mercedes-Benz 814D	Plaxton Beaver	C33F	1993	Ex Country Lion, Northampton, 1997
430	L232FRX	Mercedes-Benz 814D	Plaxton Beaver	C33F	1993	Ex Coles, Eversley, 1997
431	R3BOY	Volvo B10M-62	Van Hool Alizée 2	C49FT	1998	
432	CAZ2819	Volvo B10M-60	Van Hool Alizée H	C53F	1991	Ex Shearings, 1998
434	BAZ6527	Volvo B10M-60	Van Hool Alizée H	C53F	1990	Ex Shearings, 1997
435	YXI9253	Volvo B10M-61	Van Hool Alizée H	C53F	1989	Ex Shearings, 1996
458	YOI7145	Iveco 79.14	Caetano Viana	C19F	1986	Ex Link Line, Harlesden, 1986

Previous registrations:-

BAZ6527	G847RNC	YOI7353	B473UNB
CAZ2819	H189DVM	YOI7374	J763ONK
YOI949	L247YNV, A12CLN	YOI7725	J760ONK
YOI1214	F264RPH, A10NPT	YOI7744	G587LUX
YOI2642	J761ONK	YOI7757	C333DND
YOI2805	F777GNA	YOI8271	F722SML
YOI5475	WJM812T	YXI3049	F731ENE
YOI5997	G876VNA, BAZ8576	YXI3057	F735ENE
YOI7079	KAR986Y	YXI8897	F747ENE
YOI7145	C358LVV	YXI9253	F749ENE

Named   Vehicles:- BAZ6527 *Miss Annie*; CAZ2819 *Miss Angela*; K966GWR *Miss Carol*; L232FRX *Miss Jane*; M635UCT *Miss Grainne*; R3BOY *Master John*; YOI949 *Miss Sinead*; YOI1214 *Miss Patricia*; YOI2642 *Miss Sheila*; YOI2805 *Miss Marian*; YOI5997 *Miss Rosie*; YOI7145 *Miss Teresa*; YOI7353 *Miss Jacqueline*; YOI7374 *Miss Bridget* YOI7744 *Miss Lily*; YOI7757 *Miss Geraldine*; YXI3049 *Miss Margaret*; YXI3057 *Miss Kathleen*; YXI8897 *Miss Maria*; YXI9253 *Miss Mary*;

Livery:- Gold, red and black

GOLDLINE

Waylands Ltd, Unit 9 College Lane, Worlingham, Beccles, Norfolk, NR34 7SA

A23FVT	Mercedes-Benz L307D	Reeve Burgess	M12	1983	Ex Chalmers, Whitburn, 1996
C463SJU	Ford Transit 190	Robin Hood	B16F	1985	Ex Expresslines, Bedford, 1996
D140TFM	Ford Transit 190	Dormobile	B16F	1986	
D140NDT	Mercedes-Benz L307D	Whittaker	M12	1986	Ex Knights, Beccles, 1997
D177MOV	Renault Master T35	Coachcraft	M13	1987	Ex Stringer, Pontefract, 1996
F715UBX	Renault Trafic	Cymric	M8	1989	Ex Waylands, Worlingham, 1996
G294OTV	Renault Trafic	Holdsworth	M13	1989	Ex Waylands, Worlingham, 1996
G897MTH	Renault Master T35	Cymric	M16	1990	Ex Swansea Coach Company, 1997
J142LKC	Renault Trafic	......	M..	1992	Ex private owner, 1997
K30GGY	Iveco Daily 49.10	Marshall C29	B23F	1993	Ex MTL, 1997
L4WMS	Renault Master T35	Cymric	M16	1993	Ex Waylands, Worlingham, 1996
L691XLK	Renault Trafic	....	M..	1994	Ex private owner, 1997
L34VBX	Renault Trafic	Cymric	M8	1994	Ex van conversion, 1996
M4WMS	Renault Master T35	Cymric	M16	1994	Ex Waylands, Worlingham, 1996
N4WMS	Renault Master T35	Cymric	M16	1995	Ex Waylands, Worlingham, 1996
N781OGA	Renault Master T35	Cymric	M16	1996	
P134RBX	Renault Master T35	Cymric	M16	1997	

Previous registration:-
G897MTH   G200ABX, A20SCC

Named Vehicle:- L34VBX *Bridget;*

Livery:- white

All but one of the Van Hool Alizée coaches operated by Golden Boy originated with Shearings. The Alizée model is renowned for its attractive 'dateless' styling and quality build which have been an attraction to coach operators accountants. Pictured here is 417, YXI3049, which carries the name *Miss Margaret.* 1998 saw the entry in UK service of the new T9 series Alizée 2 and Golden Boy were one of the first operators to receive one. *Colin Lloyd*

GOODWIN'S OF BRAINTREE

A M Goodwin, Alwynn, 265 London Road, Braintree, Essex, CM7 8QQ

Depot:- Goldcrest Industrial Estate, Driberg Way, Braintree.

APL777T	Bedford YLQ	Plaxton Supreme IV	C45F	1979	Ex Regan, Ware, 1984
987UYA	Volvo B58-61	Plaxton Viewmaster IV	C51F	1979	Ex Easton, Brandiston, 1989
AFN297V	Bedford YMT	Plaxton Supreme IV	C53F	1980	Ex Bovington, Margate, 1993
XMW279W	Bedford YMQ	Plaxton Supreme IV	C30F	1981	Ex Tigerways, Harlow, 1997
840FAY	Volvo B10M-61	Berkhof Everest 370	C49FT	1982	Ex Watson Enterprises, Corringham, 1991
A147RMJ	Leyland Tiger TRCTL11/3R	Van Hool Alizée SH	C51D	1984	Ex Freestones, Norwich, 1998
E422BMY	Peugeot-Talbot Express	Crystals	M14	1987	

Previous registrations:-

840FAY	FHJ841Y		987UYA	EPC904V		A147RMJ	A147RMJ, GDZ541

Livery:- White, blue and grey.

Goodwin's of Braintree operate a small fleet which includes 987UYA, a Volvo B58 fitted with a Plaxton Viewmaster body, though the observant expert will note the front panel is that of the Paramount model. The vehicle is pictured passing the London Victoria branch of the Midland Bank. *Colin Lloyd*

The East Anglia Bus Handbook

GRAHAMS

G M & R A Ellis, 14 Station Road, Kelvedon, Essex, CO5 9NP

HUP766T	Bristol VRT/SL3/6LXB	Eastern Coach Works	H43/31F	1978	Ex Warren, Alton, 1996
E856ENR	Volkswagen LT55	Optare City Pacer	B25F	1987	Ex Ely, Woodston, 1997
E23EFW	Ford Transit VE6	Deansgate	M11	1988	Ex Sleaford Taxi, Sleaford, 1997
E786MEU	Ford Transit VE6	Steedrive	M13	1988	
G805RNC	Scania K93CRB	Plaxton Paramount 3200 III	C53F	1990	Ex Lowland, 1995
G32HKY	Scania K93CRB	Plaxton Paramount 3200 III	C49FT	1990	Ex Lodge, High Easter, 1997
G885VNA	Scania K93CRB	Plaxton Paramount 3200 III	C53F	1990	Ex Shearings, 1995
H392CFT	Toyota Coaster HDB30R	Caetano Optimo II	C21F	1991	Ex Neal's Travel, Isleham, 1995
M345UVX	Mercedes-Benz 811D	Plaxton Beaver	B31F	1994	
R441PCK	LDV Convoy	LDV	M16	1998	

Livery:- White and two tone blue.

The large touring coach operators, such as Shearings, Wallace Arnold, Park's and Excelsior etc maintain low average age profiles, replacing their vehicles after only a few years use in the same way many motorists replace their cars on a three year basis. The pattern makes available large numbers of good relatively young coaches onto the dealer market. New to Shearings, G805RNC spent a spell on seasonal hire to Lowland before joining the fleet of Grahams. This Scania features the low-driving position version of the Plaxton Paramount 3200 body. *David Heath*

GRETTON'S

R E Gretton, 8 Thurlaston Close, Peterborough, Cambridgeshire, PE3 6LD

Depot:- Newark Road, Peterborough

GAL967	Bedford OWB	Duple Vista (1952)	C29F	1944	Ex preservation, 1997
GJF286N	Scania BR111DH	MCW Metropolitan	H45/28D	1975	Ex Leicester Citybus, 1991
GJF302N	Scania BR111DH	MCW Metropolitan	H45/28D	1975	Ex Leicester Citybus, 1991
JAG406N	Scania BR111DH	MCW Metropolitan	H44/29F	1975	Ex Camms, Nottingham, 1988
RYG664R	Scania BR111DH	MCW Metropolitan	H44/31F	1976	Ex West Yorkshire PTE, 1985
OCU769R	Scania BR111DH	MCW Metropolitan	H45/29F	1977	Ex Tyne & Wear PTE, 1986
OKY89R	AEC Reliance 6U3ZR	Plaxton Supreme III	C55F	1977	Ex Jennings, Arrington, 1987
XRW506S	AEC Reliance 6U3ZR	Plaxton Supreme III	C53F	1978	Ex Ironside, Sevenoaks, 1984
SJI2953	Bedford YMP	Plaxton Paramount 3200 III	C35F	1985	Ex Chivers, Wallington, 1995
RNC478	Scania K112CRS	Plaxton Paramount 3200 II	C53F	1985	Ex PMT, 1990
VUN678	Scania K92CRS	Plaxton Paramount 3200 II	C53F	1985	Ex Boro'line Maidstone, 1992
TJI6707	Scania K112CRB	Berkhof Esprite 350	C53F	1985	Ex Heyfordian, Upper Heyford, 1996
RJI6859	Scania K112CRS	Plaxton Paramount 3200 II	C48FT	1986	
SIB8528	Bedford YMP	Plaxton Paramount 3200 III	C35F	1987	Ex Air-Sea, Dunstable, 1995
E827EUT	Scania K112CRB	Plaxton Paramount 3500 III	C55F	1987	Ex Harry Crawford, Neilston, 1989
NJI5892	Scania K112TRB	Jonckheere Jubilee P99	CH55/19CT	1988	Ex Turner, Bristol, 1997
E309DMA	Volvo B10M-61	Plaxton Paramount 3500 III	C53F	1988	Ex Vale of Llangollen, Cefn Mawr, 1997
G553CRF	Scania K93CRB	Plaxton Paramount 3200 III	C53F	1990	Ex Hurst's of Wigan, 1993
H721VWU	Scania K93CRB	Plaxton Paramount 3200 III	C53F	1991	Ex Dodsworth, Boroughbridge, 1993
J275TVU	Scania K113CRB	Plaxton Paramount 3500 III	C49FT	1992	Ex Shearings, 1996

Previous registrations:-

E309DMA	E421CCA, VLT191, 9975VT	SIB8528	971OHT, D856XJL
GAL967	From new	SJI2953	B268TLJ
J275TVU	SPR35	TJI6707	C829LJN, 9467MU, C775KWL
NJI5892	E213GNV	VUN678	C92DTM, 794SKO, C874YKE
RJI6859	D559BAV	XRW506S	XRW506S, VUN678
RNC478	C112DTM, 5702PL, C447YFA		

Livery:- Silver, burgundy and maroon

Representing
Gretton's well
standardised fleet is
Scania H721VWU, a
K93 model with
Plaxton Paramount
3200 bodywork.
This is the mark III
version of the body
styling. The vehicle
is seen at South
Mimms motorway
service area.
Colin Lloyd

The East Anglia Bus Handbook

GREYS OF ELY

D R & A C Grey, 41 Sedgeway, Witchford, Ely, Cambridgeshire, CB6 2HY

WSU484	Bedford SB5	Duple Dominant	C41F	1975	Ex Elliott, Appleby, 1980
LHG441T	Bristol VRT/SL3/501(6LXB)	Eastern Coach Works	H43/31F	1978	Ex Southend, 1997
KPJ269W	Leyland Atlantean AN68B/1R	Roe	H43/30F	1981	Ex Kentish Bus, 1997
ESU389	Bedford YNT	Plaxton Paramount 3200 II	C53F	1985	Ex Premier Albanian, Watford, 1987
WSU485	Mercedes-Benz L608D	Plaxton Mini-Supreme	C25F	1986	Ex Felix, Long Melford, 1995
ESU378	Dennis Javelin 12SDA1907	Duple 320	C57F	1989	Ex Maybury, Verwood, 1994
WSU483	Mercedes-Benz 811D	Optare StarRider	B26F	1989	Ex Metroline, 1996
F647JHO	Citroen C25D	Citroen	M8	1989	Ex van, 1991
ESU320	Dennis Javelin 12SDA1907	Duple 320	C57F	1989	Ex Culverbeck, Berinsfield, 1992
ESU369	Dennis Javelin 8.5SDA1915	Duple 320	C35F	1990	Ex Felix, Long Melford, 1993
ESU238	Dennis Javelin 12SDA1907	Duple 320	C53F	1991	Ex Ardenvale, Knowle, 1994
ESU394	Dennis Javelin 12SDA2131	Plaxton Premiére 320	C57F	1994	Ex Harrod, Wormegay, 1997
L960VFL	Renault Trafic	Holdsworth	M8	1994	Ex MoD, 1997
ESU350	Dennis Javelin	Plaxton Premiére 350	C49FT	1995	Ex Grangeburn, Motherwell, 1997
N167BCE	Renault Trafic	Holdsworth	M8	1996	Ex MoD, 1997
ESU307	Dennis Javelin	Berkhof Excellence 1000	C51FT	1997	
ESU308	Dennis Javelin	Berkhof Excellence 1000	C57F	1997	
ESU629	Mercedes-Benz Sprinter 614	Concept Coachcraft	C24F	1998	

Previous registrations:-

ESU238	H272GRY	ESU369	G530GSC	F450GGP	J229OKX, J9WMS
ESU307	From new	ESU378	F625SAY	JNM747Y	WSU483 F154FWY
ESU308	From new	ESU389	B104XKX, ESU308	WSU483	?
ESU320	G218SWL	ESU394	L224BUT	WSU484	KPC219P
ESU350	N564CHE	ESU629	From new	WSU485	C930LMW

Livery:- Cream and two tone green

Private index plates are becoming increasingly common, with many pages of the weekend motoring press devoted to their sales. Imaginatively, Greys operate ESU320 on a Duple 320 coach and ESU350, as seen here, has been placed on Plaxton Premiére 350
Geoff Rixon

HAPPY WANDERER TOURS

Leiston Motor Hire Ltd, 15 High Street, Leiston, Suffolk, IP16 4EL

YRT240	Leyland Leopard PSU3C/4R	Plaxton Supreme III	C53F	1976	Ex Bygone, Biddenden, 1992
CFR297V	Leyland Leopard PSU3F/4R	Plaxton Supreme IV	C53F	1980	Ex Wyre Coaches, Preesall, 1996
PNB806W	Leyland Leopard PSU3F/5R	Plaxton Supreme IV	C53F	1981	Ex Meale, Reepham, 1995
PNW314W	Leyland Leopard PSU3F/4R	Plaxton Supreme IV	C49FT	1981	Ex Athelstan, Chippenham, 1990
447HWT	Leyland Tiger TRCTL11/2R	Plaxton Paramount 3200 E.	C49FT	1983	Ex Hill's, Tredegar, 1991
HIW233	Van Hool T813	Van Hool Alizée	C49FT	1983	Ex Bicknell, Godalming, 1986
47HWT	Van Hool T815	Van Hool Alicon	C53F	1985	Ex Bicknell, Godalming, 1989
HIW471	Mercedes-Benz 811D	Happy Wanderer (1990)	C21F	1987	
HIW9901	Volvo B10M-61	Plaxton Paramount 3500 III	C53F	1988	Ex Turner, Bristol, 1996
G541AGV	Van Hool T815	Van Hool Alicron	C49FT	1990	
K2HWT	MAN 16.290	Jonckheere Deauville P599	C49FT	1992	

Previous registrations:-

47HWT	C73PPE	HIW471	D606XNH
447HWT	RNY306Y	HIW9901	F868TLJ, 3138DP, F868TLJ
CFR297V	LUA286V, VVL266	PNW314W	PNW314W, YRT240
HIW233	MSU855Y, YRT240	YRT240	PNK158R, 302TKR, ?

Livery:- Black, orange and white.

Happy Wanderer Tours use a bold black and orange colour scheme. The only Leyland Tiger operated is Plaxton-bodied 447HWT, pictured near Romford. The body incorporates the Express doorway comprising two inward-folding panels. *Kevin Vincent*

HARRIS BUS / FRANK HARRIS COACHES

Harris Bus Company Ltd, Frank Harris (Coaches) Ltd,
Parker House, Manor Road, West Thurrock, Grays, Essex, RM20 4EH

Depots:- Manor Road West Thurrock, Grange Farm Tillingham; Crabtree Manor Way North, Belvedere.

34	M519NCG	Volvo B10M-62	Plaxton Premiére 320	C49FT	1995	Ex Excelsior, Bournemouth, 1997
35	M515NCG	Volvo B10M-62	Plaxton Premiére 320	C49FT	1995	Ex Excelsior, Bournemouth, 1997
42	K95GEV	DAF SB3000DKVF601	Van Hool Alizée HE	C48FT	1993	
44	L93OAR	Neoplan N122/3	Neoplan Skyliner	CH54/16CT	1994	
46	L98PTW	Toyota Coaster HZB50R	Caetano Optimo III	C21F	1994	
48	M501XWC	DAF SB3000WS601	Van Hool Alizée HE	C49FT	1995	
49	M502XWC	DAF SB3000WS601	Van Hool Alizée HE	C49FT	1995	
50	M503XWC	DAF SB3000WS601	Van Hool Alizée HE	C49FT	1995	
51	M504XWC	Neoplan N122/3	Neoplan Skyliner	CH54/16DT	1995	
52	N505CVW	DAF DE33WSSB3000	Van Hool Alizée HE	C49FT	1995	
53	N601EEV	Neoplan N212H	Neoplan Jetliner	C35FT	1996	
54	N602EEV	Neoplan N116	Neoplan Cityliner	C35FT	1996	
55	N603EEV	DAF DE33WSSB3000	Van Hool Alizée HE	C49FT	1996	
56	N604EEV	DAF DE33WSSB3000	Van Hool Alizée HE	C49FT	1996	
57	P701NHJ	DAF DE33WSSB3000	Ikarus Blue Danube 350	C49FT	1997	
58	P702NHJ	DAF DE33WSSB3000	Ikarus Blue Danube 350	C49FT	1997	
59	P703NHJ	DAF DE33WSSB3000	Ikarus Blue Danube 350	C49FT	1997	

Since the expansion into bus work the Harris coach fleet has received fleet numbers. Pictured here is M502XWC which, at the time the picture was taken, didn't display its fleet number 49. The DAF SB3000 is seen in the two-tone green UK-Europe livery on its trip to Derby Day at Epsom races.
Kevin Vincent

	K97GEV	DAF SB3000DKVF601	Van Hool Alizée HE	C48FT	1993
	N316VNT	LDV 200	LDV	M8	1996	Ex private owner, 1997
302	J582WVX	Mercedes-Benz 709D	Alexander Sprint	B25F	1991
303	J583WVX	Mercedes-Benz 709D	Alexander Sprint	B25F	1991
305	L475GOV	Peugeot-Talbot Freeway	TBP	B18FL	1994
306	L476GOV	Peugeot-Talbot Freeway	TBP	B18FL	1994
307	N25COO	LDV 400	LDV	M16	1995
308	M52WEV	LDV 400	LDV	M16	1995
310	F310OVW	MCW Metrorider MF150/112	MCW	B24F	1988
315	J51GCX	DAF SB220LC550	Ikarus Citibus	B48F	1992	Ex Strathclyde, 1994
316	J52GCX	DAF SB220LC550	Ikarus Citibus	B48F	1992	Ex Strathclyde, 1994
317	P317KTW	DAF DB250RS505	Northern Counties Palatine II	H47/30F	1996
318	P318KTW	DAF DB250RS505	Northern Counties Palatine II	H47/30F	1996
319	M649RCP	DAF DB250RS505	Northern Counties Palatine II	H47/30F	1995	Ex Bee Line, 1996
320	P320KAR	Optare L1070	Optare Excel	B35F	1996
321	P321KAR	Optare L1070	Optare Excel	B35F	1996
322	P322KAR	Optare L1070	Optare Excel	B35F	1996
323	P323KAR	Optare L1070	Optare Excel	B35F	1996

324-334   Optare L1070   Optare Excel   B35F   1997

324	P324NHJ	327	P327NHJ	329	P329NHJ	331	P331NHJ	333	P333HBC
325	P325NHJ	328	P328NHJ	330	P330NHJ	332	P332NHJ	334	P334NHJ
326	P326NHJ								

335	P335ROO	DAF DB250RS505	Northern Counties Palatine II	H43/25D	1997
336	P336ROO	DAF DB250RS505	Northern Counties Palatine II	H43/25D	1997
337	P337ROO	DAF DB250RS505	Northern Counties Palatine II	H43/25D	1997

338-350   Volvo Olympian   East Lancashire Pyoneer   H51/28D   1997

338	P338ROO	341	P341ROO	344	P344ROO	347	P347ROO	349	P349ROO
339	P339ROO	342	P342ROO	345	P345ROO	348	P348ROO	350	P350ROO
340	P340ROO	343	P343ROO	346	P346ROO				

351-359   Volvo Olympian   East Lancashire Pyoneer   H51/35F   1997

351	P351ROO	353	P353ROO	355	R355XVX	357	R357XVX	359	R359XVX
352	P352ROO	354	R354XVX	356	R356XVX	358	R358XVX		

360-372   Volvo Olympian   East Lancashire Pyoneer   H51/28D   1998

360	R360DJN	363	R363DJN	366	R366DJN	369	R369DJN	371	R371DJN
361	R361DJN	364	R364DJN	367	R367DJN	370	R370DJN	372	R372DJN
362	R362DJN	365	R365DJN	368	R368DJN				

373-380   Optare L1070   Optare Excel   B35F   1997/8

373	R373DJN	375	R375DJN	377	R377DJN	379	R379DJN	380	R380DJN
374	R374DJN	376	R376DJN	378	R378DJN				

Previous registrations:-

M515NCG   A7EXC   M519NCG   A9EXC

Livery:- Blue and lime green (buses); green, grey and white (coaches); blue, purple and pink (Harris Holidays) 53, 54; green (UK Europe) 49, 55; white, red and blue (Eurolines) 42, 50, 52, 57.

Opposite, top:- **Carrying the colours of Harris Holidays is Neoplan Jetliner 53, N601EEV. The Jetliner is the shortest of the current coach models that Neoplan are marketing in Britain at only 9.85 metres. The model includes a Mercedes-Benz engine and ZF six-speed gearbox.** *David Heath*
Opposite, bottom:- **Harris Bus commenced operating LRT tendered services in 1997 when it took over operation of route 108 in April. The company now operate six routes in south east and east London. Pictured on Route 129 is Volvo Olympian 344, P344ROO. The bodywork is East Lancashire Pyoneer, this example to London Transport's dual-door layout.** *Colin Lloyd*

D & H HARROD

D & H Harrod (Coaches) Ltd, West View, Wormegay, Kings Lynn, Norfolk, PE33 0SG

Depot:- Castle Road, Wormegay.

NDF158P	AEC Reliance 6U2R	Duple Dominant	C57F	1976	Ex Gobig, Mirfield, 1989
PNU133R	Bedford YRQ	Plaxton Supreme III	C45F	1976	Ex Butler Bros, Kirkby-in-Ashfield, 1983
AAL480A	Leyland Leopard PSU5D/4R	Plaxton P'mount 3200 III(1988) C53F		1980	Ex Tellings-Golden Miller, Cardiff, 1992
AAL456A	Leyland Leopard PSU5D/4R	Plaxton P'mount 3200 III(1988) C53F		1980	Ex Tellings-Golden Miller, Cardiff, 1992
PBC648W	Bedford YMT	Plaxton Supreme IV	C53F	1981	Ex Heginbotham, N. Runcton, 1996
OHE282X	Leyland Tiger TRCTL11/3R	Plaxton Supreme V	C53F	1982	Ex Garratt, Ashby, 1995
YPD104Y	Leyland Tiger TRCTL11/2R	Duple Dominant IV Express	C53F	1983	Ex The Delaine, Bourne, 1997
YPD105Y	Leyland Tiger TRCTL11/2R	Duple Dominant IV Express	C53F	1983	Ex The Delaine, Bourne, 1997
F882RFP	Dennis Javelin 12SDA1907	Plaxton Paramount 3200 III	C57F	1989	
F883RFP	Dennis Javelin 12SDA1907	Plaxton Paramount 3200 III	C57F	1989	

Previous registrations:-

AAL456A	BUH228V		AAL480A	BUH227V

Livery:- White and black

Several former-NBC coaches are now operated in the fleet of D&H Harrod. Leyland Tiger OHE282X is one of these and was new to National Travel East. The vehicle can be dated by the Plaxton Supreme body which ceased production shortly after the Leyland Tiger was introduced. Here we see OHE282X setting out on school contract work in Kings Lynn. *Kevin Vincent*

HEDINGHAM

Hedingham & District Omnibus Ltd, Wethersfield Road, Sible Hedingham,
Halstead, Essex, CO9 3LB

Depots:- *CN* Brunel Road and Stephensons Road, Clacton; *CR* Church Lane, Little Tey; *HD* Wethersfield Road, Sible Hedingham; *KN* High Street, Kelvedon; *SY* Meekings Road, Sudbury and *TY* New Road, Tollesbury.

	EX6566	Leyland Titan PD2/1	Leyland	H30/26R	1950	
L84	RGV284N	Leyland Leopard PSU3B/4R	Willowbrook	B55F	1974	
L87	PHK387R	Bedford YRQ	Duple Dominant	B47F	1976	
L88	REV188R	Bedford YLQ	Duple Dominant	B47F	1976	
L89	CEV89T	Bedford YLQ	Duple Dominant	B47F	1978	
L94	GVW894T	Bedford YMT	Plaxton Supreme III Express	C53F	1979	
L95	JAR495V	Bedford YLQ	Duple Dominant	B47F	1979	
L96	NFX446P	Bedford YMT	Plaxton Supreme III	C53F	1976	Ex Shamrock & Rambler, Bournemouth, 1979
L98	SPU898W	Bedford YMQ	Duple Dominant	B47F	1980	
L100	UNO100W	Bedford YMT	Plaxton Supreme IV Express	C53F	1981	
L103	BAR103X	Leyland Leopard PSU3E/4R	Plaxton Bustler	B55F	1982	
L105	BEV105X	Leyland Leopard PSU3E/4R	Plaxton Supreme IV Express	C53F	1982	
L111	UVX4S	Bristol LH6L	Eastern Coach Works	B43F	1977	Ex Eastern National, 1982
L112	UVX5S	Bristol LH6L	Eastern Coach Works	B43F	1977	Ex Eastern National, 1982
L113	UVX6S	Bristol LH6L	Eastern Coach Works	B43F	1977	Ex Eastern National, 1982
L114	UVX7S	Bristol LH6L	Eastern Coach Works	B43F	1977	Ex Eastern National, 1982
L115	FEV115Y	Leyland Leopard PSU3E/4R	Plaxton Supreme IV	C53F	1982	
L121	DBH452X	Leyland Leopard PSU5C/4R	Plaxton Supreme IV	C57F	1982	Ex Flights, Birmingham, 1983
L122	A122PAR	Leyland Tiger TRCTL11/2R	Plaxton Paramount 3200 E	C53F	1983	
L124	B124BOO	Leyland Tiger TRCTL11/2R	Plaxton Paramount 3200	C53F	1985	

One of the smaller National Bus Company fleets of Bristol LHs was that of Eastern National which operated just four, all of which passed to Hedingham when only five years old. The quartet are still active, often to be found on school duties which is where L111 was heading when pictured departing Clacton depot. *Steve Maskell*

L125	BNO700T	Bedford YMT	Duple Dominant II Express	C53F	1979	Ex Eastern National, 1984
L126	BNO703T	Bedford YMT	Duple Dominant II Express	C53F	1979	Ex Eastern National, 1984
L133	BHK710X	Bedford YNT	Plaxton Supreme IV Express	C53F	1982	Ex Springett, Ashen, 1984
L135	KGS489Y	Leyland Tiger TRCTL11/3R	Plaxton Paramount 3500	C50F	1983	Ex Travellers, Hounslow, 1985
L136	D136XVW	Bedford YMQ	Plaxton Derwent II	B47F	1987	
L137	D137XVW	Bedford YMQ	Plaxton Derwent II	B47F	1987	
L138	B273AMG	Leyland Tiger TRCTL11/3R	Plaxton Paramount 3200	C57F	1985	Ex Goldenport, Wandsworth, 1987
L139	FCY287W	Bedford YMQ	Duple Dominant	B43F	1980	Ex South Wales, 1987
L140	FCY288W	Bedford YMQ	Duple Dominant	B43F	1980	Ex South Wales, 1987
L141	FCY289W	Bedford YMQ	Duple Dominant	B43F	1980	Ex South Wales, 1987
L146	FCY287W	Bedford YMQ	Duple Dominant	DP45F	1981	Ex Armchair, Brentford, 1988
L147	NCD553M	Bristol VRT/SL2/6G	Eastern Coach Works	H43/31F	1973	Ex Southdown, 1988
L148	WPH135Y	Leyland Tiger TRCTL11/2R	East Lancs EL2000 (1994)	B55F	1982	Ex Kentish Bus, 1988
L149	E79HVX	Iveco Daily 49.10	Carlyle Dailybus	B25F	1988	
L150	F150LTW	Leyland Lynx LX112L10ZR1	Leyland Lynx	B51F	1988	
L151	F151NPU	Leyland LBM6T	Wadham Stringer Vanguard II	B39F	1988	
L152	D576VBV	Freight-Rover Sherpa	Dormobile	B16F	1986	Ex Ribble, 1988
L153	D345WPE	Ford Transit 190	Carlyle	B16F	1986	Ex Alder Valley South, 1989
L156	NPU979M	Bristol VRT/SL2/6G	Eastern Coach Works	H39/31F	1973	Ex Eastern National, 1989
L158	VOD590S	Bristol VRT/SL3/6LXB	Eastern Coach Works	H43/31F	1978	Ex Thames Transit (South Midland), 1989
L159	TBW451P	Bristol VRT/SL3/6LXB	Eastern Coach Works	H43/31F	1978	Ex Thames Transit (South Midland), 1989
L160	H160HJN	Leyland Olympian ONCL10/1RZ	Alexander RL	H47/32F	1990	
L161	SNJ591R	Bristol VRT/SL3/6LXB	Eastern Coach Works	H43/31F	1977	Ex Brighton & Hove, 1990
L162	MOD569P	Bristol VRT/SL3/6LXB	Eastern Coach Works	H43/32F	1976	Ex United, 1990
L163	MGR672P	Bristol VRT/SL3/6LXB	Eastern Coach Works	H43/31F	1975	Ex United, 1990
L164	SUP685R	Bristol VRT/SL3/6LXB	Eastern Coach Works	H43/31F	1976	Ex United, 1990
L165	LRA801P	Bristol VRT/SL3/501(6LXB)	Eastern Coach Works	H43/34F	1976	Ex Trent, 1990
L166	MRB802P	Bristol VRT/SL3/6LXB	Eastern Coach Works	H43/34F	1976	Ex Trent, 1990
L167	JWT757V	Bristol VRT/SL3/6LXB	Eastern Coach Works	H43/31F	1979	Ex Keighley & District, 1991
L168	PWY43W	Bristol VRT/SL3/6LXB	Eastern Coach Works	H43/31F	1981	Ex Keighley & District, 1991
L169	JKV414V	Bedford YMT	Plaxton Supreme IV	C53F	1979	Ex Kemp, Clacton, 1991
L170	WOO903W	Bedford YMT	Plaxton Supreme IV	C53F	1981	Ex Kemp, Clacton, 1991
L178	DWU294T	Bristol VRT/SL3/6LXB	Eastern Coach Works	H43/31F	1978	Ex Keighley & District, 1991
L193	D600MVR	Leyland Tiger TRCTL11/3RZ	Plaxton Paramount 3200 III	C53F	1987	Ex Shearings, 1991
L194	JWV271W	Bristol VRT/SL3/680	Eastern Coach Works	H43/31F	1981	Ex Brighton & Hove, 1991
L195	D584MVR	Leyland Tiger TRCTL11/3RZ	Plaxton Paramount 3200 III	C53F	1987	Ex Shearings, 1992
L196	H48NDU	Leyland Lynx LX2R11C15Z4R	Leyland Lynx II	B51F	1990	Ex VL Bus, Warwick, 1992
L197	GGM108W	Bristol VRT/SL3/6LXB	Eastern Coach Works	H43/31F	1980	Ex Oxford Bus Company, 1992
L198	K198EVW	Dennis Dart 9.8SDL3013	Alexander Dash	B43F	1992	
L199	HJB464W	Bristol VRT/SL3/6LXB	Eastern Coach Works	H43/31F	1980	Ex Oxford Bus Company, 1992
L200	J295TWK	Leyland Lynx LX2R11C14Z4S	Leyland Lynx II	B51F	1992	Ex VL Bus, Warwick, 1992
L201	F781GNA	Leyland Tiger TRCTL11/3ARZA	Plaxton Paramount 3200 III	C53F	1989	Ex Shearings, 1993
L202	BRC836T	Bristol VRT/SL3/6LXB	Eastern Coach Works	H43/31F	1979	Ex Trent, 1993
L203	BRC839T	Bristol VRT/SL3/6LXB	Eastern Coach Works	H43/31F	1979	Ex Trent, 1993
L204	AUD461R	Bristol VRT/SL3/6LXB	Eastern Coach Works	H43/31F	1977	Ex Delivered-in-Style, Syston, 1993
L205	E668UNE	Leyland Tiger TRCTL11/3RZ	Plaxton Paramount 3200 III	C53F	1988	Ex Shearings, 1994
L206	J724KBC	Leyland Lynx LX2R11V18Z4S	Leyland Lynx II	B51F	1992	Ex Westbus, Ashford, 1994
L207	L207RNO	Volvo B6-9.9m	Alexander Dash	B41F	1994	
L208	L208RNO	Volvo B6-9.9m	Alexander Dash	B41F	1994	
L209	H645UWR	Volvo B10M-60	Plaxton Paramount 3200 III	C53F	1991	Ex Wallace Arnold, 1994
L210	M210VEV	Dennis Dart 9SDL3031	Plaxton Pointer	B34F	1994	
L211	M211WHJ	Dennis Lance SLF	Wright Pathfinder 320	N40F	1995	
L212	M212WHJ	Dennis Lance SLF	Wright Pathfinder 320	N40F	1995	
L215	MKK458P	Bedford YRT	Plaxton Supreme III	C53F	1976	Ex Partridge, Hadleigh, 1994
L221	229LRB	Leyland Leopard PSU5C/4R	Plaxton Supreme III	C53F	1979	Ex Partridge, Hadleigh, 1994
L224	A486FPV	Bedford YNT	Duple Laser	C53F	1983	Ex Partridge, Hadleigh, 1994
L225	A487FPV	Bedford YNT	Duple Laser	C53F	1983	Ex Partridge, Hadleigh, 1994
L229	F464NRT	Leyland Tiger TRCTL11/3RZ	Duple 320	C61F	1988	Ex Partridge, Hadleigh, 1994
L230	F145SPV	Leyland Tiger TRCTL11/3ARZ	Plaxton Paramount 3200 III	C57F	1989	Ex Partridge, Hadleigh, 1994
L231	F146SPV	Leyland Tiger TRCTL11/3ARZ	Plaxton Paramount 3200 III	C57F	1989	Ex Partridge, Hadleigh, 1994
L232	F147SPV	Leyland Tiger TRCTL11/3ARZ	Plaxton Paramount 3200 III	C57F	1989	Ex Partridge, Hadleigh, 1994
L233	F148SPV	Leyland Tiger TRCTL11/3ARZ	Plaxton Paramount 3200 III	C57F	1989	Ex Partridge, Hadleigh, 1994

Opposite, top:- **A batch of Eastern Coach Works-bodied Leyland Tigers were delivered to London Country in 1982 and these formed the TL class. TL35 passed to Hedingham and after some five years of operation in its original condition, the vehicle was rebodied with an East Lancashire EL2000 bus body. It was pictured leaving Colchester bus station for Nayland.** *Malcolm King*
Opposite, bottom:- **Plaxton Pointer bodywork is carried on the two Dennis Darts operated by Hedingham while the Volvo B6 fleet numbers six. Illustrated here is L241, N241EWC.** *Paul Goodison*

The East Anglia Bus Handbook

L235	WJM831T	Bristol VRT/SL3/6LXB	Eastern Coach Works	H43/31F	1979	Ex The Bee Line, 1995
L236	CJH143V	Bristol VRT/SL3/6LXB	Eastern Coach Works	H43/31F	1980	Ex The Bee Line, 1995
L237	GGM84W	Bristol VRT/SL3/6LXB	Eastern Coach Works	H43/31F	1980	Ex The Bee Line, 1995
L240	XPW877X	Leyland Leopard PSU3G/4R	Eastern Coach Works B51	C47F	1982	Ex Carter, Colchester, 1995
L241	N241EWC	Dennis Dart 9SDL3051	Plaxton Pointer	B35F	1996	
L242	J734CWT	Volvo B10M-60	Plaxton Excalibur	C53F	1992	Ex Wallace Arnold, 1996
L243	M262KWK	Volvo B6-9.9m	Alexander Dash	B40F	1995	Ex Volvo, Warwick, 1996
L244	M988NAA	Volvo B10M-62	Plaxton Premiére 320	C53F	1995	Ex Excelsior, Bournemouth, 1996
L245	SGR780V	Bristol VRT/SL3/6LXB	Eastern Coach Works	H43/31F	1979	Ex NE Bus (Tees), 1996
L246	APT813W	Bristol VRT/SL3/6LXB	Eastern Coach Works	H43/31F	1980	Ex NE Bus (Tees), 1996
L247	CPT731S	Bristol VRT/SL3/6LXB	Eastern Coach Works	H43/31F	1978	Ex Ellis, Kelvedon, 1996
L248	HJB455W	Bristol VRT/SL3/6LXB	Eastern Coach Works	H43/31F	1980	Ex Oxford Bus Company, 1996
L249	HJB456W	Bristol VRT/SL3/6LXB	Eastern Coach Works	H43/31F	1980	Ex Oxford Bus Company, 1996
L250	HJB459W	Bristol VRT/SL3/6LXB	Eastern Coach Works	H43/31F	1980	Ex Oxford Bus Company, 1996
L251	MRJ8W	Bristol VRT/SL3/6LXB	Eastern Coach Works	DPH41/29F	1980	Ex Oxford Bus Company, 1996
L252	MRJ9W	Bristol VRT/SL3/6LXB	Eastern Coach Works	DPH41/29F	1980	Ex Oxford Bus Company, 1996
L253	PWY39W	Bristol VRT/SL3/6LXB	Eastern Coach Works	H43/31F	1980	Ex Cambus (Viscount), 1996
L254	RAH260W	Bristol VRT/SL3/6LXB	Eastern Coach Works	H43/31F	1980	Ex Cambus, 1996
L255	STW30W	Bristol VRT/SL3/6LXC	Eastern Coach Works	H43/31F	1980	Ex Cambus, 1996
L256	SUB791W	Bristol VRT/SL3/6LXB	Eastern Coach Works	H43/31F	1981	Ex Cambus (Viscount), 1996
L257	PWY46W	Bristol VRT/SL3/6LXB	Eastern Coach Works	H43/31F	1981	Ex Cambus (Viscount), 1996
L258	M261KWK	Volvo B6-9.9m	Plaxton Pointer	B40F	1995	Ex Volvo, Warwick, 1997
L259	TJI1688	Volvo B10M-60	Plaxton Paramount 3500 III	C49FT	1990	Ex Osborne, Tollesbury, 1997
L260	BHJ368S	Bristol VRT/SL3/6LXB	Eastern Coach Works	H43/31F	1978	Ex Osborne, Tollesbury, 1997
L261	CJH115V	Bristol VRT/SL3/6LXB	Eastern Coach Works	H43/31F	1979	Ex Osborne, Tollesbury, 1997
L262	CJH141V	Bristol VRT/SL3/6LXB	Eastern Coach Works	H43/31F	1980	Ex Osborne, Tollesbury, 1997
L268	XGS767X	Leyland Tiger TRCTL11/3R	Plaxton Supreme V	C57F	1981	Ex Osborne, Tollesbury, 1997
L269	GVS948Y	Leyland Tiger TRCTL11/2R	Plaxton Supreme VI Express	C53F	1983	Ex Osborne, Tollesbury, 1997
L270	CPU125X	Leyland Tiger TRCTL11/2R	Plaxton Supreme VI Express	C53F	1982	Ex Osborne, Tollesbury, 1997
L271	KBC2V	Volvo B58-61	Plaxton Supreme IV	C57F	1980	Ex Osborne, Tollesbury, 1997
L275	RWC41W	Leyland Leopard PSU3E/4R	Plaxton Supreme IV Express	C49F	1981	Ex Osborne, Tollesbury, 1997
L276	LUA289V	Leyland Leopard PSU3E/4R	Plaxton Supreme IV	C53F	1980	Ex Osborne, Tollesbury, 1997
L277	EWW213T	Leyland Leopard PSU3E/4R	Plaxton Supreme IV	C53F	1979	Ex Osborne, Tollesbury, 1997
L280	JIL5623	Leyland Tiger TRCTL11/3R	Plaxton Paramount 3200	C57F	1983	Ex Osborne, Tollesbury, 1997
L281	M107UWY	Volvo B10M-62	Plaxton Premiére 320	C50F	1995	Ex Wallace Arnold, 1997
L282	M571XKY	Volvo B10M-62	Plaxton Premiére 350	C49FT	1995	Ex A&R International, Bedfont, 1997
L283	L202HYE	Volvo B6-9.9m	Plaxton Pointer	DP29F	1994	Ex Terminus, Crawley, 1997
L284	L203HYE	Volvo B6-9.9m	Plaxton Pointer	DP29F	1994	Ex Terminus, Crawley, 1997
L285	M517NCG	Volvo B10M-62	Plaxton Premiére 350	C53F	1995	Ex Excelsior, Bournemouth, 1997
L286	P530CLJ	Volvo B10M-62	Plaxton Premiére 320	C53F	1996	Ex Excelsior, Bournemouth, 1998

Previous registrations:-

229LRB	VAS589T, 162EKH, VWS976T, VAS589T	M517NCG	XEL606
BHJ368S	VPF282S, HIL9273	P530CLJ	A13XEL
EX6566	From new	TJI1688	G88RGG
JIL5623	FNM860Y		

Livery:- Red and cream.

In 1995, Hedingham added two new Dennis Lance SLFs to the fleet, and these carry bodywork by Wrights. The body for the early Lance is the Pathfinder 320 and L212 from that pair is shown here.

IPSWICH BUSES

Ipswich Buses Ltd, Constantine Road, Ipswich, Suffolk, IP1 2DL

| 9 | MRT9P | Leyland Atlantean AN68/1R | Roe | | O43/26D | 1976 | | |

18-35

Leyland Atlantean AN68A/1R   Roe   H43/29D   1976-77

18	RDX18R	22	SDX22R	25	SDX25R	30	SDX30R	33	SDX33R
19	RDX19R	23	SDX23R	27	SDX27R	31	SDX31R	34	SDX34R
20	RDX20R	24	SDX24R	29	SDX29R	32	SDX32R	35	SDX35R

40	M640EPV	Volvo Olympian YN2RV18V3	East Lancashire	H49/31D	1995	
41	M41EPV	Volvo Olympian YN2RV18V3	East Lancashire	H49/31D	1995	
42	M42EPV	Volvo Olympian YN2RV18V3	East Lancashire	H49/31D	1995	
43	B714HVO	Leyland Olympian ONLXB/1RV	Eastern Coach Works	H45/30F	1985	Ex Trent, 1998
44	C722NNN	Leyland Olympian ONLXB/1RV	Eastern Coach Works	H45/30F	1985	Ex Trent, 1998
81	F81ODX	Dennis Dominator DDA1019	East Lancashire	H45/26D	1988	
82	B82NDX	Dennis Dominator DDA907	East Lancashire	DPH43/27D	1985	
101	YDX101Y	Dennis Falcon HC SDA408	East Lancashire	B44D	1983	
104	YDX104Y	Dennis Falcon HC SDA408	East Lancashire	B44D	1983	
106	C106SDX	Dennis Falcon HC SDA416	East Lancashire	B44D	1985	

114-124

Dennis Falcon HC SDA419*   East Lancashire   B44D   1988-89 *118-24 are SDA420

114	E114KDX	117	E117KDX	119	G119VDX	121	G121VDX	123	G123VDX
115	E115KDX	118	G118VDX	120	G120VDX	122	G122VDX	124	G124VDX
116	E116KDX								

130	P130PPV	Dennis Dart SLF	East Lancashire Spryte	N42F	1997	
131	P131PPV	Dennis Dart SLF	East Lancashire Spryte	N42F	1997	
132	P132PPV	Dennis Dart SLF	East Lancashire Spryte	N42F	1997	
133	R133SBJ	Dennis Dart SLF	East Lancashire Spryte	N42F	1997	
134	R134SBJ	Dennis Dart SLF	East Lancashire Spryte	N42F	1997	
144	B114LDX	Bristol B21	Alexander N	B49D	1985	
145	B115LDX	Bristol B21	Alexander N	B49D	1985	
146	B116LDX	Bristol B21	Alexander N	B47D	1985	
147	WOI607	Bristol B21	Alexander N	B53F	1985	
149	TDX124W	Bristol B21	Alexander	B53F	1981	Ex Ulsterbus, 1991
150	XRT931X	Bristol B21	Alexander	B53F	1981	Ex Citybus, 1991
151	TDX120W	Bristol B21	Alexander	B53F	1981	Ex Citybus, 1992
152	XRT932X	Bristol B21	Alexander	B53F	1981	Ex Citybus, 1992
153	XRT947X	Bristol B21	Alexander	B53F	1981	Ex Citybus, 1992

The latest double-deck buses with Ipswich are a trio of Volvo Olympians delivered in 1995, though two older Olympians have since been acquired from Trent. Pictured at Baker Street station on rail-replacement contracts during February 1998 is 41, M41EPV.
Keith Grimes

160	J160LPV	Dennis Lance 11SDA3101	East Lancashire EL2000	B45D	1992	
161	L161ADX	Dennis Lance 11SDA3113	East Lancashire EL2000	B41D	1994	
162	L162ADX	Dennis Lance 11SDA3113	East Lancashire EL2000	B41D	1994	
169	L169ADX	Dennis Lance 11SDA3113	Optare Sigma	B41D	1994	
180	H180HPV	DAF SB220LC550	Optare Delta	B45D	1991	
181	L181ADX	DAF SB220LC550	Optare Delta	B44D	1994	
182	L182ADX	DAF SB220LC550	Optare Delta	B44D	1994	
183	L183APV	DAF SB220LC550	Optare Delta	B44D	1994	
184	L184APV	DAF SB220LC550	Optare Delta	B44D	1994	

185-189 Optare L1150 — Optare Excel — B37F — 1997

185	R185DDX	186	R186DDX	187	R187DDX	188	R197DDX	189	R189DDX

190	P190SGV	Optare L1150	Optare Excel	B38F	1997	
191	P191SGV	Optare L1150	Optare Excel	B38F	1997	
192	P192SGV	Optare L1150	Optare Excel	B38F	1997	
193	P443SWX	Optare L1150	Optare Excel	B37F	1997	Ex Optare demonstrator, 1997
194	P194SGV	Optare L1150	Optare Excel	B38F	1997	
195	P195SGV	Optare L1150	Optare Excel	B38F	1997	
196	P196SGV	Optare L1150	Optare Excel	B38F	1997	
213	M213EDX	Optare MetroRider MR17	Optare	B29F	1994	
214	M214EDX	Optare MetroRider MR17	Optare	B29F	1994	
215	M215EDX	Optare MetroRider MR17	Optare	B29F	1994	
216	M216EDX	Optare MetroRider MR17	Optare	B29F	1994	
217	L832MWT	Optare MetroRider MR07	Optare	B27F	1993	Ex Optare demonstrator, 1993
218	J218NRT	Optare MetroRider MR05	Optare	B31F	1992	
219	K219PPV	Optare MetroRider MR05	Optare	B31F	1992	

221-228 Optare MetroRider MF158* — Optare — B31F — 1989-90 223-8 are MetroRider MR01

221	G221VDX	223	G223VDX	225	H225EDX	227	H227EDX	228	J228JDX
222	G222VDX	224	G224VDX	226	H226EDX				

229	K100LCT	Optare MetroRider MR01	Optare	DP31F	1992	Ex Lancaster, 1993

Previous registrations:-

TDX124W	WOI3002		WOI607	B117LDX		XRT932X	WOI3003
TDX120W	WOI3001		XRT931X	WOI3005		XRT947X	WOI3004

9 *Eastern Belle*; 18 *Memory*; 19 *Mirosa*; 20 *Northdown*; 22 *Perseus*; 23 *Phoenician*; 24 *Pride of Ipswich*; 25 *Reminder*; 26 *Reporter*; 27 *Saxon*; 29 *Sunbeam*; 30 *Thalatta*; 31 *Tollesbury*; 32 *Triton*; 33 *Vanguard*; 34 *Veronica*; 35 *Xylonite*; 40 *Beatrice Maud*; 41 *May*; 42 *Vigilant*; 75 *Eastbourne Queen*; 81 *British Oak*; 82 *Margaret Catchpole*; 101 *Alaric*; 104 *Alma*; 106 *Ardwina*; 114 *Avocet*; 115 *Eldred Watkins*; 116 *Excelsior*; 117 *Felix*; 118 *Lady Daphne*; 119 *Lady Jean*; 120 *Marjorie*; 121 *Nautilus*; 122 *Orinoco*; 123 *Pudge*; 124 *Venture*; 130 *HMS Grafton*, 131 *Will Everard*, 132 *Raybel*, 144 *Great Western*; 145 *Great Eastern*; 146 *Godspeed*; 147 *Bristolian*; 149 *Hibernia*; 150 *Shamrock*; 151 *Esmeralda*; 152 *Kathleen*; 153 *Muriel*; 160 *Barbara Jean*; 161 *Adie*; 162 *Doris*; 169 *King John*; 180 *New Spirit of Ipswich*; 181 *Peter Bruff*; 182 *Leonard Squirrell*; 183 HN *'Jimmy' James*; 184 *Thomas Cobbold*, 190 *Chantry Infant School*, 191 *Gusford Primary School*, 192 *Handford Hall Primary School & Nursery*; 193 *Orwell Junior Traveller*, 194 *Saint Matthews School*, 195 *Sprites Infants School*, 196 *St Mark's RC Primary School*, 213 *Ariel*; 214 *Miranda*; 215 *Oberon*; 216 *Umbriel*; 217 *Diana Princess of Wales 1961-1997*, 218 *Apollo*; 219 *Thisbe*; 221 *Dione*; 222 *Mimas*; 223 *Rhea*; 224 *Tethys*; 225 *Eros*; 226 *Pallas*; 227 *Vesta*; 228 *Icarus*; 229 *Lancastrian*.

Livery:- Two tone green and cream; purple (Park & Ride) 185-189.

Opposite,top:- **Recent deliveries have introduced the Dennis Dart SLF to the Ipswich fleet. These buses carry East Lancashire Spryte bodywork, the name now adopted by East Lancashire for all lengths of the low floor buses built at Blackburn.** *Colin Lloyd*
Opposite, bottom:- **Minibus requirements at Ipswich are met by sixteen Optare MetroRider, just one of the Optare products which have been introduced into Ipswich in recent times. The latest arrivals at Ipswich are examples of the Excel.***Malcolm King*

JACKSONS COACHES

M J Jackson, Bicknacre House, Leighams Road, Bicknacre,
Chelmsford, Essex, CM3 4NF

2	MJI3376	Bova EL26/581	Bova Europa	C50F	1982	Ex Harris, West Thurrock, 1990
3	L738NMU	Mercedes-Benz 609D	Autobus Classique	C23F	1993	
4	MJI2374	Neoplan N122/3	Neoplan Skyliner	CH56/22CT	1985	Ex APT, Rayleigh, 1993
5	BDZ5198	DAF 2300DHS585	Plaxton Paramount 3200 II	C49FT	1988	Ex Thomas, West Ewell, 1991
6	MJI2550	Dennis Javelin 12SDA1907	Plaxton Paramount 3200 III	C53F	1989	Ex Wainfleet, Nuneaton, 1995
7	F303RMH	Mercedes-Benz L307D	Reeve Burgess	M12	1988	
8	PRA12R	Leyland Leopard PSU3C/4R	Alexander AT	C49FT	1976	Ex Porter, Great Totham, 1995
9	F321SMD	Mercedes-Benz 811D	Optare StarRider	C29F	1988	Ex Brentwood Coaches, 1993
10	B897AGJ	Mercedes-Benz 307D	Devon Conversions	M10	1984	Ex Kent Transmission, Sidcup, 1990
11	OSR192R	Bristol VRT/SL3/6LXB	Alexander AL	H49/34F	1977	Ex City of Nottingham, 1994
12	OSR194R	Bristol VRT/SL3/6LXB	Alexander AL	H49/34F	1977	Ex City of Nottingham, 1994
45	C245OFE	Mercedes-Benz L608D	Reeve Burgess	B20F	1988	Ex RoadCar, 1995
	MJI1306	Neoplan N122/3	Neoplan Skyliner	CH57/20CT	1990	Ex APT, Rayleigh, 1997
	CDT322T	Bedford YMT	Duple Dominant II	C53F	1979	Ex APT, Rayleigh, 1997
	K96GEV	DAF SB3000DKFV601	Van Hool Alizée HE	C48FT	1993	Ex Harris, Grays, 1997

Previous registrations:-

BDZ5198	C335UFT	MJI2374	2803PK, B701JYJ
CDT322T	APU513T, CIB3683	MJI2550	F78VWK, MIW5791, F868RFP
MJI1306	G300XAC	MJI3376	8947FH, AOO101X

Livery:- Cream with purple and yellow relief.

JANS COACHES

R C, S and J Edwards, 23 Townsend, Soham, Cambridgeshire, CB7 5DD

PJJ18S	Bristol VRT/SL3/6LXB	Willowbrook	H43/31F	1978	Ex East Kent, 1992
VOI3252	Bedford YNT	Duple Dominant IV	C53F	1981	Ex Barrett, Gt Mongeham, 1990
B671DVL	Neoplan N122/3	Neoplan Skyliner	CH55/20DT	1985	Ex Anglo-French, Chislehurst, 1988
D164TCX	ACE Cheetah	Van Hool Alizée H	C49FT	1986	Ex King, Bordon, 1992
D343CPB	LAG G355Z	LAG Panoramic	C49FT	1987	Ex Goldline, Wimbourne, 1995
E92VWA	Neoplan N122/3	Neoplan Skyliner	CH57/20CT	1987	Ex Express Travel, Perth, 1994
299SAE	Van Hool T815	Van Hool Alicron	C51FT	1991	Ex Swanbrook, Cheltenham, 1996
K112YFL	Leyland-DAF 400	Leyland-DAF	M16	1993	Ex private owner, 1996
R	MAN 18.350	Neoplan Transliner	C F	1998	

Named Vehicles:- 299SAE *Eurocruiser I*; B671DVL *Eurocruiser II*; D343CPB *Eurocruiser III*

Previous registrations:-

299SAE	H131JFH	VOI3252	JAX24W

Livery:- White and black

KENZIES

Kenzies Coaches Ltd, 6 Angel Lane, Shepreth, Cambridgeshire, SG8 6QH

JBY804	Bedford OB	Duple Vista	C29F	1951	Ex Barber, Mitcham, 1963
GUP743C	Bedford VAL14	Plaxton Panorama	C52F	1965	Ex Carr, New Silksworth, 1981
PJE999J	Bedford YRQ	Plaxton Panorama Elite	C45F	1971	
PEB2R	Bedford YMT	Plaxton Supreme III	C45F	1977	
YJE3T	Bedford YMT	Plaxton Supreme IV	C53F	1979	
XVE8T	Volvo B58-61	Plaxton Supreme IV	C57F	1979	
CVE12V	Volvo B58-61	Plaxton Supreme IV	C50F	1980	
HFL14W	Bedford YMQ	Plaxton Supreme IV	C45F	1981	
LEW16W	Volvo B10M-61	Plaxton Supreme IV	C53F	1981	
C25KAV	Volvo B10M-61	Van Hool Alizée H	C57F	1985	
C28RFL	Volvo B10M-46	Van Hool Alizée H	C41F	1986	
D30BEW	Volvo B10M-61	Van Hool Alizée H	C57F	1987	
G40SAV	Volvo B10M-60	Van Hool Alizée H	C57F	1990	
K49TER	Volvo B10M-60	Van Hool Alizée HE	C48FT	1993	
K51TER	Volvo B10M-60	Van Hool Alizée HE	C48FT	1993	
K52TER	Volvo B10M-60	Van Hool Alizée HE	C48FT	1993	
L56REW	Volvo B10M-62	Van Hool Alizée HE	C53F	1994	
L57REW	Volvo B10M-62	Van Hool Alizée HE	C48F	1994	
M61WEB	Volvo B10M-62	Van Hool Alizée HE	C49FT	1995	
M64WEB	Volvo B10M-62	Van Hool Alizée HE	C48F	1995	
M65WEB	Volvo B10M-62	Van Hool Alizée HE	C48F	1995	
M67WEB	Volvo B10M-62	Van Hool Alizée HE	C48F	1995	
N68WEW	Volvo B10M-62	Van Hool Alizée HE	C48F	1995	
N69WEW	Volvo B10M-62	Van Hool Alizée HE	C48F	1995	
N71WEW	Volvo B10M-62	Van Hool Alizée HE	C48F	1995	
N72WEW	Volvo B10M-62	Van Hool Alizée HE	C48F	1995	
N73WEW	Volvo B10M-62	Van Hool Alizée HE	C48F	1995	
N74WEW	Volvo B10M-62	Van Hool Alizée HE	C48F	1995	
N75WEW	Volvo B10M-62	Van Hool Alizée HE	C48F	1995	
P76OEW	Volvo B10M-62	Van Hool Alizée HE	C48F	1997	
P78OEW	Volvo B10M-62	Plaxton Premiére 350	C48F	1997	
P79OEW	Volvo B10M-62	Van Hool Alizée HE	C48F	1997	
R81NAV	Volvo B10M-62	Van Hool Alizée 2	C49FT	1998	
R82NAV	Volvo B10M-62	Van Hool Alizée 2	C49FT	1998	
R83NAV	Volvo B10M-62	Van Hool Alizée 2	C49FT	1998	

Livery:- Two tone blue, orange, white and silver; white and red (Globus):- L57REW, M64/5/7WEB, N69/71/3-5WEW, P76/8/9DEW

Kenzies of Shepreth operate a modern fleet of high-specification coaches mostly on contracted tour work. One of the older coaches, which are used on more local duties, is LEW16W, an early Volvo B10M with Plaxton Supreme IV coachwork.
David Heath

KINGS

A B Cousins, 364 London Road, Stanway, Colchester, Essex, CO3 5LT

C718NHJ	Volvo B10M-61	Van Hool Alizée	C52DT	1986	Ex Travelrich, Clacton, 1996
C27OFL	Volvo B10M-61	Van Hool Alizée	C52DT	1986	Ex Kenzie, Shepreth, 1994
C404LRP	Volvo B10M-46	Jonckheere Jubilee P50	C35FT	1986	Ex Budden, Woodfalls, 1990
D685JVF	Van Hool T815	Van Hool Acron	C53FT	1987	Ex Boon, Boreham, 1992
F613HGO	DAF SB2305DHS585	Van Hool Alizée DH	C53F	1989	Ex London Coaches, 1995
G976KJX	DAF SB3000DKV601	Van Hool Alizée	C53FT	1990	Ex Duguid, Aberdeen, 1993
P111ABC	Bova FHD 12.330	Bova Futura	C55F	1997	

Previous registration:-
C718NHJ   C26OFL, 5765DZ

Livery:- White and green

The Van Hool Alizée is built on a variety of chassis as well as being an integral product. The standard model is the 3.41-metre H model, also available with low driving position as the DH. This variant is shown here by F613HGO, a DAF SB2305 rear-engined example operated by Kings. *David Heath*

KIDDLES / ST IVES TRAVEL

R Willmore, 10 East Street, St Ives, Huntingdon, Cambridgeshire, PE17 4PB

KBV211S	Bedford YMT	Plaxton Supreme III	C53F	1978	Ex Stainton, Kendle, 1995
UFT914T	Bedford YMT	Plaxton Supreme III	C53F	1978	Ex St Peters School, Huntingdon, 1995
GRT500V	Bedford YMT	Plaxton Supreme IV	C53F	1979	Ex Kiddles, St Ives, 1995
CAZ6829	Volvo B58-61	Plaxton Supreme IV	C53F	1980	Ex Kiddles, St Ives, 1995
UHJ797Y	Bedford YNT	Plaxton Supreme VI	C53F	1982	Ex Kiddles, St Ives, 1995
FDZ5347	Volvo B10M-61	Van Hool Alizée H	C46FT	1983	Ex Spring, Evesham, 1996
RIW9057	Volvo B10M-61	Duple Caribbean	C49FT	1984	Ex Kiddles, St Ives, 1995
A154RUM	Bova FHD12.280	Bova Futura	C57F	1984	Ex B&H Tours, Mirfield, 1997
D560CJF	Bedford YNT	Plaxton Paramount 3200 III	C53F	1987	Ex Kiddles, St Ives, 1995
RIW9456	LAG G355Z	LAG Panoramic	C49FT	1989	Ex Kiddles, St Ives, 1995

Previous registrations:-

A154RUM	A698TNO, 3553FH	RIW9057	A232GNR
CAZ6829	NNS241V, 885FOC	RIW9456	F423EEG
FDZ5347	PGC519Y	UHJ797Y	PTX332Y, 9424RU
KBV211S	WPJ9S, LIB3626		

Livery:- White and black (Kiddles); white, blue and gold (St.Ives);

KIRBY'S RAYLEIGH

E Kirby, 2 Princess Road, Rayleigh, Essex, SS6 8HR

OTW116K	Kässbohrer Setra S130	Kassbohrer	C53F	1971	
WNO115X	Kässbohrer Setra S215HD	Kässbohrer Tornado	C47F	1981	
LHK589Y	Kässbohrer Setra S215HD	Kässbohrer Tornado	C49F	1981	
VWX361X	Kässbohrer Setra S215H	Kässbohrer Optimal	C53F	1982	Ex Wallace Arnold, 1986
F993MTW	Kässbohrer Setra S215HD	Kässbohrer Tornado	C49FT	1989	Ex Loveridge, Marks Tey, 1989
NMC873	Kässbohrer Setra S215HD	Kässbohrer Tornado	C53FT	1982	Ex North Mymms, Potters Bar, 1990
WVY596	Kässbohrer Setra S215H	Kässbohrer Optimal	C53F	1983	Ex SSS, Euston, 1993
G636CAF	Kässbohrer Setra S215HD	Kässbohrer Tornado	C49FT	1990	Ex Deeble, Darley Ford, 1995
K13BYS	Kässbohrer Setra S250	Kässbohrer Special	C48FT	1996	

Previous registrations:-

NMC873	RWF313X	WVY596	FUA406Y

Livery:- Silver, blue and lilac.

LAMBERT'S

Lamberts Coaches (Beccles) Ltd, Unit 7 Ellough Industrial Estate,
Beccles, Suffolk, NR34 7TD

BFL503V	Bedford YMT	Plaxton Supreme IV	C53F	1979	Ex Mathews Blue, Shouldham, 1992
FIL2296	Bedford YMT	Plaxton Supreme IV	C53F	1980	Ex Lambert, Ditchingham, 1987
NFP115W	Bedford YMT	Plaxton Supreme IV	C49F	1980	Ex Easton's Coaches, Stratton Strawless, 1997
NRR36W	Bedford YMT	Plaxton Supreme IV Express	C53F	1981	Ex Ryan, Langridge, 1996
TVN330X	Bedford YNT	Plaxton Supreme VI	C53F	1982	Ex Cropper, Leeds, 1991
856GKH	Bova FHD12.280	Bova Futura	C53FT	1984	Ex Easton's Coaches, Stratton Strawless, 1994
MIL9423	Bedford Venturer YNV (Volvo)	Plaxton Paramount 3200 II	C57F	1985	Ex Easton's Coaches, Stratton Strawless, 1996
5019BT	Volvo B10M-61	Plaxton Paramount 3500 III	C48FT	1987	Ex Easton's Coaches, Stratton Strawless, 1996
M441CVG	Volvo B6-9.9m	Plaxton Pointer	B40F	1995	
M832CVG	Volvo B6-9.9m	Plaxton Pointer	B40F	1995	

Previous registrations:-

856GKH	A585GPE	FIL2296	MWU186V
5019BT	D204LWX	MIL9423	B272KUF, TSV757, B422RDY

Livery:- Two tone blue and white.

Two Plaxton Pointer-bodied Volvo B6 buses are operated by Lambert's on tendered services. These joined the fleet in 1995 and M832CVG is seen in Great Yarmouth wearing Lambert's blue and white.
Richard Godfrey

LEROY COACHES / A & P TRAVEL

P J Brown, North View, Barway Farm, Barway, Ely, Cambridgeshire, CB7 5UB

Q856MEV	Leyland Leopard PSU3A/2R	Berkhof Esprite 340 (1985)	C53F	1971	Ex Travelmate, Wareham, 1993
TPJ780M	Bedford YRT	Duple Dominant	C53F	1973	Ex D J, Fordham, 1996
PHH408R	Bristol VRT/SL3/501	Eastern Coach Works	H43/31F	1976	Ex Stephenson, Rochford, 1996
TMA329R	Bristol VRT/SL3/6LXB	Eastern Coach Works	H43/31F	1976	Ex Cityfleet, Aintree, 1993
OCY913R	Bristol VRT/SL3/501	Eastern Coach Works	H43/31F	1977	Ex Pratt, Moreton Valence, 1996
RDC103R	Bristol VRT/SL3/6LXB	Northern Counties	H43/31F	1977	Ex SM, Roydon, 1996
CBV10S	Bristol VRT/SL3/501	Eastern Coach Works	H43/31F	1977	Ex APT, Rayleigh, 1997
SKG901S	Bristol VRT/SL3/501	Eastern Coach Works	H43/31F	1977	Ex Pratt, Moreton Valence, 1996
TYE707S	Bedford YMT	Duple Dominant II	C49F	1977	Ex Newmarket Transport Training, 1996
VBH97S	Bedford YMT	Duple Dominant II	C53F	1977	Ex Premier-Albanian, Watford, 1985
RJI4078	Ford Transit 190	Reeve Burgess	M16	1979	Ex BarkerBus, Roydon, 1994
LJI1613	Volvo B58-61	Jonckheere Bermuda	C49FT	1979	Ex Brandons, Blackmore End, 1996
YYL775T	Leyland Leopard PSU5C/4R	Duple Dominant II	C55F	1979	Ex Storey, Littleport, 1996
KOF663	Volvo B58-61	Plaxton Supreme IV	C51F	1980	Ex KGS, Pencoed, 1996
RAY160W	Bedford YMT	Caetano Alpha	C53F	1981	Ex Reliant, Ibstock, 1993
TVU716X	Bedford YMT	Duple Dominant IV	C53F	1982	Ex Barnes, Bury St Edmunds, 1997
Q290FDF	Leyland Leopard PSU5E/5R	Willowbrook Crusader(1990)	C53F	1982	Ex Boulton, Eastington, 1996
JIL7540	Leyland Tiger TRCTL11/2R	Duple Laser	C55F	1982	Ex Dent, North Kelsey, 1995
JIW3889	Bedford YNT	Plaxton Paramount 3200	C53F	1983	Ex Clarke, Elmswell, 1996
PJB614R	Leyland Tiger TRCTL11/2R	Plaxton Paramount 3500	C53F	1983	Ex Finglands, Rusholme, 1992
FVS893Y	Ford Transit 190	Dormobile	M11L	1983	Ex Rimmer, Stowupland, 1996
A129MFL	Dennis Dorchester SDA805	Duple Caribbean	C49FT	1984	Ex Davian, Enfield, 1995
A776TYL	Ford Transit 190	Ford	M8	1984	Ex British Rail, 1996
B660OVU	Ford Transit 190	Mellor	M16	1984	Ex Chambers, Stevenage, 1996
B44DNY	Bedford YNT	Duple Laser 2	C53F	1985	Ex GP Travel, Highbury, 1988
C802FMC	Leyland Royal Tiger RT	Plaxton Paramount 3500	C53F	1986	Ex Happy Wanderer, Leiston, 1997
C902JOF	MCW Metroliner DR130/30	MCW	CH53/17CT	1986	Ex Ashall, Manchester, 1996
C989KUK	Ford Transit 190	Ford	M7	1986	Ex private owner, 1993
C463SRT	Ford Transit 190	Ford	M	1986	Ex private owner, 1996
D429SKD	Bedford Venturer YNV	Duple 320	C53F	1986	Ex Regency, Cambridge, 1997
E699GNH	Iveco 79.14	Caetano Viana	DP25F	1987	Ex Shamrock, Pontypridd, 1996
E554UWF	Ford Transit VE6	Crystals	M16	1987	Ex private owner, 1991
F626SAY	Toyota Coaster HB31R	Caetano Optimo	C21F	1989	Ex Dereham Coachways, 1995
F29SBL	Freight-Rover Sherpa	Freight-Rover	M8	1989	Ex Grey, Ely, 1987
F769OBY	Ford Transit VE6	Dormobile	M4L	1989	Ex private owner, 1997
G27XBK	Iveco Daily 49.10	Phoenix	B25F	1990	Ex Lofty, Bridge Trafford, 1997
H521YCX	DAF SB2305DHS585	Duple 340	C53FT	1991	Ex Arvonia, Llanrug, 1997

Named Vehicle:- PJB614R *Super Cruiser*

Previous registrations:-

JIL7540	BDF202Y, USV803, HSB585Y	PJB614R	BNA2Y, SIA6180, GNF985Y
JIW3889	XRA61Y	Q290FDF	51AC00
KOF663	OYA695V, 794PAF, FGL281V	Q856MEV	CHA425K
LJI1613	GMJ838T, 612CCH, HSG92T	RJI4078	FKX145T

Livery:- White with orange, red and yellow relief

LEWIS'S

A M Lewis, 27 Acacia Avenue, Bury St Edmunds, Suffolk, IP32 6HN

Depot:- Rougham Industrial Estate, Rougham.

YGC295W	Bedford YMT	Unicar Urko	C53F	1981	Ex Travel the Wright Way, Brandon, 1993
RIB3929	Volvo B58-61	Jonckheere Bermuda	C53F	1981	Ex PR Coaches, Southall, 1990
LIB2006	Volvo B58-61	Jonckheere Bermuda	C49FT	1981	Ex Hunter, Grange-over-Sands, 1991
VNK49W	Bedford YNT	Duple Dominant IV	C53F	1981	Ex Meale, Reepham, 1995
GJI832	Volvo B10M-61	Irizar Pyrenean	C49FT	1985	Ex Pedigree, Abertillery, 1994
B862XYR	Volvo B10M-61	Plaxton Paramount 3500 II	C53F	1985	Ex Metroline (Brents), 1996
B869XYR	Volvo B10M-61	Plaxton Paramount 3500 II	C53F	1985	Ex Metroline (Brents), 1996
B116DTG	Bedford YNT	Duple Laser 2	C53F	1985	Ex East London & City Health, 1997
C393FBO	Bedford YNT	Duple Laser 2	C53F	1985	Ex City & Hackney HA, 1997
E966VKY	Mercedes-Benz 609D	Whittaker	C24F	1987	Ex Atkinson, Kirkby Malzeard, 1996
E861TNG	Bedford Venturer YNV	Duple 320	C57F	1988	Ex Woollon, Feltham, 1996

Previous registrations:-

B862XYR	B859XYR		LIB2006	XRP751W
GJI832	B833AUS		RIB3929	XNV139W

Named Vehicle:- GJI832 *Aidan*; RIB3929 *Ashley*; YGC295W *Hannah*.

Livery:- Yellow and gold.

LODGE'S

J W Lodge & Sons Ltd, The Garage, High Easter, Chelmsford, Essex, CM1 4QS

	MJB481	Bedford SBG	Duple	C41F	1956	Ex Traject, Halifax, 1994
	XNM820S	Bedford YMT	Duple Dominant II	C53F	1978	Ex Armchair, Brentford, 1979
	YMJ555S	Bedford YMT	Duple Dominant II	C53F	1978	
w	ACP832V	Ford R1114	Plaxton Supreme IV	C53F	1980	Ex Grahams, Kelvedon, 1997
	C995ERO	Bedford YNT	Plaxton Paramount 3200 II	C53F	1986	Ex Ford, Athorne, 1998
	D519FYL	Iveco Daily 49.10	Robin Hood City Nippy	B21F	1986	Ex The Shires, 1995
	160EBK	Scania K112CRB	Van Hool Alizée	C53FT	1988	Ex Wessex, 1993
	46AEW	Scania K112CRB	Van Hool Alizée	C49FT	1988	Ex Wessex, 1993
	LIL2592	Scania K112CRB	Van Hool Alizée	C55FT	1988	Ex Snells, Newton Abbot, 1998
	K442BMO	Scania K113CRB	Berkhof Excellence 2000	C51FT	1993	Ex Lucketts, Fareham, 1998
	L705CNR	DAF SB3000WS601	Caetano Algarve II	C53F	1994	Ex Osborne, Tollesbury, 1997
	M7SLC	Scania K113CRB	Van Hool Alizée HE	C51F	1995	
	N369GPU	Scania K113CRB	Van Hool Alizée HE	C49FT	1996	

Previous registrations:-

46AEW	E665YDT	160EBK	E663YDT	LIL2592	?

Livery:- Cream, blue and pink.

Two Plaxton Paramount-bodied Volvo B10Ms in the Lewis Travel fleet have stayed together since they were new to Grey-Green. Even though they have had several operators, they arrived with Lewis's after the Brent operation was acquired by Metroline. B862XYR is seen in Parliament Square, London. *Colin Lloyd*

Lodge's of High Easter acquired a pair of DAF SB3000s from Osborne of Tollesbury in 1997. These are fitted with Caetano Algarve II bodywork and the only vehicle remaining is the sole Portuguese-bodied coach in the fleet. L705CNR shows the upsweep of the driver's side window, the main difference between the mark 1 and mark 2 models. *Phillip Stephenson*

M & E COACHWAYS

M E & F A E Jones, Fleet House, 59 Vanguard Way,
Shoeburyness, Essex, SS3 9QY

KOU796P	Bristol VRT/SL3/6LXB	Eastern Coach Works	H43/31F	1976	Ex Stephenson, Rochford, 1997
CJH123V	Bristol VRT/SL3/6LXB	Eastern Coach Works	DPH41/25F	1980	Ex Alder Valley, 1992
BAZ6877	Bova EL26/581	Bova Europa	C53F	1981	Ex Thorn, Hadleigh, 1995
711BHR	Leyland Tiger TRCTL11/3R	Plaxton Supreme V	C53F	1982	Ex Supreme, Hadleigh, 1991
TIA5819	Magirus-Deutz M260L117	Ayats Apollo	C55FT	1982	Ex Trathens, Plymouth, 1996
HOI7624	Leyland Tiger TRCTL11/3R	Berkhof Esprite 340	C53F	1983	Ex Hall & Lapworth, Romford, 1992
C964GCV	Mercedes-Benz L608D	Reeve Burgess	DP19F	1986	Ex Stephenson, Rochford, 1987

Previous registrations:-

711BHR	LEC195X	HOI7624	JVW157Y
BAZ6877	JHR672W, BGS71A	TIA5819	DVC357Y, TOI4578

Livery:- Two tone green and white.

MATTHEWS BLUE

J P Lloyd, The Garage, Westgate Street, Shouldham, Kings Lynn, Norfolk, PE33 0BN

ANX330X	Bedford YMT	Plaxton Supreme IV	C53F	1982	Ex Horseshoe, Tottenham, 1984
B389DCA	Bedford YNT	Plaxton Paramount 3200 II	C53F	1985	Ex Hanmer, Wrexham, 1987
D636CNP	Bedford YNT	Plaxton Paramount 3200 III	C53F	1987	Ex Lugg Valley, Leominster, 1990
D137SWE	Bedford YNT	Plaxton Paramount 3200 III	C53F	1987	Ex Simonds, Botesdale, 1992
F728ENE	Leyland Tiger TRCL10/3ARZM	Plaxton Paramount 3200 III	C53F	1988	Ex Shearings, 1995
F620HWE	Leyland Tiger TRCL10/3ARZM	Plaxton Paramount 3200 III	C53F	1989	Ex Larratt Pepper, Thurnscoe, 1994
G454PGO	Dennis Javelin 12SDA1907	Plaxton Paramount 3200 III	C53F	1990	Ex Monahan, Kentford, 1993
G531EAD	Leyland Tiger TRCL10/3ARZM	Plaxton Paramount 3200 III	C53F	1990	Ex G-Line, Lytham St. Annes, 1996
H177EJU	Dennis Javelin 12SDA1928	Plaxton Paramount 3200 III	C53F	1991	Ex Westercroft Coaches, Queensbury, 1997
J318LNL	Leyland-DAF 400	Autobus Classique	M16	1992	

Previous registration:-

F620HWE	F704ENE, YWP752

Livery:- White, blue and gold.

MIKE BOGGIS TRAVEL

Flowsecure Ltd, 14 Alley Road, Kirton, Ipswich, Suffolk, IP10 0NN

Depots:- Clopton Commercial Park Woodbridge and Felixstowe Dock.

ACG70V	Volvo B58-61	Plaxton Supreme IV	C53F	1980	Ex Smith, Edwardstone, 1996
A479FBA	Dennis Dorchester SDA807	Duple Caribbean 2	C49F	1984	Ex Red & Green, Chislehurst, 1997
A810LEL	Quest 80VM	Plaxton Paramount 3200	C53F	1984	Ex S E Driver Training, Sidcup, 1997
MBZ4739	Leyland Tiger TRCTL11/3R	Duple Laser	C51F	1984	Ex Castle, Clanfield, 1998
C260GOF	Freight-Rover Sherpa	Chassis Developments	C16F	1986	Ex Awaydays, Ipswich, 1997
G878SKE	Peugeot-Talbot Pullman	Talbot	B22F	1990	Ex Kentish Bus, 1997

Previous registration:-

A479FBA	A959GPA, BUI1484	MBZ4739	A226LFX, 8683LJ, A533NJK

Around a dozen Ayats-bodied coaches were imported to Britiain in the early 1980s. One of these now-rare vehicles built on Magirus Deutz chassis is TIA5819 which serves with M&E Coachways of Shoeburyness.
David Heath

The majority of coaches in the Matthews fleet carry Plaxton Paramount 3200 bodywork. Chassis are mixed between Bedford, Dennis and Leyland. Representing the fleet is D636CNP, a Bedford pictured in Norwich.
Trevor Bookes

A479FBA is a Duple-bodied Dennis Dorchester. Only 67 Dorchester underframes were built over a five year period, with all bar ten being coaches. Duple bodied only four for the home market and this example was seen shortly after being acquired by Mike Boggis.
Trevor Brookes

MIKES COACHES

M S Orphan, 46 Rokells, Basildon, Essex, SS14 2BP

Depot:- The Granary, Pipps Hill Road North, Crays Hill, Billericay.

PIW4795	Bedford YRT	Plaxton Pranorama Elite III	C53F	1974	Ex Ingatestone Coaches, 1996
TJI6277	Bedford YMT	Duple Dominant II	C53F	1977	Ex Pandora Coaches, Pitsea, 1996
SJI7477	Volvo B58-56	Van Hool Aragon	C53F	1980	Ex Day, Kilnhurst, 1997
OSE739W	Volvo B58-56	Plaxton Supreme IV	C53F	1981	Ex Mitchell, Plean, 1997
GSV905	Volvo B58-61	Jonckheere Bermuda	C51FT	1981	Ex Knight, Sidcup, 1996
A162KLK	Bedford YMP	Plaxton Paramount 3200	C31F	1984	Ex Kemp, Chillenden, 1997
OXI2381	DAF MB200DKVL600	Plaxton Paramount 3500 II	C46FT	1985	Ex Royles, Rochford, 1997
RJI1682	Mercedes-Benz LP813D	More-Style	C28F	1985	Ex Palmer, Lemington, 1993
E463NVT	Mercedes-Benz 609D	Made-to-Measure	C20F	1988	Ex Webb, Barham, 1995

Previous registrations:-

E463NVT	E416KBF, VOI3577, 6727VT
GSV905	JUC516W
OXI2381	B567AHD
PIW4795	WPB77M, PIW4128

RJI1682	B333PNF
SJI7477	KWT616V
TJI6277	PEB1R, 440ELY, ESU389, SFL401R

Livery:- White, red and black.

MIL-KEN / STOREY'S COACHES

Mil-Ken Travel Ltd, Grasmere, Bury Road, Kentford, Newmarket, Suffolk, CB8 7PZ

Depots:- Bury Road, Kentford (Mil-Ken) and Lynn Road, Littleport, (Storey's)

BEG438T	Bedford YMT	Duple Dominant II	C53F	1978	Ex Mackenzie, West Row, 1994
YUJ318T	Ford R1114	Plaxton Supreme III Express	C53F	1978	Ex Bird's, Hunstanton, 1996
BGY584T	AEC Reliance 6U3ZR	Plaxton Supreme IV	C55F	1979	Ex Elesmore, Sellindge, 1997
BGY585T	AEC Reliance 6U3ZR	Plaxton Supreme IV	C55F	1979	Ex Gretton, Peterborough, 1997
ETM238T	Bedford YMT	Plaxton Supreme IV	C53F	1979	Ex Clayton, Pudsey, 1993
HIL5066	Volvo B58-61	Duple Dominant IV	C52FT	1980	Ex Hayton, Burnage, 1998
XBD556W	DAF MB200DKFL600	Jonckheere Bermuda	C51FT	1981	Ex Curnow, Hobson, 1996
227ASV	Bova EL26/581	Bova Europa	C52F	1982	Ex Storey's Coaches, Littleport, 1995
MIL1658	Bedford YNT	Plaxton Supreme IV	C53F	1982	Ex Matthews Blue, Shouldham, 1993
XLF611	Bova EL26/581	Bova Europa	C53F	1982	Ex Storey's Coaches, Littleport, 1995
GIJ4797	DAF SB2300DHS585	LAG Galaxy	C53F	1983	Ex Smith, High Wycombe, 1996
JAZ8315	Leyland Tiger TRCTL11/2R	Plaxton Paramount 3200 E	C49F	1983	Ex Storey's Coaches, Littleport, 1995
JAZ6917	DAF SB2005DHU605	Plaxton Paramount 3200	C53F	1983	Ex Storey's Coaches, Littleport, 1995
JAZ8291	Bedford YNT	Plaxton Paramount 3200	C55F	1983	Ex Burton, Bury St.Edmunds, 1989
VWL817	DAF MB200DKFL600	Plaxton Paramount 3200	C53F	1983	Ex Selwyn, Runcorn, 1990
A545TMA	Bedford YNT	Plaxton Paramount 3200	C53F	1983	Ex Matthews Blue, Shouldham, 1996
HIL6327	DAF SB2300DHS585	Berkhof Esprite 340	C57F	1985	Ex Spratt, Wreningham, 1997
HIL6328	DAF SB2300DHS585	Berkhof Esprite 340	C57F	1985	Ex Spratt, Wreningham, 1997
MJI4690	DAF SB200DKFL600	LAG Galaxy	C53F	1985	Ex Compass Royston, Stockton-on-Tees, 1994
MIL1803	Bedford YNT	Plaxton Paramount 3200 II	C53F	1985	Ex Matthews Blue, Shouldham, 1996
JAZ6914	DAF SB2300DHS585	LAG Galaxy	C53F	1985	Ex Rolyn, Barton-le-Clay, 1993
OIL6275	DAF SB2300DHS585	Duple 340	C....	1985	Ex ..
JAZ3562	DAF SB3000DKSB585	Plaxton Paramount 3500 II	C53F	1986	Ex Storey's Coaches, Littleport, 1995
JAZ6948	Bedford Venturer YNV	Willowbrook Crusader	C53F	1986	Ex Carterton Coaches, 1994
JAZ6918	DAF MB230DKFL615	Duple 340	C55FT	1986	Ex Waddon, Bedwas, 1995
JAZ7815	Dennis Javelin 11SDL1905	Duple 320	C53F	1988	Ex Mayne, Buckie, 1991
JAZ6847	Dennis Javelin 12SDA1913	Duple 320	C53FT	1988	Ex Brighton & Hove, 1996

The East Anglia Bus Handbook

Previous registrations:-

227ASV	SMY627X	JAZ6918	D618SJX
BEG438T	BUR432T, XLF611	JAZ6948	C262WBC
ETM238T	ETM238T, RIB4326	JAZ7815	E990KJF
GIJ7497	CFX424Y	JAZ8291	ECK202Y
HIL5066	AWP222W	JAZ8315	RNY307Y
HIL6327	B686BTW	MIL1658	YBJ850Y
HIL6328	B689BTW	MIL1803	B622DDW
JAZ3562	C315UFP, A10AAS, C597UEW	MJI4690	B265NUT
JAZ6847	E503EFG	OIL6275	....
JAZ6914	C753RJU	VWL817	ODM540Y
JAZ6917	HAT677Y, 600JOT, JFL807Y	XLF611	687DEW, KVS154Y

MORLEY'S

J R Morley & Sons Ltd, West End Garage, Whittlesey, Cambridgeshire, PE7 1HH

Depots:- West End Garage, Whitmore Street and Low Cross, Whittlesey.

UEB782K	Bedford YRQ	Willowbrook 001	B47F	1972	
NER610M	Bedford YRT	Duple Dominant Express	C53F	1973	
JFR397N	Leyland Atlantean AN68/1R	East Lancashire	H45/31F	1975	Ex Ribble, 1989
ODU254P	Bedford YLQ	Duple Dominant II	C45F	1976	Ex Wainfleet, Nuneaton, 1979
NDP38R	Bristol VRT/LL3/6LXB	Northern Counties	H47/29D	1976	Ex Reading, 1990
NSJ19R	Seddon Pennine 7	Alexander AY	B53F	1976	Ex Western Scottish, 1987
NSJ21R	Seddon Pennine 7	Alexander AY	B53F	1976	Ex Western Scottish, 1988
OJD192R	Leyland Fleetline FE30AGR	MCW	H45/32F	1977	Ex London Transport, 1984
OJD232R	Leyland Fleetline FE30AGR	MCW	H45/32F	1977	Ex Thamesdown, 1985
RSD978R	Seddon Pennine 7	Alexander AY	B53F	1977	Ex Western Scottish, 1987
SPA192R	Bedford YMT	Plaxton Supreme III Express	C53F	1977	Ex Jasons, St. Marys Cray, 1989
BTX39V	Ford R1114	Plaxton Supreme IV	C53F	1979	Ex Harrod, Wormegay, 1984
WYV48T	Leyland Titan TNLXB2RRSp	Park Royal	H44/26D	1979	Ex London Buses, 1984
CUL92V	Leyland Titan TNLXB2RRSp	Park Royal	H44/26D	1980	Ex Village, Garston, 1996
UAV457X	Bedford YNT	Duple Dominant IV Express	C53F	1982	
HBH411Y	Bedford YNT	Duple Dominant IV Express	C53F	1983	Ex Hornsby, Ashby, 1990
B220JPH	Mercedes-Benz L508D	Coachcraft	M15	1984	Ex Statham, Ibstock, 1989

Livery:- Red and grey

Morley's of Whittlesey operate six double-deck buses, including four from the London area, on rural services radiating from Peterborough. Recent additions include two Leyland Titans, but shown here is former DMS-class OJD192R, a MCW-bodied Leyland Fleetline. It was photographed in Peterborough.
Tony Wilson

MYALL'S

A C Myall & Son, Cherry Tree House, 75 The Causeway, Bassingbourne, Cambridgeshire, SG8 5JA

PCE637R	Bedford SB5	Plaxton Supreme III	C41F	1977	
HIL8130	Bedford YMT	Duple Dominant II	C53F	1979	Ex Roberts, Bootle, 1993
A858OVJ	Bedford SB5	Wright TT	DP40F	1984	
C822XCJ	Bedford SB5	Duple Dominant	C40F	1986	
C629XVU	Ford Transit 190	Mellor	M16	1986	
G842VAY	Hestair-Duple SDA1512	Duple 425	C63F	1989	
L967OFL	Mercedes-Benz 711D	Plaxton Beaver	DP25F	1993	
L452UEB	Dennis Dart 9.8 SDL3017	Marshall C27	B40F	1993	
M561TJL	Mercedes-Benz 811D	Autobus Classique II	C29F	1995	Ex Chalfont, Southall, 1997
M577VSF	Mercedes-Benz 709D	Alexander Sprint	B29F	1995	
N796PDS	Mercedes-Benz 811D	Mellor	C...	1995	
N211YJE	Dennis Dart 9.8 SDL3054	Alexander Dash	DP40F	1995	

Previous registration:-

HIL8130   EVC209T

Livery:- White and turquoise

N211YJE, a Dennis Dart in the Myall's fleet has an Alexander Dash body and, as can be seen from the picture, high-back seating as it waits time at Royston bus station just over the Hertfordshire border. Another Dennis Dart is in the fleet and that has one of the early bodies built by Marshall.
Colin Lloyd

NEAL'S TRAVEL

Neal's Travel Ltd, 102 Beck Road, Isleham, Ely, Cambridgeshire, CB7 5QP

E46MMT	Mercedes-Benz L307D	Reeve Burgess	M12	1987	
F651OHD	DAF SB2305DHTD585	Duple 320	C53FT	1989	Ex Grahams, Kelvedon, 1996
F652OHD	DAF SB2305DHTD585	Duple 320	C53FT	1989	Ex Grahams, Kelvedon, 1995
TJI1686	LAG G355Z	LAG Panoramic	C49FT	1989	Ex Rennie, Dunfermline, 1996
G154XJF	DAF SB2305DHS585	Caetano Algarve	C53F	1990	Ex Anderson, Bermondsey, 1996
H84RUX	MAN 10.180	Caetano Algarve	C33FT	1991	Ex Boulton, Cardington, 1995
H391CFT	Toyota Coaster HDB30R	Caetano Optimo II	C21F	1991	Ex Hudson, Bilbrough, 1994
H283TAH	Peugeot-Talbot Pullman	Talbot	B21F	1991	Ex Coach Services, Thetford, 1994
J78SNK	Mercedes-Benz 811D	Reeve Burgess Beaver	C25F	1992	
J832RNK	Mercedes-Benz 811D	Plaxton Beaver	C33F	1992	
K327EJV	Mercedes-Benz 410D	Autobus Classique	M13	1992	
K832FEE	Mercedes-Benz 814D	Autobus Classique	C33F	1993	
L484JFU	Mercedes-Benz 410D	Autobus Classique	M16	1994	
M373VER	Mercedes-Benz 709D	Marshall C19	B29F	1994	
M853WEB	Ford Transit VE6	Ford	M8	1995	
N419WJL	Mercedes-Benz 814D	Autobus Classique Nouvelle	C29F	1996	
N375EAK	Mercedes-Benz 814D	Plaxton Beaver	B33F	1996	
N376EAK	Mercedes-Benz 814D	Plaxton Beaver	B33F	1996	
P416ACT	Mercedes-Benz Sprinter 412D	Autobus Classique	M16	1996	
P430JDT	Dennis Javelin 12SDA2136	Plaxton Premiére 320	C57F	1996	
R718TRV	Dennis Javelin	UVG S320	C57F	1997	
R719TRV	Dennis Javelin	UVG S320	C57F	1997	
R281THL	Dennis Javelin GX	Neoplan Transliner	C49FT	1998	

Previous registration:-
TJI1686   G699PNW, ..., G326DJK

Livery:- White and two tone blue

NEAVE

H S Neave & Son Ltd, Fenside, The Street, Hickling Road, Catfield, Norfolk, NR29 5AA

LVS228P	Ford R1114	Duple Dominant Express	C53F	1975	Ex Jacksons, Altrincham, 1981
RYL728R	Bedford YMT	Duple Dominant II	C53F	1977	Ex Easton, Brandiston, 1989
VBH605S	Bedford YMT	Duple Dominant II	C53F	1978	Ex Smith, Blofield, 1988
XHE754T	Ford R1114	Plaxton Supreme III	C53F	1978	Ex Chambers, Stevenage, 1983
ENM10T	Bedford YMT	Plaxton Supreme III	C53F	1979	Ex Court, Fillongley, 1992
AJD24T	Bedford YMT	Plaxton Supreme IV	C47F	1979	Ex Sales, Armes & Craske, Norwich, 1994
APH511T	Volvo B58-61	Plaxton Supreme IV	C57F	1979	Ex Embling, Guyhirn, 1984
KNK539V	Bedford YMT	Caetano Estoril	C53F	1979	Ex Tate, Potten End, 1985
JKV413V	Bedford YMT	Plaxton Supreme IV	C53F	1979	Ex Wood, Kirby-le-Soken, 1984
JDG322V	Bedford YMT	Duple Dominant II Express	C53F	1980	Ex Tyler, Hitchin, 1990
GEG963W	Ford R1114	Plaxton Supreme IV Express	C53F	1980	Ex Embling, Guyhirn, 1987
NRY333W	Bedford YMT	Plaxton Supreme IV	C53F	1980	Ex Amber & Blue, Slough, 1991
UNK11W	Bedford YMT	Plaxton Supreme IV	C53F	1981	Ex Inland Travel, Flimwell, 1991
UHJ969Y	Bedford YNT	Plaxton Supreme V	C53F	1982	Ex Golden Boy, Roydon, 1992
A202LCL	Bedford YMP	Marshall Campaigner	B48F	1983	Ex Norfolk CC, 1990
C288VLF	Iveco 35.8	Elme Orion	C16F	1986	Ex Reynolds, Caister, 1996
F716PFP	Iveco Daily 49.10	Carlyle Dailybus	B25F	1989	Ex Eastern Counties, 1996

Previous registration:-
UHJ969Y   DNK582Y, YOI7374

Livery:- White, red and grey.

NIBS / NELSONS COACHES

William H Nelson (Wickford) Ltd, The Coach Station, Bruce Grove,
Wickford, Essex, SS11 8BZ

17	BIL9406	Leyland Leopard PSU3E/4R	Plaxton Supreme III	C53F	1979	
29	BIL7894	Leyland Leopard PSU3E/4R	Plaxton Supreme IV	C53F	1980	Ex Atlas Bus, Harlesden, 1983
30	BIL4539	Leyland Leopard PSU3E/4R	Plaxton Supreme III	C53F	1978	Ex Atlas Bus, Harlesden, 1983
35	GHM803N	Daimler Fleetline CRL6	MCW	H44/32F	1975	Ex London Transport, 1984
36	GHM797N	Daimler Fleetline CRL6	MCW	H44/27F	1975	Ex London Transport, 1984
43	TGX892M	Daimler Fleetline CRL6	Park Royal	H44/32F	1974	Ex Avro & Elm Park, Stanford-le-Hope, 1987
44	THM705M	Daimler Fleetline CRL6	MCW	H44/32F	1974	Ex Avro & Elm Park, Stanford-le-Hope, 1987
	SMU721N	Daimler Fleetline CRL6	MCW	H45/32F	1974	Ex Ensign, Purfleet, 1984
	SMU729N	Daimler Fleetline CRL6 (6LXB)	MCW	H........	1974	Ex Deep Purple Showband, Wickford, 1995
	GUG132N	Leyland National 11351/1R		B52F	1975	Ex M&E Coachways, Shoeburyness, 1993
	MAU142P	Bristol VRT/SL3/6LXB	Eastern Coach Works	H39/31F	1976	Ex Europa, Pitsea, 1995
	NDL652R	Bristol VRT/SL3/6LXB	Eastern Coach Works	H43/31F	1976	Ex Yorkshire Terrier, 1991
	KIB7256	Leyland Leopard PSU3D/4R	Willowbrook Spacecar 008	C49F	1977	Ex Ashall, Manchester, 1997
	AUP714S	Bristol VRT/SL3/6LXB	Eastern Coach Works	H43/31F	1977	Ex Northumbria, 1994
	DNG232T	Bristol VRT/SL3/6LXB	Eastern Coach Works	H43/31F	1979	Ex Cambus, 1997
	BIL4710	Bristol VRT/SL3/6LXB	Eastern Coach Works	H43/31F	1980	Ex Thamesway, 1991
	ARN891Y	Leyland National 2 NL116HLXB/1R		B52F	1983	Ex MTL (Merseybus), 1997
	ARN893Y	Leyland National 2 NL116HLXB/1R		B52F	1983	Ex MTL (Merseybus), 1997
	ARN894Y	Leyland National 2 NL116HLXCT/1R		B52F	1983	Ex MTL (Merseybus), 1997
	BIL4419	Renault-Dodge S56	East Lancashire	B21F	1986	Ex Ipswich, 1990
	BIL6538	Renault-Dodge S56	East Lancashire	B21F	1986	Ex Ipswich, 1990
	E101VWA	Neoplan N416	Neoplan SL11	B50F	1988	Ex Mainline, 1996
	F616CWJ	Neoplan N416	Neoplan SL11	B50F	1988	Ex Mainline, 1996
	L890UVE	Mercedes-Benz 811D	Marshall C16	B33F	1994	
	L891UVE	Mercedes-Benz 811D	Marshall C16	B33F	1994	
	N811CSC	Mercedes-Benz 811D	Alexander Sprint	B33F	1995	

Previous registrations:-

BIL4419	D201YDX		BIL7894	LVS431V
BIL4539	VMJ960S		BIL9406	CTM404T
BIL4710	STW25W		KIB7256	OKY53R
BIL6538	D202YDX			

Livery:- Yellow and white.

NIBS is an
abbreviation for
Nelsons
Independent Bus
Services, though
only the acronym is
now carried.
ARN893Y is one of
three Leyland
National 2s used on
local services, all
three being acquired
from Merseybus in
1997. They joined
by a pair of Neoplan
buses previously
used in Sheffield.
Richard Godfrey

NORFOLK GREEN

Go West Travel Ltd, Beveridge Way, Kings Lynn, Norfolk, PE30 4NS

Depot:- Beveridge Way, Kings Lynn; Colberville, Caston.

100	B906OPJ	Bedford YNT	Plaxton Paramount 3200	C53F	1984	Ex Hill, Hersham, 1996
103	B91UBM	Bedford YNT	Duple Laser 2	C53F	1984	Ex Haynes, Ringstead, 1995
105	VRC605Y	Leyland Leopard PSU3G/4R	Plaxton Supreme V Express	C51F	1982	Ex Trent, 1996
108	VRC608Y	Leyland Leopard PSU3G/4R	Plaxton Supreme V Express	C51F	1982	Ex Trent, 1996
109	VRC609Y	Leyland Leopard PSU3G/4R	Plaxton Supreme V Express	C53F	1982	Ex Trent, 1996
111	B258GWJ	Bedford Venturer YNV	Plaxton Paramount 3200 II	C57F	1985	Ex Eniway, Saham Toney, 1996
112	B500YUR	Bedford Venturer YNV	Plaxton Paramount 3200 II	C53F	1985	Ex Eniway, Saham Toney, 1996
114	PTV588X	Leyland Leopard PSU3G/4R	Plaxton Supreme IV Express	C53F	1981	Ex Trent, 1997
115	PTV583X	Leyland Leopard PSU3G/4R	Plaxton Supreme IV Express	C51F	1981	Ex Trent, 1997
116	RCH487R	Leyland Leopard PSU3C/4R	Plaxton Supreme III Express	C51F	1976	Ex Trent, 1998
117	PTV587X	Leyland Leopard PSU3G/4R	Plaxton Supreme IV Express	C51F	1981	Ex Derby Integrated, 1997
118	LNU568W	Leyland Leopard PSU3E/4R	Plaxton Supreme IV Express	C53F	1980	Ex Trent, 1998
201	G350GCK	Dennis Dart 9SDL3002	Duple Dartline	B39F	1989	Ex Reg's, Hertford, 1996
202	G624WPB	Dennis Dart 9SDL3002	Duple Dartline	B39F	1990	Ex Reg's, Hertford, 1996
204	AAS185W	Leyland National 2 NL116L11/2R		B52F	1980	Ex Merseybus, 1996
205	WAH592S	Leyland National 11351A/1R		B52F	1977	Ex Eastern Counties, 1996
207	VAE507T	Leyland National 10351B/1R		B44F	1979	Ex Cheltenham & Gloucester, 1997

Norfolk Green commenced operations in 1996 by acquiring the four-vehicle fleet of Haynes, Ringstead. Several former Trent coaches have been added, including 115, PTV583X, seen at Kings Lynn. *Tony Wilson*

301	D501NWG	Mercedes-Benz L608D	Alexander AM	B20F	1986	Ex RoadCar, 1996
303	D103DAJ	Mercedes-Benz L608D	Reeve Burgess	B20F	1986	Ex RoadCar, 1996
305	D505NWG	Mercedes-Benz L608D	Alexander AM	B20F	1986	Ex RoadCar, 1996
307	E467CGM	Mercedes-Benz 607D	Robin Hood	B20F	1987	Ex The Bee Line, 1997
308	E478CGM	Mercedes-Benz 607D	Robin Hood	B20F	1987	Ex The Bee Line, 1997
311	D511NWG	Mercedes-Benz L608D	Alexander AM	B20F	1986	Ex RoadCar, 1996
401	F401XWR	Mercedes-Benz 811D	Optare StarRider	B33F	1988	Ex Yorkshire Coastliner, 1996

Previous registrations:-

A745JPB	A840PPP, OJI8785, TSV806	B906OPJ	B272HCD, TSV717
B258GWJ	B285AMG, 98TNO, PSK619, B60WNG	FIL4168	MVN873P

Livery:- Two tone green and white.

PARTRIDGE

C J Partridge & Son Ltd; H A C Claireaux,
Mount Pleasant, George Street, Hadleigh, Suffolk, IP7 6AE

UUF332J	Leyland Leopard PSU3B/4RT	Plaxton Panorama Elite II	C47F	1971	Ex Southdown, 1988
ACF877L	Ford R226	Plaxton Panorama Elite II	C53F	1972	
759KFC	Bedford YRT	Marshall Camair	B53F	1973	Ex Hedingham & District, 1997
LHU662L	Leyland Leopard PSU3B/4R	Plaxton Panorama Elite III	C47F	1973	Ex Cheltenham & Gloucester, 1987
YWE503M	Bedford YRT	Duple Dominant	C53F	1974	Ex NCB, Yorkshire, 1985
OGV374P	Bedford YRT	Plaxton Supreme III	C53F	1975	Ex Hedingham & District, 1977
TJI3132	Ford R1114	Plaxton Supreme III	C57F	1977	Ex E&J Coaches, Batley, 1995
240FRH	Leyland Leopard PSU5B/4R	Plaxton Supreme III	C55F	1977	Ex Casters, Abridge, 1996
WTG357T	Bristol VRT/SL3/6LXB	Alexander AL	H43/31F	1979	Ex Cardiff, 1995
DNK431T	Ford R1114	Duple Dominant II	C53F	1979	Ex Hedingham & District, 1996
JIL3580	Leyland Leopard PSU3E/4R	Duple Dominant II	C53F	1979	Ex Tyler, Hitchin, 1995
DSU105	Bedford Venturer YNV	Duple 320	C57F	1986	Ex Phil Haines, Frampton West, 1995
JSK951	Neoplan N722/3	Plaxton Paramount 4000 II	CH53/18CT	1986	Ex Hedingham & District, 1996
TJI3133	Dennis Javelin 11SDL1905	Plaxton Paramount 3200 III	C53F	1988	Ex Greybird, Swalwell, 1995
LGV34	Dennis Javelin 12SDA1907	Plaxton Paramount 3200 III	C57F	1988	Ex Nesbit, Somerby, 1995

Previous registrations:-

240FRH	OKY87R	LGV34	F580PSE
759KFC	YNO481L	OGV374P	MNW731P, 759KFC
DSU105	C185LGA, PSU627, C747URS	TJI3132	SND577R
JIL3580	BWE203T	TJI3133	E490FCN
JSK951	300CUH, C366KEP, LST873		

Livery:- Blue, white and gold.

PAYNES OF PAXTON

D A Payne, Tuckwood Transport, Unit 2 Foundry Way, Little End Road Industrial Estate, Eaton Socon, Cambridgeshire, CB

BUF260C	Leyland Titan PD3/4	Northern Counties	FH39/30F	1965	Ex preservation, 1990
CSV253	Leyland Tiger TRCTL11/3R	Duple Dominant III	C50FT	1981	Ex Frampton, Hillingdon, 1990
LIL5870	Kässbohrer Setra S215HD	Kässbohrer Tornado	C49FT	1983	Ex Capital, West Drayton, 1995
C426DML	Bedford Midi	Bedford	M8	1986	Ex private owner, 1997
D356KVA	Freight-Rover Sherpa	Dormobile	B16F	1986	Ex Cambus, 1988
D139AFH	Freight-Rover Sherpa	Dormobile	B20FL	1986	Ex Gloucestershire CC, 1992
F171WFL	Mazda E2200	Made-to-Measure	M8	1988	
F172WFL	Mazda E2200	Made-to-Measure	M8	1988	
G106APC	Toyota Coaster HB31R	Caetano Optimo	C21F	1989	Ex Kiddle, Holywell, 1997
G515MWA	Ford Transit VE6	Advanced Vehicle Builders	M11	1990	Ex private owner, 1997

Previous registrations:-

CSV253	LKG19X	LIL5870	5192MW, 1816MW, FLD401Y

Livery:- Blue and pink

Many operators regard the products of Kässbohrer, the coach building subsidiary of Mercedes-Benz as the 'Rolls-Royce' of the coaching world. The company has production plants in Ulm, Germany; Ligny; France and Aabenraa in Denmark.   It was acquired by Mercedes-Benz at the beginning of 1995. Shown here is Paynes' LIL5870, a high floor S215HD Tornado model. *Colin Lloyd*

PEELINGS COACHES

J R Joplin, The Garage, Clay Hill, Tittleshall, Kings Lynn, Norfolk, PE32 2RQ

MIB3378	Bedford YMT	Duple Dominant II	C53F	1980	Ex Freestone, Beetley, 1997
RJR869Y	Ford R1114	Duple Dominant IV	C53F	1982	Ex Enterprise, Chatteris, 1998
SMR381Y	Bedford YNT	Duple Dominant IV Express	C53F	1983	Ex Lloyd, Nuneaton, 1992
B45DNY	Bedford YNT	Duple Laser 2	C53F	1985	Ex Bure Valley, Buxton, 1994,
C810FMC	Bedford YNT	Duple Laser 2	C53F	1986	Ex CITB, Bircham Newton, 1996
LSK643	Bedford Venturer YNV	Plaxton Paramount 3200 III	C53F	1986	Ex New Enterprise, Tonbridge, 1998

Previous registration:-

LSK643	C112AFX		
		MIB3378	KBC607V

Named Vehicles:- RJR869Y *Henry VIII;* MIB3378 *Woody.*

Livery:- White, blue and grey.

Duple Laser 2 bodywork was only constructed for one year - or season. Two examples are used by Peelings Coaches including B45DNYwhich was one of a batch of eight new to Bebb, Llantwit Fardre. It was photographed in Kings Lynn. *Trevor Brookes*

The East Anglia Bus Handbook

PETER GODWARD COACHES

P R & A M Godward, 4 Edwin Hall View, South Woodham Ferrers, Essex, CM3 5QL

Depot:- Downham Road, Billericay.

GND492N	Daimler Fleetline CRG6LXB	Northern Counties	H43/32F	1974	Ex Beeston, Hadleigh, 1993
JJG1P	Leyland Atlantean AN68/1R	Eastern Coach Works	H43/31F	1978	Ex Kingsley Coaches, Birtley, 1996
JIW7131	Ford R1114	Plaxton Supreme III	C53F	1979	Ex Ludlow, Halesowen, 1989
FHS768X	Volvo B58-56	Duple Goldliner IV	C46FT	1982	Ex Forest Coaches, East Ham, 1996
FDZ984	Leyland Tiger TRCTL11/3R	Duple Goldliner IV	C51F	1982	Ex Wilkinson Coaches, Basildon, 1996
VVY670	Volvo B10M-61	Berkhof Everest 370	C51FT	1983	Ex James Bevan, Lydney, 1994
IAZ6394	Leyland Tiger TRCTL11/3RH	Duple Caribbean	C46FT	1985	Ex Thamesway, 1996
FIW5447	DAF SBR2300DHS570	Jonckheere Jubilee P99	CH57/14CT	1985	Ex Amos, Daventry, 1996
D145WCC	Freight-Rover Sherpa	Carlyle	B18F	1987	Ex Dalybus, Eccles, 1994

Previous registrations:-

FDZ984	OHM831Y	JIW7131	CNR217T, 8797PL, HDH565T, 8797PL, HDH789T
FIW5447	B498CBD	VVY670	JJN182Y
IAZ6394	B336BGL		

Livery:- White with air brush artwork (Coaches).

Peter Godward Coaches also uses the Tours 'R' Us name and operates several executive coaches. VVY670 has a 3.7 metre high Berkhof Everest body on a Volvo B10M chassis. All the Berkhof imports are now sold through the AVE Berkhof organisation at Basingstoke though at one time Ensign was the importer, hence a preponderance of Essex marks for the first registrations. *David Heath*

PULLMAN

Coach Team Pullman Ltd, The Garage, 26 Scotland Road, Chippenham, Cambridgeshire, CB7 5PN

SVF896G	Bristol RELH6G	Eastern Coach Works	C47F	1969	Ex preservation, 1994
EGX982	MCW Metroliner SR130/6	MCW	CH55/19CT	1985	Ex Wordsworth, Ely, 1998
NIL5673	Scania K112CRB	Plaxton Paramount 3500 III	C49FT	1989	Ex Martindales, Ferry Hill, 1998
G954KJX	DAF SB2305DHTD585	Plaxton Paramount 3200 III	C53F	1990	Ex JBS, Bedford, 1996
J213XKY	Scania K113CRB	Plaxton Paramount 3500 III	C51FT	1991	Ex Q Drive (Limebourne), Battersea, 1997
K344BOK	Renault Trafic T1100D	Holdsworth	M8	1992	
K750UJO	Dennis Javelin 12SDA1907	Plaxton Premiere 320	C53F	1992	Ex Oxford CityLink, 1998
K752UJO	Dennis Javelin 12SDA1907	Plaxton Premiere 320	C53F	1992	Ex Oxford CityLink, 1998

Previous registrations:-

EGX982   B233XEUY, 899DXV, B431LRA   NIL5673   F173DET

Livery:- Cream and red or pink being replaced by dark green and pale green.

Pullman's rear-engined DAF SB2305 G954KJX has a Plaxton Paramount 3200 body with the low driving position option. The National Express stop in Drummer Street in Cambridge is the location of this picture taken when the vehicle was operating as a duplicate on the service to London.
Trevor Brookes

RAYLEIGH ROADWAYS

Rayleigh Roadways Ltd, 3 Moat Close, Ramsden Heath, Billericay, Essex, CM11 1NX

Depot:- Shot Farm, Southend Road, Shotgate, Wickford.

TUB1M	Leyland Leopard PSU3B/4R	Plaxton Panorama Elite III	C53F	1974	Ex Venturer, Southend, 1994
OPL215R	Bristol VRT/SL3/6LXB	Eastern Coach Works	H43/31F	1976	Ex Jolly Roger, New Earswick, 1993
NOC409R	Daimler Fleetline FE30AGR	MCW	H43/33F	1976	Ex Redline, Redditch, 1993
SAO411R	Bristol VRT/SL3/501	Eastern Coach Works	H43/31F	1977	Ex Stephenson, Rochford, 1994
BEA344Y	Ford R1114	Plaxton Supreme V	C53F	1982	Ex Nightingale, Exmouth, 1988
SIW8306	Kässbohrer Setra S215HD	Kässbohrer Tornado	C48FT	1982	Ex Silver Knight, Wickford, 1998
F878TNH	Volvo B10M-61	Caetano Algarve I	C53F	1988	Ex Harold Wood Coaches, 1994
K710RNR	Dennis Javelin 12SDA1929	Caetano Algarve 2	C53F	1992	
N878ENK	LDV 400	Crystals	M16	1996	Ex private owner, 1997

Previous Registrations:
SIW8306   PKW322X, 5092EL

Livery:- White, red and beige.

Before the launch of the Caetano Algarve II, around a handful of the original Algarve had seen a facelift with a revised grille and headlights. An example of this intermediate styling, known as the Algarve I, is K710RNR pictured at Legoland at Windsor. The Dennis Javelin was delivered new to the operator in August 1992. *David Heath*

REYNOLDS COACHES OF CAISTER

C J Reynolds, Ormesby Road, Caister-on-Sea, Great Yarmouth, Norfolk, NR30 5QJ

UVE593K	Bedford J2SZ2	Plaxton Embassy	C20F	1972	Ex NBTS, Cambridge, 1982
GDG241V	Bedford YNT	Duple Dominant II	C53F	1979	Ex Warner, Tewkesbury, 1984
BLJ721Y	Ford R1115	Plaxton Paramount 3200	C49F	1983	Ex Reliance, Benfleet, 1992
CLB779Y	Bedford YNT	Plaxton Paramount 3200	C53F	1982	Ex Patterson, Beadnell, 1989
A53NPP	Bedford YNT	Duple	C53F	1983	Ex Garratt, Birstall, 1997
A987RFO	Bedford YNT	Duple Laser	C49F	1984	Ex Halls Coaches, Henham, 1997
B136AAV	Bedford Venturer YNV	Duple Laser 2	C53F	1985	Ex Keymer, Aylsham, 1990
B620ODX	Bedford YNT	Plaxton Paramount 3200	C53F	1985	Ex Squirrell, Gt. Finborough, 1993
B94PLU	Bedford VAS5	Plaxton Supreme IV	C25F	1985	Ex Capital, West Drayton, 1992
YDE4	Bedford YMP	Plaxton Paramount 3200 II	C35F	1986	Ex Marton, West Drayton, 1991
C493KGP	Bedford Venturer YNV	Duple 320	C55F	1986	Ex Clarke, Newthorpe, 1997
NIL4810	LAG G350Z	LAG Panoramic	C53F	1986	Ex Belle, Lowestoft, 1997
D80APC	Mercedes-Benz 609D	Reeve Burgess	C19F	1987	Ex Bicknell, Godalming, 1987
E140FLD	Bedford YMP	Plaxton Paramount 3200 II	C35F	1987	Ex Capital, West Drayton, 1995
E467MRE	Vauxhall Midi	Vauxhall	M8	1993	Ex Contract Car, Lowestoft, 1996
F743TWC	Vauxhall Midi	Vauxhall	M8	1993	Ex Contract Car, Lowestoft, 1996
F963CEG	Ford Transit VE6	Ford	M11	1989	Ex private owner, 1996
K841EKW	Vauxhall Midi	Vauxhall	M8	1993	Ex Contract Car, Lowestoft, 1996

Previous registrations:-

A987RFO	A454PFO, GWO1L	NIL4810	C623UPG, OJI4755, C...
CLB779Y	CLB778Y	YDE4	C808TLF

Named Vehicles:- B136AAV *Lady June Fel*; B620ODX *Lady Heather Jane*; B94PLU *Lady Cheryl Ann*; BLJ721Y *Lady Rosemary*; CLB779Y *Lady Louise*; D80APC *Lady Grace*; GDG241V *Lady Catherine*; NIL4810 *Lady Christina*; UVE593K *Lady Ellen*

Livery:- Two tone blue and yellow.

Reynolds of Caister proudly proclaim to be Norfolk's oldest established coach operator. NIL4810 is named *Lady Christina* and this LAG Panoramic was photographed at Kings Lynn. The fleet also contains a now-rare example of the Plaxton Embassy body on a Bedford J2. *Trevor Brookes*

ROBINSON

C V & C J Robinson, Thrapston Road, Kimbolton,
Huntingdon, Cambridgeshire, PE18 0HW

RBZ2566	Bedford YRT	Plaxton Supreme III	C53F	1975	
YMJ545S	Bedford YMT	Plaxton Supreme III	C53F	1978	Ex Trina Tours, Holborn, 1984
RBZ2959	Bedford YMT	Plaxton Supreme IV	C53F	1981	
RBZ2960	Bedford Venturer YNV	Plaxton Paramount 3200 II	C57F	1986	
RBZ2562	Dennis Javelin 12SDA1907	Plaxton Paramount 3200 III	C53F	1988	
RBZ2563	Leyland Tiger TRCL10/3ARZM	Plaxton Paramount 3200 III	C53F	1989	Ex Stevenson, Mexborough, 1994
RBZ2961	Dennis Javelin 12SDA1919	Duple 320	C57F	1990	Ex Copeland, Meir, 1996
RBZ2565	Toyota Coaster HDB30R	Caetano Optimo II	C21F	1990	Ex Henning, Trimdon Station, 1993
RBZ2962	Dennis Javelin 12SDA1907	Duple 320	C57F	1991	
RBZ2564	Dennis Javelin 12SDA1929	Plaxton Paramount 3200 III	C53F	1992	Ex Lewis, Pailton, 1997

Previous registrations:-

RBZ2562	F425VEW	RBZ2959	HEW553W, 380JFM, OAV411W
RBZ2563	F707ENE, PSK619, F594HWE	RBZ2960	D383WAV
RBZ2564	J719KBC	RBZ2961	G813HOV, MIB394, G231FVT
RBZ2565	H714BRG	RBZ2962	H194BAV
RBZ2566	KEW785P		

Livery:- Cream, red and brown

Since it was photographed at Heathrow coach station, H194BAV, a Dennis Javelin with Duple 320
bodywork has now been registered in the RBZ series. Most of Robinson's coaches now carry these
letters. *Colin Lloyd*

RUFFLES

Ruffles of Castle Hedingham Ltd, The Bungalow, Church Lane, Castle
Hedingham, Essex, CO9 3DA

Depot:- Station Road, Sible Hedingham.

APH520T	Bedford YMT	Plaxton Supreme III	C53F	1979	Ex G.A.Contractors, Stevenage, 1994
TBM626W	Ford R1114	Duple Dominant IV	C53F	1981	Ex Clarke, Maldon, 1994
DNK576Y	Leyland Tiger TRCTL11/3R	Plaxton Supreme V	C57F	1982	Ex GP Travel, Highbury, 1991
SIB6176	Van Hool T815	Van Hool Acron	C48FT	1982	Ex K&T, Stratford, 1996
XIB2453	Volvo B10M-61	Berkhof Everest 370	C49FT	1983	Ex Abbey, Muswell Hill, 1996
A911LUD	Ford R1015	Reeve Burgess Riviera	DP31F	1983	Ex Croxford, Farnham, 1995
C330PEW	Leyland Tiger TRCTL11/3RZ	Plaxton Paramount 3200 II	C53F	1986	Ex Premier, Cambridge, 1995
C647YKE	Bova FHD12.280	Bova Futura	C49FT	1986	Ex Norris, Sidcup, 1993
E816UKW	Freight-Rover Sherpa	Whittaker	M16	1987	Ex Enterprise, Chatteris, 1997
E222YTU	Quest 80 J	Jonckheere Piccolo P35	C25FT	1988	Ex Coach Services, Thetford, 1993
F421RRY	Toyota Coaster HB31R	Caetano Optimo	C21F	1989	Ex Silver Knight, Wickford, 1994
G167RBD	Volvo B10M-61	Jonckheere Deauville	C51FT	1990	Ex Dereham Coachways, 1997
TJI1670	Volvo B10M-60	Plaxton Paramount 3500 III	C53F	1990	Ex Osborne, Tollesbury, 1997
TJI1685	Volvo B10M-60	Plaxton Paramount 3500 III	C53F	1990	Ex Osborne, Tollesbury, 1997
J388RRX	Mercedes-Benz 308D	Devon Conversions	M15	1992	Ex Halfpenny, Swaythling, 1997
K144PLP	Mercedes-Benz 308D	Autobus Classique	M12	1993	Ex Alamo Car Hire, 1995
K146PLP	Mercedes-Benz 308D	Autobus Classique	M12	1993	Ex Alamo Car Hire, 1995
L337HFU	Mercedes-Benz 410D	Autobus Classique	M16	1993	Ex Balcombe, Hertford, 1997
L919ABJ	LDV 400	LDV	M16	1993	Ex Airport Services, 1997
L631WLD	Ford Transit VE6	Ford	M7	1994	Ex private owner, 1997
N249GOO	Ford Transit VE6	Ford	M8	1996	Ex Ford Motor Co, 1997
P926NNO	Ford Transit VE6	Ford	M8	1997	Ex Ford Motor Co, 1997

Previous registrations:-

C647YKE	C408SRT, 279NDE	TJI1685	G85RGG
SIB6176	FKX238Y, ROF882, 9740EL	XIB2453	A830NTW
TJI1670	G70RGG		

Named Vehicle:- TJI1670 *Lady Jane*

Livery:- Cream and blue.

Castle Hedingham in Essex is the home of Ruffles, but recently sold D448PGH, a Bedford Venturer with Duple bodywork indicates it was undertaking a school contract to London when pictured in Trafalgar Square. The Bedford Venturer was the only 12-metre chassis produced for the home market by this now ceased manufacturer.
Colin Lloyd

RULES

Rule's Coaches Ltd, Boxbank, Boxford, Sudbury, Suffolk, CO10 5HH

APA46B	AEC Reliance 2U3RA	Willowbrook BET	B53F	1964	Ex Beeston, Hadleigh, 1978
DAL771J	AEC Reliance 6U2R	Plaxton Panorama Elite	C53F	1970	Ex Overton, Stockton, 1981
OGV364P	Leyland Leopard PSU5A/4R	Plaxton Supreme III	C51F	1976	Ex Duggan, Airdrie, 1990
GNK781T	AEC Reliance 6U2R	Duple Dominant II	C53F	1979	Ex Olde London Town, Luton, 1980
FBJ713T	AEC Reliance 6U3ZR	Plaxton Supreme IV Express	C53F	1979	
EPM126V	AEC Reliance 6U2R	Duple Dominant II Express	C53F	1979	Ex Mulley, Ixworth, 1995
JPE605V	Volvo B58-56	Plaxton Supreme IV	C53F	1979	Ex Fiveways, Croydon, 1997
KIB5227	Volvo B10M-61	Plaxton Supreme IV	C53F	1980	Ex Caravelle, Felixstowe, 1989
D203NON	Freight-Rover Sherpa	Van Hool Alizée	C49FT	1983	Ex Bee Line, 1991
F580RTL	Volvo B10M-60	Carlyle	B18F	1987	Ex Classic, Annfield Plain, 1997
		Van Hool Alizée	C51FT	1989	

Named Vehicle:- APA46B *Didi*

Previous registrations:-

F580RTL	F32NVL, 520FUM	KIB5227	A51UMB	OGV364P	SFV202P, LIB1611

Livery:- Red, maroon and white.

Rule's operate several services from their base at Boxford. The main fleet comprises entirely heavy-weight chassis ranging from AEC Reliances to the Volvo B10Ms. The only Leyland Leopard in the fleet is 12-metre OGV364P which was new to Ribble's National Travel North West operation as SFV202P. *Trevor Brookes*

S M TRAVEL LTD

S M Travel Ltd, Unit 9 Burnt Mill, Elizabeth Way, Harlow, Essex, CM20 2HT

NCD563M	Bristol VRT/SL2/6G	Eastern Coach Works	H43/31F	1974	Ex APT, Rayleigh, 1995
KEH976N	Daimler Fleetline CRG6	Park Royal	H43/33F	1975	Ex Roger Hill, Congleton, 1997
OKY84R	Leyland Leopard PSU5B/4R	Plaxton Supreme III	C55F	1977	Ex Golden Boy, Roydon, 1988
ULS646T	Leyland Leopard PSU3E/4R	Duple Dominant II Express	C49F	1979	Ex Crown Coaches, Bristol, 1992
KFX675	MAN SR280	MAN	C49FT	1981	Ex Brown, Barway, 1996
A319HFP	Bova EL26/581	Duple Calypso	C53F	1984	Ex Jennings, Bude, 1991
HIL2923	Bova FHD 12.280	Bova Futura	C49FT	1984	Ex Brandon, Blackmore End, 1997
C54VJU	MCW Metroliner DR130/22	MCW	CH57/22FT	1986	Ex Hemisphere, Welwyn Garden City, 1996
D39KAX	Iveco Daily 49.10	Robin Hood City Nippy	B21F	1986	Ex Acorn Mini Travel, Chester, 1994
D555HNW	Iveco Daily 49.10	Robin Hood City Nippy	DP21F	1986	Ex Pickford, Grittleton, 1993
F224AKG	Iveco Daily 49.10	Carlyle	B21F	1988	Ex Jones, Gilston, 1997
F353VRN	Leyland Swift LBM6T/2RS	Elme Orion	C35F	1988	Ex Norris, Hawkhurst, 1995
F77CJC	Iveco Daily 49.10	Carlyle Dailybus 2	C25F	1989	Ex The Shires, 1995
G743DSG	Iveco Daily 49.10	Carlyle Dailybus 2	B24F	1989	Ex Moffat & Williamson, Gauldry, 1995
N662HBY	Iveco Daily 49.10	Marshall C31	DP27F	1996	

Previous registrations:-

HIL2923	A398VML		KFX675	NFJ371W
KEH976N	GOG530N, HIL3478		N662HBY	N622HBY

Livery:- White and red.

Local bus services operated in Harlow by S M Travel Ltd use minibuses and these are also to be found in Welwyn Garden City on evening tendered operation. For the coaching side of the business a MCW Metroliner double deck coach is owned. Here C54VJU is seen in Parliament Square while working a school excursion. *Colin Lloyd*

S & M COACHES
CASTLEPOINT BUS COMPANY

Linkfast Ltd, 42-52 Benfleet Road, Hadleigh, Essex, SS7 1QB

UFC422K	Daimler Fleetline CRL6	Northern Counties	H43/27D	1971	Ex City of Oxford, 1988
MRR808K	AEC Reliance 6U2R	Plaxton PanoramaElite Exp	B60F	1972	Ex DGB Products, Lawford, 1991
TGX704M	Daimler Fleetline CRL6	Park Royal	H44/32F	1973	Ex Boon, Boreham, 1991
GHV29N	Daimler Fleetline CRL6	Park Royal	H44/27D	1974	Ex London & Country (Horsham), 1997
GHV43N	Daimler Fleetline CRL6	Park Royal	H45/32F	1975	Ex Capital Citybus, 1992
KUC154P	Daimler Fleetline CRL6	Park Royal	H45/32F	1975	Ex Capital Citybus, 1992
KUC941P	Daimler Fleetline CRL6	MCW	H45/32F	1975	Ex Capital Citybus, 1992
OUC38R	Leyland Fleetline FE30AGR	MCW	H44/24D	1976	Ex Fourways, Chelmsford, 1997
OJD167R	Leyland Fleetline FE30AGR	MCW	H45/32F	1976	Ex Metrobus, Orpington, 1993
OJD198R	Leyland Fleetline FE30AGR	MCW	H45/..F	1976	Ex Metrobus, Orpington, 1997
OJD383R	Leyland Fleetline FE30ALR	Park Royal	H44/28F	1977	Ex South London, 1992
SEL118R	Ford R1014	Plaxton Supreme III	C45F	1977	Ex Tilbury Coach, 1991
LUA288V	Leyland Leopard PSU3F/4R	Plaxton Supreme IV	C53F	1980	Ex Wallace Arnold, 1986
SPU443W	Ford R1114	Plaxton Supreme IV	C37DL	1980	Ex Lewis, Greenwich, 1997

Livery:- Two tone green and silver.

S & P COACH TRAVEL

K Lapage, The Coach House, 17 Mountbatten Drive, North Shoebury, Southend-on-Sea,
Essex, SS3 8UY

UAR930M	Bedford YRT	Plaxton Panorama Elite III	C53F	1974	Ex Playford, Welwyn Garden City, 1994
HTC729N	Bristol VRT/SL3/6G	Eastern Coach Works	H39/27D	1975	Ex M&E Coachways, Shoeburyness, 1995
VOD603S	Leyland National 11351A/1R		B49F	1978	Ex Inland Travel, Flimwell, 1996
VEJ561V	Leyland Leopard PSU3E/4R	Duple Dominant II	C53F	1979	Ex Warner, Tewkesbury, 1996
HOI7624	Leyland Tiger TRCTL11/3R	Berkhof Esprite 350	C53F	1983	Ex M & E Coachways, Shoeburyness, 1997
USV807	Leyland Tiger TRCTL11/3R	Plaxton Paramount 3200	C46FT	1983	Ex Lamcote, Radcliffe, 1995
C801FYA	Bedford Venturer YNV	Duple Laser 2	C53F	1985	Ex Willis, Denton, 1996
D913EHM	Renault Master T35	Holdsworth	M12	1987	Ex M & E Coachways, Shoeburyness, 1996

Previous registrations:-

HOI7624	JVW157Y	USV807	CDG210Y

Livery:- Mushroom, blue, green and beige.

SANDERS COACHES

N J, C E, P F & G A Sanders, Heath Drive, Hempstead Road Industrial Estate, Holt, Norfolk, NR25 6JU

No	Reg	Chassis	Body	Code	Year	Notes
1	R1SCH	Dennis Javelin	Neoplan Transliner	C49FT	1998	
2	R2SCH	Dennis Javelin	Neoplan Transliner	C49FT	1998	
3	RDV903	DAF MB230LT615	Van Hool Alizée H	C51F	1988	Ex Robinson, Gt. Harwood, 1995
4	RJI8604	Bedford Venturer YNV	Plaxton Paramount 3200 III	C53F	1987	Ex Mayne, Buckie, 1988
6	GFH6V	Bedford YMT	Plaxton Supreme IV Express	C53F	1980	Ex Harrison & Peart, Dagenham, 1992
7	J7FTG	Mercedes-Benz 811D	PMT Ami	C33F	1992	Ex Flights, Birmingham, 1995
8	J8FTG	Mercedes-Benz 811D	PMT Ami	C33F	1992	Ex Flights, Birmingham, 1995
9	YJE9T	Bedford YMT	Plaxton Supreme IV Express	C53F	1979	Ex Lloyd, Nuneaton, 1994
10	G300JEP	DAF SB2305DHS585	Duple 340	C57F	1989	Ex Burrows, Ogmore Vale, 1997
11	N11NJS	Toyota Coaster HZB50R	Caetano Optimo IV	C21F	1995	
12	ATL312X	Bedford YMT	Plaxton Supreme IV Express	C53F	1981	Ex The Delaine, Bourne, 1989
14	RJI8614	DAF MB200DKFL600	Plaxton Supreme V	C57F	1982	Ex Fowler, Holbeach Drove, 1997
15	SJI1615	Bedford YMT	Plaxton Supreme III	C53F	1978	Ex Martin, Sheffield, 1985
16	SJI1616	Bedford YMT	Plaxton Supreme IV Express	C53F	1980	Ex Torr, Gedling, 1991
17	SJI1617	Bedford YMT	Duple Dominant II	C53F	1980	Ex Matthews Blue, Shouldham, 1997
18	SJI1618	Bedford YMT	Duple Dominant II	C53F	1981	Ex Felix, Stanley, 1988
19	SJI1619	Bedford YMT	Duple Dominant IV	C53F	1981	Ex Dereham Coachways, 1990
20	SJI1620	Bedford YMT	Plaxton Supreme IV	C53F	1979	Ex Tappins, Didcot, 1993
21	SJI1621	Bedford YMT	Plaxton Supreme IV	C53F	1979	Ex Tappins, Didcot, 1993
22	SJI1622	DAF MB200DKL600	Plaxton Supreme IV	C57F	1979	Ex Crescent, N. Walsham, 1993
23	SJI1623	DAF MB200DKTL600	Plaxton Supreme IV	C51FT	1980	Ex Crescent, N. Walsham, 1993
24	SJI1624	Bedford YMT	Plaxton Supreme IV	C53F	1980	Ex Boyden, Castle Donington, 1991
25	SJI1625	Bedford YMT	Plaxton Supreme IV	C53F	1979	Ex Tappins, Didcot, 1993
26	SJI1626	Bedford Venturer YNV	Plaxton Paramount 3200 II	C57F	1987	Ex East Midland, 1992
27	SJI1627	Bedford Venturer YNV	Plaxton Paramount 3200 II	C53F	1986	Ex Williams, Camborne, 1990
28	SJI1628	Bedford Venturer YNV	Plaxton Paramount 3200 II	C53F	1985	Ex Bammant, Fakenham, 1992
29	SJI1629	Bedford Venturer YNV	Plaxton Paramount 3200 II	C53F	1985	Ex Thornes, Bubwith, 1993
30	SJI1630	Bedford Venturer YNV	Plaxton Paramount 3200 II	C53F	1986	
32	SJI1632	DAF MB200DKFL600	Plaxton Paramount 3200	C53F	1985	Ex Mayne, Buckie, 1995
33	N33SCS	Mercedes-Benz 811D	Plaxton Beaver	DP31F	1996	
34	P34KWA	Mercedes-Benz 814D	Plaxton Beaver	C32F	1997	
35	P35KWA	Mercedes-Benz 811D	Plaxton Beaver	C32F	1997	
37	PVF377	DAF SB2305DHS585	Van Hool Alizée DH	C53F	1989	Ex London Coaches (Kent), Northfleet, 1997
38	JGU938V	Bedford YMT	Duple Dominant II	C53F	1980	Ex ABC, Whetstone, 1988
39	3990ME	DAF SB3000DKV601	Van Hool Alizée	C53F	1992	Ex Jowitt, Tankersley, 1996
40	MNM40V	DAF MB200DKTL600	Plaxton Supreme IV	C57F	1980	Ex Dhanoia, Orsett, 1995
41	D441CEW	Mercedes-Benz 609D	Reeve Burgess	C23F	1987	Ex Grey, Ely, 1990
42	P542SCL	Mercedes-Benz 814D	Plaxton Beaver	DP31F	1997	
43	P543SCL	Mercedes-Benz 814D	Plaxton Beaver	DP31F	1997	
44	N44SCS	Mercedes-Benz 814D	Plaxton Beaver	DP32F	1996	
47	OGR647	DAF MB230DKFL615	Plaxton Paramount 3500 III	C55F	1987	Ex Grey-Green, 1995
48	PJI7348	Bedford Venturer YNV	Plaxton Paramount 3200 II	C57F	1986	Ex Larratt Pepper, Thurnscoe, 1993
49	BIL8949	DAF MB200DKTL600	Plaxton Supreme V	C57F	1982	Ex Irvine, Law, 1994
50	JDN506L	Bedford YRT	Plaxton Panorama Elite III	C53F	1973	Ex York Pullman, 1981
51	JNK551N	Bedford YRT	Plaxton Panorama Elite III	C53F	1975	Ex Allen & Shingfield, Foulden, 1982
52	SJI5629	DAF MB200DKTL600	Plaxton Supreme IV	C57F	1981	Ex Brijan Tours, Bishops Waltham, 1995
53	WXI9253	DAF MB200DKTL600	Plaxton Supreme IV	C57F	1980	Ex Embling, Guyhirn, 1994
54	354TRT	DAF MB200DKTL600	Plaxton Supreme IV	C57F	1980	Ex Kingsman, Matlock, 1995
55	FTO551V	Bedford YMT	Plaxton Supreme IV Express	DP53F	1979	Ex Baker, Weston-super-Mare, 1994
56	PJI5637	DAF MB200DKL600	Plaxton Supreme IV	C57F	1979	Ex Dogwood, Ringstead, 1994
57	FTO557V	Bedford YMT	Plaxton Supreme IV Express	DP53F	1979	Ex Baker, Weston-Super-Mare, 1994
59	259VYC	Bova FLD12.250	Bova Futura	C57F	1986	Ex Marchwood Motorways, Totton, 1993
61	MIW3561	DAF MB200DKVL600	Duple Caribbean 2	C49FT	1986	Ex Ward, Mundesley, 1994
62	D624KJT	Mercedes-Benz 609D	Yeates	C19F	1987	Ex Excelsior, Bournemouth, 1990
63	N63MDW	Mercedes-Benz 814D	Auto Classique Nouvelle	B33F	1996	Ex Bebb, Llantwit Fardre, 1998
64	GOE264V	DAF MB200DKL600	Plaxton Supreme IV	C57F	1979	Ex de Courcey, Coventry, 1995

The Sanders family still own over fifty Bedford coaches and operate over a large network of routes in north Norfolk. *Opposite, top* is Bedford VAL 125, SNT925H which was seen at Showbus in 1997. *Opposite, bottom* shows 59, 259VYC, one of four Bova Futura coaches currently employed. *Colin Lloyd/David Heath*

The East Anglia Bus Handbook

Very few Dennis Javelins have been taken into the Sanders fleet in recent years. However, a pair with Plaxton Premiére bodywork were purchased in 1996. Pictured in central London is 67, P767PCL, which carries the name Bob Alexander beneath the windscreen. *Colin Lloyd*

65	SGF965	Bedford Venturer YNV	Plaxton Paramount 3200 II	C57F	1988	Ex Cooper, Kirkstall, 1995
66	N65MDW	Mercedes-Benz 814D	Auto Classique Nouvelle	B33F	1996	Ex Bebb, Llantwit Fardre, 1998
67	P767PCL	Dennis Javelin	Plaxton Premiére 350	C57F	1996	
68	P768PCL	Dennis Javelin	Plaxton Premiére 350	C57F	1996	
69	N68MDW	Mercedes-Benz 814D	Auto Classique Nouvelle	B33F	1996	Ex Bebb, Llantwit Fardre, 1998
70	N71MDW	Mercedes-Benz 814D	Auto Classique Nouvelle	B33F	1996	Ex Bebb, Llantwit Fardre, 1998
71	M971CVG	Mercedes-Benz 711D	Plaxton Beaver	C25F	1995	
74	KAU574V	Bedford YMT	Plaxton Supreme IV Express	DP53F	1980	Ex Baker, Weston-Super-Mare, 1994
75	KAU575V	Bedford YMT	Plaxton Supreme IV Express	DP53F	1980	Ex Baker, Weston-Super-Mare, 1994
76	YVJ677	DAF MB200DKFL600	Van Hool Alizée	C51FT	1983	Ex Crescent, N. Walsham, 1993
77	P77SCS	Mercedes-Benz 811D	Plaxton Beaver	B31F	1996	
78	EAC878T	Bedford YMT	Plaxton Supreme IV Express	C53F	1979	Ex Lloyd, Nuneaton, 1994
81	LNU581W	Bedford YMT	Plaxton Supreme IV Express	DP53F	1980	Ex Baker, Weston-Super-Mare, 1994
82	VKC832V	Bedford YMT	Plaxton Supreme IV	C53F	1980	Ex Christian, Liverpool, 1983
83	VKC833V	Bedford YMT	Plaxton Supreme IV	C53F	1980	Ex Christian, Liverpool, 1983
84	BIL8430	Bedford YMT	Plaxton Supreme IV	C53F	1979	Ex Collins, E. Hardwick, 1986
87	PJI8327	Bova FHD12.290	Bova Futura	C49FT	1988	Ex Bird, Hunstanton, 1996
88	WJI3488	DAF SB2305DHS585	Duple 340	C55F	1988	Ex Whippet, Fenstanton, 1997
89	WJI3489	DAF SB2305DHS585	Duple 340	C55F	1988	Ex Whippet, Fenstanton, 1997
90	MIB9067	Bedford YNT	Plaxton Supreme IV	C53F	1981	Ex Dore, Leafield, 1992
93	FIL8693	DAF MB200DKTL600	Plaxton Supreme V	C53F	1982	Ex Crescent, N. Walsham, 1993
95	DHE695V	Bedford YMT	Plaxton Supreme IV	C53F	1980	Ex Boyden, Castle Donington, 1991
97	HGG997T	Bedford YMT	Plaxton Supreme IV	C53F	1979	Ex Constable, Felixstowe, 1984
99	BWK9T	Bedford YMT	Plaxton Supreme IV Express	C53F	1979	Ex Lloyd, Nuneaton, 1994
100	RRT100W	Bedford YNT	Plaxton Supreme IV Express	C53F	1981	Ex Bammant, Fakenham, 1992
101	D601RGJ	Bedford YMT	Plaxton Derwent II	B53F	1987	Ex Fowler, Holbeach Drove, 1997
102	SFC2T	Bedford YMT	Plaxton Supreme IV	C53F	1979	Ex Blunsdon, Bladon, 1990
104	D604RGJ	Bedford YMT	Plaxton Derwent II	B53F	1987	Ex Fowler, Holbeach Drove, 1997
107	RJI8607	Bedford VenturerYNV	Plaxton Paramount 3200 III	C57F	1987	Ex Owen, Oswestry, 1989
108	CVA108V	Bedford YMT	Plaxton Supreme IV	C53F	1980	Ex Crescent, N Walsham, 1993
109	MMJ547V	Bedford YMT	Duple Dominant II	C53F	1980	Ex Jones & Hoerty, Birkenhead, 1987
111	HEX211Y	Bedford YNT	Plaxton Paramount 3200 E.	C49F	1983	Ex Clarke, Burbage, 1992
113	H113DVM	Mercedes-Benz 609D	Reeve Burgess	DP16F	1991	Ex Shearings, 1995
116	D447PGH	Bedford Venturer YNV	Duple 320	C55F	1987	Ex McColl, Balloch, 1995
117w	LAH817A	AEC Reliance 2U3RA	Plaxton Elite II (1972)	C49F	1962	Ex preservation, 1994
122	B223OJU	Bedford Venturer YNV	Duple Laser 2	C57F	1985	Ex PR Coaches, Southall, 1997

123	D823UBH	Bedford YMT	Plaxton Derwent II	B53F	1986	Ex Fowler, Holbeach Drove, 1997
124	LIL2493	DAF SB3000DKV601	Van Hool Alizée	C53F	1990	Ex Galloway, Mendlesham, 1997
125	SNT925H	Bedford VAL70	Plaxton Panorama Elite	C53F	1970	Ex Woolley, Llanedwen, 1993
129	D129SHE	Bedford Venturer YNV	Caetano Algarve	C57F	1987	Ex McColl, Balloch, 1995
134	E134PLJ	Bedford Venturer YNV	Caetano Algarve	C53F	1988	Ex Kershaw, Halifax, 1997

Previous registrations:-

259VYC	C954VAY	SGF965	C821EUG
354TRT	MNM44V	SJI1615	DVY755S
3990ME	J61GCX	SJI1616	FRR686V
BIL8430	KUM983V	SJI1617	NPV307W, PVF377
BIL8949	TND421X, RDV903	SJI1618	ORA688W
BWK9T	EAC877T	SJI1619	RJU259W
D624KJT	D901JFX, 21MMM	SJI1620	YAN814T, 3990ME
D823UBH	D620PWA, 760BUS	SJI1621	YAN822T, WOA521
FIL8693	TND408X, KIW4010	SJI1622	SWP666V
GOE264V	LBM146V, MJI2367	SJI1623	JJU68V, 3367PP, NPW444V
HEX211Y	LCJ633Y, SJI1632	SJI1624	HDB353V
J7FTG	J457UFS	SJI1625	YAN821T, SGF965
LAH817A	521FN	SJI1626	D342SWB
LIL2493	F254RJX, 5516PP, F53UDX	SJI1627	C115AFX
MIB9067	KHB14W	SJI1628	B283AMG
MIW3561	C789MVH	SJI1629	B918SPR
N33SCS	N33SJS	SJI1630	C294BVF
OGR647	E160TVR	SJI1632	C301CFP, CXI7390, C57USS,
PJI5637	FTW131T		CXI7390, C134USS
PJI7348	C840KDS, XAE695, C514MWJ	SJI5629	RAY7W, UVY412
PJI8327	F58JTA, A10BCT	WJI3488	E178OEW
PVF377	F616HGO	WJI3489	E177OEW
RDV903	E221KFV	WXI9253	PNM666W
RJI8604	E440MSE	YJE9T	FDU807T
RJI8607	E917EAY	YVJ677	ORP204Y
RJI8614	UFP136X		

Named Vehicles:- 34 *Matthew Charles*; 67 *Bob Alexander*; 88 *USS Enterprise*; 97 *Higgie*.

Livery:- White, blue and orange

Allocations:-

Fakenham (Clay Pit Lane)

Bedford	20	28	29	65	102	108	109
	111	116	122	129			
DAF	32	76					
Mercedes-Benz	66	70	71	113			

Holt (Heath Drive)

Bedford	4	6	16	19	21	25	26	27
	30	38	48	50	51	74	75	78
	82	83	84	90	100	101	104	107
	123	125	134					
DAF	10	37	88	89	124			
Mercedes-Benz	7	8	34	35	41	63	68	
AEC Reliance	117			Toyota	11			
Dennis Javelin	1	2	67	68		Bova	1	87

North Walsham (Cornish Way)

Bedford	9	12	15	17	18	24	55	57
	81	95	97	99				
Bova	59							
DAF	3	14	22	23	39	40	47	49
	52	53	54	56	61	64	93	
Mercedes-Benz	33	42	43	44	62	77.		

SEMMENCE

H Semmence & Company Ltd, 34, Norwich Road, Wymondham, Norfolk, NR18 0NS

w	EPH27V	Bedford YLQ	Duple Dominant	B52F	1979	Ex Tillingbourne, Cranleigh, 1985	
	JKV420V	Bedford YMT	Plaxton Supreme IV	C53F	1979	Ex Wood, Billericay, 1989	
	JKV422V	Bedford YMT	Plaxton Supreme IV	C53F	1979	Ex Clarke & Goodman, Pailton, 1986	
	JGV336V	Bedford YMT	Plaxton Supreme IV	C53F	1979	Ex Morley, West Row, 1985	
	KNR310V	Bedford YMT	Duple Dominant II	C53F	1980	Ex Orsborn, Wollaston, 1985	
	GWO111W	Bedford YMT	Plaxton Supreme IV	C53F	1980	Ex Hunt, Alford, 1986	
	NUF990W	Bedford YMT	Plaxton Supreme IV	C53F	1981	Ex The Kings Ferry, 1986	
	TKV18W	Bedford YNT	Plaxton Supreme IV	C53F	1981	Ex Lambert, Bungay, 1987	
	CBE882X	Bedford YMT	Plaxton Supreme IV Express	C53F	1981	Ex Enterprise & Silver Dawn, Waddington, 1988	
	PTV597X	Bedford YNT	Plaxton Supreme IV Express	C53F	1981	Ex Gagg, Bunny, 1988	
	WAY456X	Bedford YNT	Duple Dominant IV	C57F	1982	Ex Bexleyheath Transport, 1987	
	XNR997Y	Bedford YNT	Duple Dominant IV	C57F	1982	Ex Torquay Travel, 1988	
w	CKM140Y	Bedford YMT	Wright TT	B61F	1982	Ex Maidstone & District, 1992	
w	CKM141Y	Bedford YMT	Wright TT	B61F	1982	Ex Maidstone & District, 1992	
	EUB552Y	Bedford YNT	Plaxton Paramount 3200	C57F	1982	Ex Dereham, Caochways, 1990	
	XBJ876	Bedford YNT	Plaxton Paramount 3200	C53F	1983	Ex Palmer, Dunstable, 1989	
	PVV312	Bova EL26/581	Bova Europa	C52F	1983	Ex County, Ratby, 1989	
	PVV313	Bova EL26/581	Bova Europa	C52F	1983	Ex County, Ratby, 1989	
	OSU314	Bedford YNT	Plaxton Paramount 3200	C57F	1983	Ex Jamieson, Cullivoe, 1989	
	149GJF	DAF SB2300DHS585	Plaxton Paramount 3200	C53F	1984	Ex Fleet Coaches, 1993	
	A266BTY	Bedford YNT	Plaxton Paramount 3200	C53F	1984	Ex R & M, Hexham, 1993	
	A583MEH	Bova FLD12.250	Bova Futura	C53F	1984	Ex Stoddard, Cheadle, 1993	
	A301KFP	Bova FLD12.250	Bova Futura	C53F	1984	Ex Sykes, Appleton Roebuck, 1993	
	A33UGA	Bova EL28/581	Duple Calypso	C57F	1984	Ex Crawford, Neilston, 1990	

Semmence is another East Anglian coach operator which has built up a fleet dominated by Bedford products but has latterly taken to the Dennis Javelin as a replacement. Representing the Bedfords is EUB552Y which was seen outside the depot. *Glynn Matthews*

The Dennis Javelins with Semmence mostly carry Duple 320 coachwork which reflects production in that Duple out-numbered Plaxton in building bodywork on early Javelins. Representing the type is H157DJU which joined the fleet in 1997. *Glyn Matthews*

B512JJR	Bedford YNT	Plaxton Paramount 3200 II	C57F	1985	Ex Luxury Coaches, Wallsend, 1991
B513JJR	Bedford YNT	Plaxton Paramount 3200 II	C57F	1985	Ex Luxury Coaches, Wallsend, 1991
BXI3079	DAF SB2300DHS585	Plaxton Paramount 3500 II	C53F	1985	Ex Burgin, Sheffield, 1994
C72HDT	Bedford YNT	Plaxton Paramount 3200 II	C53F	1985	Ex Cropper, Leeds, 1992
434YAH	DAF SB2300DHS585	Duple 340	C53F	1987	Ex Wilson, Carnwath, 1993
XCF297	Mercedes-Benz 609D	Reeve Burgess	C25F	1988	Ex Stonebridge, Biggleswade, 1994
E667UND	Mercedes-Benz 609D	Made-to-Measure	C24F	1988	Ex Cunningham Carriage Co, Corringham, 1994
RJI5723	Dennis Javelin 12SDA1907	Plaxton Paramount 3200 III	C53F	1988	Ex Baker, Weston-super-Mare, 1994
RJI5721	Dennis Javelin 12SDA1907	Plaxton Paramount 3200 III	C57F	1988	Ex Baker, Weston-super-Mare, 1994
G851VAY	Dennis Javelin 12SDA1907	Duple 320	C57F	1989	Ex Top Marks Travel, Crayford, 1995
G852VAY	Dennis Javelin 12SDA1907	Duple 320	C57F	1989	Ex Top Marks Travel, Crayford, 1995
TAZ4517	Dennis Javelin 12SDA1907	Duple 320	C57F	1990	Ex Voel, Dyserth, 1998
TAZ4518	Dennis Javelin 12SDA1907	Duple 320	C57F	1990	Ex Voel, Dyserth, 1998
G407DPD	Iveco Daily 49.10	Carlyle Dailybus	DP25F	1989	Ex Metrobus, Orpington, 1994
G49HDW	Dennis Javelin 12SDA1907	Duple 320	C53F	1990	Ex Wilson, Carnwath, 1997
H157DJU	Dennis Javelin 12SDA1907	Duple 320	C57F	1990	Ex KB Coaches, Eastington, 1997

Previous registrations:-

149GJF	A272KEL	PVV313	JRO614Y
434YAH	D616YCX	RJI5721	F421PSE
A301KFP	WDL124, 124YTW	RJI5723	E761HJF
A583MEH	A866XOP, A20MPS	TAZ4517	G415YAY, 776VC
BXI3079	B643OFP	TAZ4518	G425YAY, 1760VC
OSU314	RPS380Y	XBJ876	HBH422Y
PVV312	JRO613Y	XCF297	E218ARM

Livery:- Cream with orange, red and brown relief.

SHAWS OF MAXEY

Newborough Coaches Ltd; C J Shaw, R E Shaw & J Duffelen,
49 High Street, Maxey, Peterborough, Cambridgeshire, PE6 9EF

1	F484WFX	Mercedes-Benz 811D	Reeve Burgess Beaver	C29F	1989	Ex Excelsior, Bournemouth, 1991
3	D557MVR	Volvo B10M-61	Van Hool Alizée H	C53F	1987	Ex Shearings, 1992
4	ELP554T	Bedford YMT	Plaxton Supreme IV	C53F	1979	Ex Paul James Coaches, Ratcliffe, 1993
5	F259OFP	Volvo B10M-61	Plaxton Paramount 3200 III	C53F	1989	Ex Dunn-Line, Nottingham, 1993
6	J427HDS	Volvo B10M-60	Plaxton Excalibur	C49F	1992	Ex Park's, Hamilton, 1993
8	L966FLJ	Renault Master T35	Holloway Commercials	M15	1994	Ex private owner, 1995
9	FNR100V	Bedford YMT	Plaxton Supreme IV	C53F	1979	Ex Hodgkinson, Langley Mill, 1997
59	HFL950N	Bedford YRT	Plaxton Supreme III	C53F	1975	
67	PFL963R	Bedford YMT	Plaxton Supreme III	C53F	1977	
68	PFL964R	Bedford YMT	Plaxton Supreme III	C53F	1977	
69	PFL965R	Bedford YMT	Plaxton Supreme III	C53F	1977	
76	XEW322T	Bedford YMT	Plaxton Supreme IV	C53F	1979	
77	XEW323T	Bedford YMT	Plaxton Supreme IV	C53F	1979	
78	XEW324T	Bedford YMT	Plaxton Supreme IV	C53F	1979	
80	BFL504V	Bedford YMT	Plaxton Supreme IV	C53F	1979	
85	HEW174Y	Bedford YNT	Plaxton Paramount 3200	C53F	1983	
86	A65UEW	Bedford YNT	Plaxton Paramount 3200	C53F	1984	
87A	A66UEW	Bedford YNT	Plaxton Paramount 3200	C53F	1984	
93	A335VTU	Bedford YNT	Plaxton Paramount 3200	C53F	1984	Ex Narburgh, Alveley, 1987
95	D298XCX	DAF SB2300DHTD585	Plaxton Paramount 3200 III	C53F	1987	Ex Smith, Alcester, 1988
96	D279XCX	DAF SB2305DHS585	Van Hool Alizée	C49FT	1987	Ex Smith, Alcester, 1988
97	F225RJX	DAF SB2305DHTD585	Plaxton Paramount 3200 III	C53F	1989	
98	F226RJX	DAF SB2305DHTD585	Plaxton Paramount 3200 III	C53F	1989	
99	G959KJX	DAF SB2305DHS585	Plaxton Paramount 3200 III	C53F	1990	
100	H515YCX	DAF SB2305DHS585	Van Hool Alizée	C49FT	1991	
..	M534NCG	Volvo B10M-62	Plaxton Première 350	C53F	1995	Ex Excelsior, Bournemouth, 1997

Previous registration:-
M534NCG   A13XEL

Livery:- White and blue

Following on from a
sucession of new
Bedford coaches,
Shaws of Maxey
next adopted DAF
products. A 1990
example, G959KJX,
is seen leaving
Hampton Court
flower show for
home. Interestingly,
the fleet numbering
recommenced at 1
after reaching 100.
Geoff Rixon

SOAMES / FORGET-ME-NOT

Forget-Me-Not (Travel) Ltd, Chapel Road, Otley, Woodbridge, Suffolk, IP6 9NP

Depots:- Chapel Road, Otley; Clopton Commercial Park, Debach and Station Road Woodbridge.

TBJ545W	Volvo B58-61	Plaxton Supreme IV	C53F	1981	Ex Fosdike, Bramfield, 1988
WAW353Y	Ford R1114	Plaxton Paramount 3200 E	C53F	1983	Ex Owen, Oswestry, 1985
B812XNK	Volvo B10M-61	Plaxton Paramount 3500	C49FT	1984	Ex Bird, Hunstanton, 1990
B916SPR	Volvo B10M-61	Plaxton Paramount 3200 II	C53F	1985	Ex Excelsior, Bournemouth, 1986
C373CTP	Volvo B10M-61	Plaxton Paramount 3200 II	C57F	1986	Ex Coliseum, West End, 1994
D939HMU	Volvo B10M-61	Plaxton Paramount 3200 II	C53F	1986	Ex Henry Crawford, Neilston, 1989
E280HRY	Volvo B10M-61	Van Hool Alizée SH	C49FT	1988	Ex BFN Travel, Ipswich, 1992
E32MCE	Volvo B10M-61	Plaxton Paramount 3200 III	C49FT	1988	Ex Kenzie, Shepreth, 1990
11PKN	Volvo B10M-61	Plaxton Paramount 3500 III	C53F	1988	Ex Graham's, Talke, 1993
F22HGG	Volvo B10M-60	Plaxton Paramount 3500 III	C53F	1989	Ex Park's, Hamilton, 1992
F428DUG	Volvo B10M-60	Plaxton Paramount 3200 III	C50F	1989	Ex Dodsworth, Boroughbridge, 1996
F436DUG	Volvo B10M-60	Plaxton Paramount 3200 III	C53F	1989	Ex Wallace Arnold, 1992
F39EEG	Volvo B10M-60	Van Hool Alizée H	C51FT	1989	Ex Kenzie, Shepreth, 1995
G718NWY	Volvo B10M-60	Plaxton Paramount 3500 III	C57F	1990	Ex Dodsworth, Boroughbridge, 1994
L46CNY	Volvo B10M-60	Plaxton Premiére 320	C53F	1993	Ex Bebb, Llantwit Fardre, 1996
L659ADS	Volvo B10M-60	Van Hool Alizée H	C49FT	1989	Ex Dereham Coachways, 1998
M513MFX	Volvo B10M-62	Plaxton Premiére 320	C49FT	1995	Ex Excelsior, Bournemouth, 1996
R233SEF	Mercedes-Benz Vario O814	Autobus Classique 2	C24F	1997	

Previous registrations:-

11PKN	E150MRF	C373CTP	636VHX

Livery:- Blue; white and blue (David Urquhart Travel) M513MFX

Falmouth Moor provides the backdrop to Plaxton-bodied Volvo B10M G718NWY. While all the large coaches in the fleet have been acquired pre-owned it will be noted that many 3-5 year old vehicles from major fleets have been targetted. *Tony Wilson*

SIMONDS

Simonds of Botesdale Ltd, The Garage, Botesdale, Diss, Norfolk, IP22 1BX

Depots:- The Garage, Botesdale; Victoria Road, Diss and Broad Street, Harleston.

w	UUB402	Commer Avenger III	Plaxton Venturer	C35F	1955	Ex Hardwick, Scarborough, 1961
w	UUB403	Commer Avenger III	Plaxton Venturer	C35F	1955	Ex Hardwick, Scarborough, 1961
w	UUB404	Commer Avenger III	Plaxton Venturer	C35F	1955	Ex Rennie, Dunfermline, 1961
w	482SBJ	Commer Avenger IV	Plaxton Embassy II	C41F	1963	
w	TCS352J	Ford R226	Plaxton Panorama Elite II	C53F	1971	Ex Mullany, Watford, 1981
	HIB644	Bedford YMT	Plaxton Supreme IV	C53F	1979	Ex Sovereign Chicken, Eye, 1991
	FDX230T	Bedford YMT	Duple Dominant	B63F	1979	
	XVA545T	Ford R1114	Plaxton Supreme IV	C53F	1979	Ex Safford, Little Gransden, 1984
	XCG264V	Ford R1014	Plaxton Supreme IV	C33F	1979	Ex Summerfield, Southampton, 1983
	4512UR	Bedford YNT	Plaxton Supreme IV	C53F	1981	Ex Amport & District, 1986
	460UEV	Bedford YNT	Plaxton Supreme V	C53F	1981	Ex Kiddle, St Ives, 1990
	XJO46	Bedford YNT	Plaxton Supreme VI Express	C53F	1982	Ex Barry Gill Motors, Wadebridge, 1985
	166UMB	Bedford YNT	Plaxton Supreme V Express	C53F	1982	Ex Chapel End Coaches, Nuneaton, 1986
	WDX663X	Ford R1114	Plaxton Supreme VI Express	C53F	1982	
	JGV929	Bedford YMT	Plaxton Supreme IV	C53F	1982	Ex Sovereign Chicken, Eye, 1992
	TCF496	Bedford YNT	Plaxton Supreme V	C53F	1982	Ex Freeman, Uffington, 1988
	TVG397	Bedford YNT	Plaxton Paramount 3200	C53F	1983	Ex Davies Bros, Pencader, 1986
	LIB226	Volvo B10M-61	Plaxton Paramount 3200 E	C53F	1983	Ex Crawley Luxury Coaches, 1997
	TJI7515	Leyland Tiger TRCTL11/3R	Plaxton Paramount 3200 E	C57F	1983	Ex John's, Stowmarket, 1997
	SIA488	Volvo B10M-61	Plaxton Paramount 3200	C53F	1983	Ex Berkeley, Paulton, 1993
	YVF158	Bedford YNT	Plaxton Paramount 3200	C53F	1983	Ex Glennie, New Mill, 1989
	8333UR	Bedford YNT	Plaxton Paramount 3200 II	C53F	1985	Ex CTC, Caerphilly, 1988
	538ELX	Bedford Venturer YNV	Plaxton Paramount 3200 II	DP69F	1985	
	DSU116	Leyland Tiger TRCTL11/3RZ	Plaxton Paramount 3200 II	C53F	1985	Ex Littlewood, Nottingham, 1995
	7236PW	Volvo B10M-61	Plaxton Paramount 3500 II	C49FT	1985	Ex Worthing Coaches, 1988
	98TNO	Volvo B10M-61	Plaxton Paramount 3500 II	C49FT	1986	Ex Moon, Warnham, 1989
	4940VF	Volvo B10M-61	Plaxton Paramount 3500 III	C53F	1987	Ex Berkeley, Paulton, 1992
	VRY841	Volvo B10M-61	Plaxton Paramount 3500 III	C53F	1987	Ex Berkeley, Paulton, 1992
	SIJ82	Volvo B10M-61	Plaxton Paramount 3200 III	C53F	1987	Ex Excelsior, Bournemouth, 1989
	224ENG	Volvo B10M-61	Plaxton Paramount 3200 III	C53F	1987	Ex Sadhra, Cranford, 1997
	256JPA	Volvo B10M-61	Plaxton Paramount 3500 III	C49FT	1987	Ex Dodsworth, Boroughbridge, 1992
	SLK886	Mercedes-Benz 609D	Reeve Burgess	C19F	1987	
	378BNG	Leyland Tiger TRCTL11/3RZ	Plaxton Paramount 3200 III	C53F	1988	Ex Thamesway, 1996
	WJI1722	Leyland Tiger TRCTL11/3RZ	Plaxton Paramount 3200 III	C53F	1988	Ex The Shires, 1998
	WJI1723	Leyland Tiger TRCTL11/3RZ	Plaxton Paramount 3200 III	C53F	1988	Ex The Shires, 1998
	WJI1724	Leyland Tiger TRCTL11/3RZ	Plaxton Paramount 3200 III	C53F	1988	Ex The Shires, 1998
	KIA891	Volvo B10M-61	Plaxton Paramount 3500 III	C49FT	1988	Ex National Plant, Bilsthorpe, 1993
	9983PW	Volvo B10M-61	Van Hool Alizée H	C49F	1988	Ex Excelsior, Bournemouth, 1991
	DSK648	Volvo B10M-61	Van Hool Alizée H	C53F	1989	Ex Kenzie, Shepreth, 1994
	9383MX	Volvo B10M-60	Van Hool Alizée H	C53F	1990	Ex Kenzie, Shepreth, 1995
	L54REW	Volvo B10M-62	Van Hool Alizée HE	C49FT	1994	Ex Kenzie, Shepreth, 1997
	M341MRU	Volvo B10M-62	Plaxton Premiére 350	C49FT	1995	Ex Excelsior, Bournemouth, 1996
	M2SOB	Toyota Coaster HZB50R	Caetano Optimo III	C21F	1995	
	M3SOB	Volvo B10M-62	Plaxton Excalibur	C49FT	1995	
	N988FWT	DAF DE02LTSB220	Ikarus Citibus	B49F	1996	
	P531CLJ	Volvo B10M-62	Plaxton Premiére 320	C49FT	1997	Ex Excelsior, Bournemouth, 1996
	R486AVG	Volvo B10M-62	Van Hool Alizée	C49FT	1997	

Opposite:- **Contrasting Plaxton products in the Simonds of Botesdale fleet are RLJ93X now re-registered 4512UR, a Bedford YNT with Supreme IV bodywork and M3SOB, an Excalibur model built on a Volvo B10M. The later coaches display more modern livery applications made available through new technology, though M3SOB is currently liveried for David Urquhart Travel.**
Phillip Stephenson/Roger Harrison

The East Anglia Bus Handbook

Previous registrations:-

166UMB	XVC9X, CEC61, AAC866X	LIB226	A799TGG, 5142SC, A613TCR,
224ENG	D254HFX		A12ESS, A48SHD
256JPA	D709MWX	M341MRU	A13EXC
378BNG	E677UNE	SIA488	OOU855Y
428SBJ	From new	SIJ82	D252HFX
4512UR	RLJ93X	SLK886	E346HBJ
460UEV	TRY6X	TCF496	YRU296Y
4940VF	D402HEU	TJI7515	?
538ELX	From new	TVG397	OBX454Y, 9983PW
7236PW	C196WJT	UUB402	From new
8333UR	B631DDW	UUB403	From new
9383MX	G41SAV	UUB404	From new
98TNO	C547RWV	VRY841	D807SGB
9983PW	E306OPR, XEL941, E407SEL	WJI1722	E661AWJ
DSK648	F38DAV	WJI1723	E662AWJ
DSU116	B620CKG	WJI1724	E663AWJ
HIB644	APH510T	XJO46	NGL276X
JGV929	AVS632X	YVF158	A807ASE
KIA891	E582UHS, A1NPT		

Named Vehicle:- LIB226 *Volvoliner*

Livery:- Red, white and gold; white (Grand UK Holidays) L54REW; white (David Urquhart Travel) M3SOB

SPRATTS

Spratt's Coaches (East Anglian & Continental) Ltd, The Garage, Wreningham, Norfolk, NR16 1AZ

RGS598R	Bedford YMT	Duple Dominant II	C57F	1977	Ex Eagre, Morton, 1995
TYE708S	Bedford YMT	Duple Dominant II	C53F	1977	Ex Grey-Green, 1981
NRY22W	Bedford YLQ	Duple Dominant IV	C45F	1980	
HIL7394	Bedford YNT	Duple Dominant IV	C49DL	1982	Ex Kings, Stanway, 1987
C357FBO	Bedford Venturer YNV	Plaxton Paramount 3200 II	C57F	1985	Ex Gregory, Netherton, 1994
HIL7477	Scania K112CRS	Van Hool Alizée	C49FT	1985	
HIL7478	Scania K92CRS	Berkhof Esprite 350	C53F	1986	Ex The Kings Ferry, 1987
HIL6919	Bedford YMP	Plaxton Paramount 3200 II	C35F	1986	Ex Coachmaster, Coulsdon, 1987
HIL7391	Bedford Venturer YNV	Plaxton Paramount 3200 II	C57F	1987	
E99ODH	Bova FHD12.280	Bova Futura	C38DTL	1987	Ex Holyhead, Tettenhall, 1995
F569MCH	Mercedes-Benz ?	?	?	19?	
HIL7479	Scania K92CRB	Van Hool Alizée	C55F	1988	Ex Harry Shaw, Coventry, 1991
CJS447	Scania K113CRB	Van Hool Alizée	C49FT	1989	Ex Elite, Stockport, 1992
H182DVM	Volvo B10M-60	Van Hool Alizée H	C49FT	1991	Ex Shearings, 1997
J234XKY	Scania K93CRB	Van Hool Alizée	C55F	1992	Ex Embling, Guyhirn, 1997
RCS754	Scania K113CRB	Berkhof Excel. 2000L(1994)	C49FT	1992	Ex The Kings Ferry, 1994
R972CJS	MAN 11.220	Berkhof Axial	C33F	1998	

Previous registrations:-

CJS447	G999HKW	HIL7394	CTM791X	HIL7479	684DYX, E648NHP
HIL6919	C535JTG	HIL7477	C22YEX	RCS754	J3KFC
HIL7391	D422KVF	HIL7478	C593KVW		

Livery:- White and blue or silver, blue and red.

STAGECOACH CAMBUS

Cambus Ltd, 100 Cowley Road, Cambridge CB4 4DN
Viscount Bus & Coach Co Ltd, 351 Lincoln Road, Peterborough, PE1 2PG

81	GAZ4381	Optare MetroRider MR17		Optare	B29F	1999	CNG Powered		
82	GAZ4382	Optare MetroRider MR17		Optare	B29F	1999	CNG Powered		

155-169

Volvo B6-9M — Marshall C32 — B32F — 1993

155	L655MFL	158	L658MFL	161	L661MFL	164	L664MFL	168	L668MFL
156	L656MFL	159	L659MFL	162	L662MFL	165	L665MFL	169	L669MFL
157	L657MFL	160	L660MFL	163	L663MFL	167	L667MFL		

200-211

Mercedes-Benz 709D — Alexander Sprint — B25F — 1996 — Ex Western, 1996

200	N614VSS	203	N619VSS	206	N616VSS	208	N620VSS	210	N643VSS
201	N615VSS	204	N641VSS	207	N618VSS	209	N642VSS	211	N644VSS
202	N617VSS	205	N613VSS						

310	F167SMT	Leyland Lynx LX112L10ZR1S	Leyland Lynx	B49F	1989	Ex Miller, Foxton, 1992
311	F168SMT	Leyland Lynx LX112L10ZR1S	Leyland Lynx	B49F	1989	Ex Miller, Foxton, 1992
312	F171SMT	Leyland Lynx LX112L10ZR1S	Leyland Lynx	B49F	1989	Ex Miller, Foxton, 1992

315-319

Volvo B10M-55 — Alexander PS — B49F — 1996

315	P315EFL	316	P316EFL	317	P317EFL	318	P318EFL	319	P319EFL

320	P320EFL	Volvo B6BLE	Alexander ALX200	N35F	1997	
321	P321EFL	Volvo B6BLE	Alexander ALX200	N35F	1997	
322	P322EFL	Dennis Dart SLF	Alexander ALX200	N39F	1997	
323	P323EFL	Dennis Dart SLF	Alexander ALX200	N39F	1997	
324	P324EFL	Dennis Dart SLF	Alexander ALX200	N39F	1997	
350	N350YFL	Dennis Dart	Alexander Dash	B40F	1996	
351	N351YFL	Dennis Dart	Alexander Dash	B40F	1996	
352	N352YFL	Dennis Dart	Alexander Dash	B40F	1996	
353	R353LER	Dennis Dart SLF	Alexander ALX200	N37F	1997	
354	R354LER	Dennis Dart SLF	Alexander ALX200	N37F	1997	
355	R355LER	Dennis Dart SLF	Alexander ALX200	N37F	1997	
356	R356LER	Dennis Dart SLF	Alexander ALX200	N37F	1997	
364	P364APM	Dennis Dart SLF	Plaxton Pointer	N40F	1996	Ex demonstrator, 1997
365	R365JVA	Dennis Dart SLF	Alexander ALX200	N37F	1998	
366	R366JVA	Dennis Dart SLF	Alexander ALX200	N37F	1998	

Two Optare MetroRiders that operate on compressed natural gas wear this special green and yellow livery to emphasise the point. The circular service they work on connects several colleges with the central area of Cambridge. Shown here is 81, GAZ4381.
Phillip Stephenson

157

407	H407GAV	Volvo B10M-60	Plaxton Paramount 3500 III	C53F	1991
408	J408TEW	Volvo B10M-60	Plaxton Paramount 3500 III	C53F	1992
409	J409TEW	Volvo B10M-60	Plaxton Paramount 3500 III	C49FT	1992
421	K911RGE	Volvo B10M-60	Jonckheere Deauville P599	C49FT	1993	Ex Park's, Hamilton, 1994
422	K912RGE	Volvo B10M-60	Jonckheere Deauville P599	C49FT	1993	Ex Park's, Hamilton, 1994
425	G525LWU	Volvo B10M-60	Plaxton Paramount 3500 III	C49FT	1990	Ex Wallace Arnold, 1994

431-435   Volvo B10M-60   Plaxton Paramount 3500 III   C48FT*   1991   Ex Wallace Arnold, 1994
*431 is C49FT

431	H649UWR	432	H642UWR	433	H643UWR	434	H652UWR	435	H653UWR

439-444   Volvo B10M-60   Plaxton Premiére 350   C48FT   1992   Ex Wallace Arnold, 1994

439	J739CWT	441	J741CWT	442	J742CWT	443	J743CWT	444	J744CWT
440	J740CWT								

445-456   Volvo B10M-62   Plaxton Expressliner 2   C49FT   1995-97

445	N445XVA	448	N448XVA	451	N451XVA	453	R453FCE	455	R455FCE
446	N446XVA	449	N449XVA	452	N452XVA	454	R454FCE	456	R456FCE
447	N447XVA	450	N450XVA						

481	A681KDV	Leyland Olympian ONLXB/1R	Eastern Coach Works	H45/32F	1983	Ex North Devon, 1996
482	A561KWY	Leyland Olympian ONLXB/1R	Eastern Coach Works	H45/32F	1983	Ex Selby & District, 1996
483	A683KDV	Leyland Olympian ONLXB/1R	Eastern Coach Works	H45/32F	1983	Ex North Devon, 1996
500	E500LFL	Leyland Olympian ONLXCT/1RH	Optare	DPH43/27F	1988	
501	E501LFL	Leyland Olympian ONLXCT/1RH	Optare	DPH43/27F	1988	
502	E502LFL	Leyland Olympian ONLXCT/1RH	Optare	DPH43/27F	1988	
503	UWW3X	Leyland Olympian ONLXB/1R	Roe	H47/29F	1982	Ex West Yorkshire PTE, 1987
504	UWW4X	Leyland Olympian ONLXB/1R	Roe	H47/29F	1982	Ex West Yorkshire PTE, 1987
505	UWW8X	Leyland Olympian ONLXB/1R	Roe	H47/29F	1982	Ex West Yorkshire PTE, 1987

506-517   Leyland Olympian ONLXB/1RZ   Northern Counties   H45/30F   1989

506	F506NJE	509	F509NJE	512	F512NJE	514	F514NJE	516	F516NJE
507	F507NJE	510	F510NJE	513	F513NJE	515	F515NJE	517	F517NJE
508	F508NJE	511	F511NJE						

518	N518XER	Volvo Olympian YN2RV18Z4	Northern Counties Palatine	DPH45/31F	1995	
519	N519XER	Volvo Olympian YN2RV18Z4	Northern Counties Palatine	DPH45/31F	1995	
520	N520XER	Volvo Olympian YN2RV18Z4	Northern Counties Palatine	DPH45/31F	1995	
523	H473CEG	Leyland Olympian ON2R50G13Z4 Leyland		H47/31F	1990	
524	H474CEG	Leyland Olympian ON2R50G13Z4 Leyland		H47/31F	1990	
525	H475CEG	Leyland Olympian ON2R50G13Z4 Leyland		H47/31F	1990	

526-579   Volvo Olympian YN2RV18V3   Northern Counties Palatine   H49/33F   1996

526	P526EFL	537	P537EFL	548	P548EFL	559	P559EFL	570	P570EFL
527	P527EFL	538	P538EFL	549	P549EFL	561	P561EFL	571	P571EFL
528	P528EFL	539	P539EFL	550	P550EFL	562	P562EFL	572	P572EFL
529	P529EFL	540	P540EFL	551	P551EFL	563	P563EFL	573	P573EFL
530	P530EFL	541	P541EFL	552	P552EFL	564	P564EFL	574	P574EFL
531	P531EFL	542	P542EFL	553	P553EFL	565	P565EFL	575	P575EFL
532	P532EFL	543	P543EFL	554	P554EFL	566	P566EFL	576	P576EFL
533	P533EFL	544	P544EFL	556	P556EFL	567	P567EFL	577	P577EFL
534	P534EFL	545	P545EFL	557	P557EFL	568	P568EFL	578	P578EFL
535	P535EFL	546	P546EFL	558	P558EFL	569	P569EFL	579	P579EFL
536	P536EFL	547	P547EFL						

580-586   Volvo Olympian   Alexander RL   H45/27F   1998

580	R580JVA	582	R582JVA	584	R584JVA	585	R585JVA	586	R586JVA
581	R581JVA	583	R583JVA						

Opposite, top:- **The combination of Alexander's PS-type bodywork and Volvo B10M chassis was the Stagecoach Group's main single deck product. The last PS-type buses have now been delivered and the ALX300, which is available on several low floor chassis has replaced it. After a short batch for Busways, the main Stagecoach intake will be on MAN chassis in 1998. Pictured here is Cambus 315, P315EFL and one of five of the PS style in the Park & Ride livery.** *Phillip Stephenson*
Opposite, bottom:- **To improve the age profile of the Cambus fleet and to reduce maintenance costs almost sixty Volvo Olympians have recently arrived in the fleet. Northern Counties bodywork is seen on 549, P549EFL, which being based at Peterborough, carries Viscount fleet names.** *Colin Brown*

Cambus Holdings acquired regular batches of new Optare Metrobuses and one batch of Iveco minibuses before becoming part of Stagecoach.   Of the latter type, 955, K175CAV, is seen in Peterborough and displays its Cambridge-built Marshall bodywork. *Colin Brown*

735	PWY37W	Bristol VRT/SL3/6LXB	Eastern Coach Works	H43/31F	1981	Ex York City & District, 1990
737w	SUB795W	Bristol VRT/SL3/6LXB	Eastern Coach Works	H43/31F	1981	Ex York City & District, 1990
739	URP943W	Bristol VRT/SL3/501	Eastern Coach Works	H43/31F	1981	Ex Buckinghamshire Road Car, 1994

742-746

Bristol VRT/SL3/6LXB   Eastern Coach Works   H43/31F   1980-81

742	VEX295X	**743**	VEX300X	**744**	VEX296X	**745w**	VEX303X	**746w**	VEX304X

747	STW24W	Bristol VRT/SL3/6LXB	Eastern Coach Works	H39/31F	1981	Ex Green, Kirkintilloch, 1991
751w	VEX298X	Bristol VRT/SL3/6LXB	Eastern Coach Works	H43/31F	1981	
753	VEX289X	Bristol VRT/SL3/6LXB	Eastern Coach Works	H43/31F	1981	
754w	KVF245V	Bristol VRT/SL3/6LXB	Eastern Coach Works	H43/31F	1980	
755	VEX293X	Bristol VRT/SL3/6LXB	Eastern Coach Works	H43/31F	1981	
760w	KVF250V	Bristol VRT/SL3/6LXB	Eastern Coach Works	H43/31F	1980	
770	SUB790W	Bristol VRT/SL3/6LXB	Eastern Coach Works	H43/31F	1981	Ex Keighley & District, 1990
772	SUB792W	Bristol VRT/SL3/6LXB	Eastern Coach Works	H43/31F	1981	Ex York City & District, 1990
773	SUB793W	Bristol VRT/SL3/6LXB	Eastern Coach Works	H43/31F	1981	Ex York City & District, 1990
775	PWY45W	Bristol VRT/SL3/6LXB	Eastern Coach Works	H43/31F	1981	Ex Keighley & District, 1990
777	PWY47W	Bristol VRT/SL3/6LXB	Eastern Coach Works	H43/31F	1981	Ex Keighley & District, 1990
779	PWY49W	Bristol VRT/SL3/6LXB	Eastern Coach Works	H43/31F	1981	Ex Keighley & District, 1990
780	PWY50W	Bristol VRT/SL3/6LXB	Eastern Coach Works	H43/31F	1981	Ex Keighley & District, 1990
781	VEX301X	Bristol VRT/SL3/6LXB	Eastern Coach Works	H43/31F	1981	
782	VEX299X	Bristol VRT/SL3/6LXB	Eastern Coach Works	H43/31F	1981	
784	RAH264W	Bristol VRT/SL3/6LXB	Eastern Coach Works	H43/31F	1980	
788	VAH278X	Bristol VRT/SL3/6LXB	Eastern Coach Works	H43/31F	1981	
789	VAH279X	Bristol VRT/SL3/6LXB	Eastern Coach Works	H43/31F	1981	
790	VAH280X	Bristol VRT/SL3/6LXB	Eastern Coach Works	H43/31F	1981	
791	VEX291X	Bristol VRT/SL3/6LXB	Eastern Coach Works	H43/31F	1981	
796w	KVF246V	Bristol VRT/SL3/6LXB	Eastern Coach Works	H43/31F	1980	

952-957

Iveco TurboDaily 59-12   Marshall C31   B25F   1992

951	K171CAV	**953**	K173CAV	**955**	K175CAV	**956**	K176CAV	**957**	K177CAV
952	K172CAV	**954**	K174CAV						

Alexander's latest product range are pre-fixed with ALX letters. First to be built was the ALX200 which displaces the Dash. The new style is seen on low floor Dennis Darts and Volvo B6s in the Cambus fleet and 321, P321EFL shows the Volvo variant. The Stagecoach order for 1997 included 90 of this combination. *Colin Lloyd*

960-974

				Optare MetroRider		Optare	B29F	1992-93		
960	J960DWX	963	K963HUB	966	K966HUB	969	K969HUB	972	K972HUB
961	J961DWX	964	K964HUB	967	K967HUB	970	K970HUB	973	K973HUB
962	J962DWX	965	K965HUB	968	K968HUB	971	K971HUB	974	K974HUB

975-979

			Optare MetroRider MR17		Optare	B29F	1995		
975	M975WWR	976	M976WWR	977	M977WWR	978	M978WWR	979	M979VWY

980	K390KUA	Optare MetroRider	Optare	B29F	1993	
981	K391KUA	Optare MetroRider	Optare	B29F	1993	
982	K392KUA	Optare MetroRider	Optare	B29F	1993	
983	K393KUA	Optare MetroRider	Optare	B29F	1993	
984	K975KUB	Optare MetroRider	Optare	B29F	1993	
985	J805DWW	Optare MetroRider	Optare	B29F	1992	
986	J806DWW	Optare MetroRider	Optare	B29F	1992	
987	J807DWW	Optare MetroRider	Optare	B29F	1992	
988	M808WWR	Optare MetroRider	Optare	B29F	1995	
989	M809WWR	Optare MetroRider	Optare	B29F	1995	
990	M810WWR	Optare MetroRider	Optare	B29F	1995	
2305	E305BWL	Mercedes-Benz 709D	Reeve Burgess Beaver	DP25F	1988	Ex Stagecoach Oxford, 1998
2306	E306BWL	Mercedes-Benz 709D	Reeve Burgess Beaver	DP25F	1988	Ex Stagecoach Oxford, 1998
2312	F312EJO	Mercedes-Benz 709D	Reeve Burgess Beaver	DP25F	1988	Ex Stagecoach Oxford, 1998

Ancilliary & Heritage vehicles:-

65	OFB965R	Bristol LH6L	Eastern Coach Works	B43F	1977	Ex Prince Henry HS, Otley, 1992
73	SFL373R	AEC Reliance 6U3ZR	Plaxton Supreme III Express	C43F	1976	Ex Premier Travel, 1990
453	JAH553D	Bristol FLF6G	Eastern Coach Works	H38/32F	1966	
552	JAH552D	Bristol FLF6G	Eastern Coach Works	O38/32F	1966	

Note: All vehicles were formerly Eastern Counties in 1984 subsequently operating for Cambus, Premier or Viscount unless shown otherwise or new later.

Allocations:-

Cambridge (Cowley Road) - Cambus - National Express ♠ - Park & Ride ♥

Outstations: - Bassingbourne; Ely; Fowlmere; Haverhill; Littleport; Longstowe; Market Deeping; Newmarket; Royston; St Ives; Sawston and Soham.

Bristol VR	735	739	742	743	744	747	753	755
Olympian	483	500	501	502	503	504	505	512
	513	514	515	516	517	518	519	520
	526	527	528	529	530	531	532	533
	534	535	541	542	543	544	545	551
	552	553	554	556	563	564	565	566
	567	571	572	573	574	575	576	577
	578	579						
Volvo PS	315	316	317	318	319			
Dart	322	323	324	350♥	351♥	352♥	353	354
	355	356	364	365	366			
Volvo B6	155	156	157	158	159	160	161	162
	163	164	165	167	168	169		
Iveco	952							
MetroRider	81	82	960	961	962	963	964	965
	966	967	968	969	970	971	972	973
	974	975	976	977	978	979	980	984
	990							
Mercedes-Benz	205	206	207	208	209	210	211	2305
	2306	2312						
Volvo B10M	407	408	409	421	422	431	439♠	440♠
	441♠	442♠	443♠	444♠	445♠	446♠	447♠	448♠
	449♠	450♠	451♠	452♠	453♠	454♠	455	

Peterborough (Lincoln Road) - Viscount - National Express ♠ -

Outstations: Browland; March; Oundle; Stamford; Sutton and Wisbech.

Bristol VR	770	772	773	775	777	779	780	781
	782	784	788	789	790	791		
Olympian	481	482	506	507	508	509	510	511
	523	524	525	536	537	538	539	540
	546	547	548	549	550	557	558	559
	561	562	568	569	570	580	581	582
	583	584	585	586				
Leyland Lynx	311	312						
Volvo B6	320	321						
Iveco	954	955	956	957				
MetroRider	981	982	983	985	986	987	988	989
Mercedes-Benz	200	201	202	203	204			
Volvo B10M	432♠	433♠	434♠	435♠	456			

Temporarily unallocated:

Leyland Lynx	310	
Iveco	951	953
Volvo coach	425	

The East Anglia Bus Handbook

STEPHENSON'S COACHES
SUPER SIMIEN COACHES

Stephenson's Coaches Ltd, Riverside Industrial Estate, South Street, Rochford, Essex, SS

Depots:- South Street and 1 Cottis Yard, Purdeys Way, Rochford.

A741TTW	Daimler CRL6/Ensign JP1	PRV/Ensign Enterprise(84)	CH43/22C	1973	Ex Mercury, Hoo, 1995
HIL4346	Leyland Atlantean AN68/2R	East Lancs EL2000 (1992)	B46F	1974	Ex Catch A Bus, East Boldon, 1995
HIL4349	Leyland Atlantean AN68/2R	East Lancs EL2000 (1992)	B46F	1974	Ex Catch A Bus, East Boldon, 1995
GBF79N	Bristol VRT/SL2/6G	Eastern Coach Works	H43/31F	1974	Ex Happy Days, Woodseaves, 1996
OJD195R	Leyland Fleetline FE30ALR	MCW	H45/32F	1976	Ex Eastern Counties, 1998
MBZ7140	Bristol VRT/SL3/501	Eastern Coach Works	O43/31F	1976	Ex Stagecoach Bluebird, 1994
TNH870R	Bristol VRT/SL3/6LXB	Eastern Coach Works	H43/31F	1977	Ex United Counies, 1998
RHT505S	Bristol VRT/SL3/6LXB	Eastern Coach Works	H43/27F	1978	Ex Overseas Development, SW1,1995
URF666S	Bristol VRT/SL3/501	Eastern Coach Works	H43/31F	1978	Ex JBS, Bedford, 1996
VHB672S	Bristol VRT/SL3/501	Eastern Coach Works	H43/31F	1978	Ex JBS, Bedford, 1996
VHB677S	Bristol VRT/SL3/501	Eastern Coach Works	CO43/31F	1978	Ex Northern Bus, Anston, 1998
VHB678S	Bristol VRT/SL3/501	Eastern Coach Works	CO43/31F	1978	Ex Northern Bus, Anston, 1998
OJI1681	Ford R1114	Plaxton Supreme III	C53F	1978	Ex Davies, Reddish, 1996
GSC855T	Leyland Fleetline FE30AGR	Eastern Coach Works	H43/32F	1978	Ex Eastern Counties, 1998
BKE839T	Bristol VRT/SL3/6LXB	Eastern Coach Works	H43/31F	1978	Ex Maidstone & District, 1997
AAP648T	Bristol VRT/SL3/6LXB	Eastern Coach Works	H43/31F	1978	Ex Stagecoach South (SC), 1996
FRP911T	Bristol VRT/SL3/6LXB	Eastern Coach Works	H43/31F	1979	Ex United Counties, 1998
AJD26T	Bedford YMT	Plaxton Supreme III	C41F	1979	Ex Catteralls, Southam, 1996
YAE518V	Bristol LH6L	Eastern Coach Works	B43F	1979	Ex Teeside, 1996
OSG55V	Leyland Fleetline FE30AGR	Eastern Coach Works	H43/32F	1979	Ex Eastern Counties, 1998
OSG67V	Leyland Fleetline FE30AGR	Eastern Coach Works	H43/32F	1979	Ex Eastern Counties, 1998
JGV321V	Bedford YMT	Plaxton Supreme IV	C53F	1980	Ex Super Simien, Canvey, 1997
MFA719V	Bristol VRT/SL3/501	Eastern Coach Works	DPH39/28F	1980	Ex Kent Coach Tours, Ashford,1997
GGM109W	Bristol VRT/SL3/6LXB	Eastern Coach Works	H43/31F	1980	Ex Walls, Sharston, 1996
NEH724W	Bristol VRT/SL3/501	Eastern Coach Works	DPH39/28F	1980	Ex Watson, Sefton, 1996

During the summer of 1997 Stephensons used open-top VRT MBZ7140 in the Southend area. The vehicle wears a livery of cream relieved by green lettering. It is seen on a clear day at Leigh-on-Sea. Stephensons are also dealers and many vehicles may be noted that are not included in the operational fleet. *Richard Godfrey*

Stephensons regularly operate rail-replacement contracts, particularly during weekend engineering work. Daimler Fleetline JTD393P was photographed at Loughton Underground station while operating an all-stations journey while London Underground's Central Line was out of action. This vehicle is one of the long-wheelbase variants new to Southend and is fitted with a Northern Counties low-height body. It left the fleet as the book went to press. *Richard Godfrey*

NEH726W	Bristol VRT/SL3/501	Eastern Coach Works	DPH39/28F	1980	Ex Watson, Sefton, 1997
TWR465W	Bristol VRT/SL3/6LXB	Eastern Coach Works	H43/31F	1981	Ex London & Country, 1998
OJI2830	Bova EL26/581	Bova Europa	C49FT	1981	Ex Super Simien, Canvey, 1997
Q287HNR	Leyland Leopard PSU3E/4R	Willowbrook Crusader (19..)	C53F	1982	Ex Boulton, Eastington, 1996
BKR835Y	Leyland Leopard PSU3G/4R	Eastern Coach Works B51	C49F	1982	Ex Northern Bus, Anston, 1996
GKE441Y	Leyland Olympian ONTL11/2R	Eastern Coach Works	CH45/28F	1983	Ex Maidstone & District, 1997
TJI4824	Leyland Tiger TRCTL11/3R	Plaxton Paramount 3500	C50F	1983	Ex The Bee Line, 1997
TJI4821	Leyland Tiger TRCTL11/3R	Plaxton Paramount 3500	C50F	1983	Ex The Bee Line, 1997
HJI3932	Leyland Olympian ONTL11/2RSp	Eastern Coach Works	CH45/28F	1983	Ex Northern Bus, Anston, 1998
HSB312Y	Leyland Olympian ONTL11/2R	Eastern Coach Works	CH45/28F	1983	Ex ABC, Ainsdale, 1997
B694BPU	Leyland Olympian ONTL11/2R	Eastern Coach Works	CH45/28F	1985	Ex MTL (Liverbus), 1997
C485BHY	Mercedes-Benz L608D	Reeve Burgess	B20F	1985	Ex Essex Buses (Eastern National), 1998
C204HJN	Mercedes-Benz L608D	Reeve Burgess	B20F	1985	Ex Essex Buses (Eastern National), 1998
C212HJN	Mercedes-Benz L608D	Reeve Burgess	B20F	1985	Ex Essex Buses (Eastern National), 1997
C756BEX	Mercedes-Benz L608D	Reeve Burgess	B20F	1986	Ex Eastern Counties, 1997
C253SPC	Leyland Tiger TRCTL11/3RH	Duple 320	C53F	1986	Ex Arriva East Herts & Essex, 1998
C263SPC	Leyland Tiger TRCTL11/3RH	Duple 320	C53F	1986	Ex Arriva East Herts & Essex, 1998
D212PPU	Mercedes-Benz L608D	Reeve Burgess	B20F	1986	Ex Essex Buses (Eastern National), 1997
D225PPU	Mercedes-Benz L608D	Reeve Burgess	B20F	1986	Ex Essex Buses (Thamesway), 1997
D540FAE	Mercedes-Benz L608D	Dormobile	B20F	1986	Ex Eastern Counties, 1997
D547FAE	Mercedes-Benz L608D	Dormobile	B20F	1986	Ex First Eastern Counties, 1998
OIB5401	Leyland Royal Tiger RTC	Leyland Doyen	C48FT	1987	Ex Rossendale, 1993
OIB5402	Leyland Royal Tiger RTC	Leyland Doyen	C53F	1987	Ex Rossendale, 1993
E700EHJ	Iveco Daily 49.10	Dormobile Routemaker	DP25F	1988	Ex Super Simien, Canvey, 1997

Previous registrations:-

A741TTW	MLK590L
HSB312Y	YPJ503Y, 341AYF, HSB312Y, ABC75Y
HIL4346	SUG561M
HIL4349	SUG595M
HJI3932	YPJ502Y
MBZ7140	OTO151R
OIB5401	D892PNB

OIB5402	D387VAO
OJI1681	ENP444S
OJI2830	PNT605X, 3572NT, SUJ239X
Q287HNR	50AC02
TJI4821	YPJ203Y
TJI4824	YPJ206Y

Livery:- White, green and orange (Stephenson's); white, red and blue (Super Simien); Cream and green (Summertime Special) MBZ7140.

The East Anglia Bus Handbook

STORT VALLEY   TRAVELLERS

Stort Valley (Stansted) Ltd, Unit 1 Stort Hill Industrial Estate, Stansted, Essex

JPL185K	Leyland Atlantean PDR1A/1spl	Park Royal	H43/29D	1972	Ex Buzz, Harlow, 1997
SIB7359	Leyland Leopard PSU3C/4R	Duple Dominant II	C53F	1976	ExNorman Hayes, Connah's Quay, 1994
UWV860R	Bedford YMT	Plaxton Supreme III Express	C53F	1977	Ex Jason, St Mary Cray, 1993
THX285S	Leyland Fleetline FE30ALR	MCW	H44/24D	1977	Ex Jason, St Mary Cray, 1993
OWV819	Volvo B10M-61	Plaxton Paramount 3200 III	C53F	1988	Ex Hills, Hersham, 1997
J4TCC	Kässbohrer Setra S215HD	Kässbohrer Tornado	C47FT	1992	Ex Travellers, Hounslow, 1997
N60TCC	Toyota Coaster HZB50R	Caetano Optimo III	C18F	1995	Ex Travellers, Hounslow, 1997
N70TCC	Toyota Coaster HZB50R	Caetano Optimo III	C18F	1995	Ex Travellers, Hounslow, 1997
N80TCC	Toyota Coaster HZB50R	Caetano Optimo III	C18F	1995	Ex Travellers, Hounslow, 1997
N600TCC	Volvo B10M-62	Plaxton Premiére 350	C48F	1996	Ex Travellers, Hounslow, 1997
N20TCC	Dennis Javelin 12SDA2159	Plaxton Premiére 350	C53F	1996	Ex Travellers, Hounslow, 1997
LRU822	Dennis Javelin 12SDA2155	Plaxton Premiére 320	C49FT	1996	
P421JDT	Dennis Javelin 12SDA2155	Plaxton Premiére 320	C51F	1996	
P422JDT	Dennis Javelin 12SDA2155	Plaxton Premiére 320	C49FT	1996	
P423JDT	Dennis Javelin 12SDA2155	Plaxton Premiére 320	C49FT	1996	
P424JDT	Dennis Javelin 12SDA2155	Plaxton Premiére 320	C49FT	1996	
P425JDT	Dennis Javelin 12SDA2155	Plaxton Premiére 320	C53F	1996	
P426JDT	Dennis Javelin 12SDA2155	Plaxton Premiére 320	C53F	1996	
P427JDT	Dennis Javelin 12SDA2155	Plaxton Premiére 320	C53F	1996	
P428JDT	Dennis Javelin 12SDA2155	Plaxton Premiére 320	C49FT	1996	
P22TCC	Dennis Javelin	Plaxton Premiére 350	C53F	1997	Ex Travellers, Hounslow, 1997
P55TCC	Dennis Javelin	Plaxton Premiére 350	C53F	1997	Ex Travellers, Hounslow, 1997
P88TCC	Dennis Javelin	Plaxton Premiére 350	C53F	1997	Ex Travellers, Hounslow, 1997
P99TCC	Dennis Javelin	Plaxton Premiére 350	C53F	1997	Ex Travellers, Hounslow, 1997
P333TCC	Dennis Javelin	Plaxton Premiére 350	C53F	1997	Ex Travellers, Hounslow, 1997
P700TCC	Kässbohrer Setra S250	Kässbohrer Special	C48FT	1997	Ex Travellers, Hounslow, 1997
P800TCC	Kässbohrer Setra S250	Kässbohrer Special	C48FT	1997	Ex Travellers, Hounslow, 1997
R179TKU	Dennis Javelin	Plaxton Premiére 350	C53F	1997	
R129XWF	Dennis Javelin	Plaxton Premiére 350	C53F	1998	

Previous registrations:-

LRU822	N959DWJ		SIB7359	NNW112P, YIA258
OWV819	E307OMG		UWV860R	RGS88R, LRU822

Livery:- White, green and grey (Story Valley), silver, red, white and blue (Travellers).

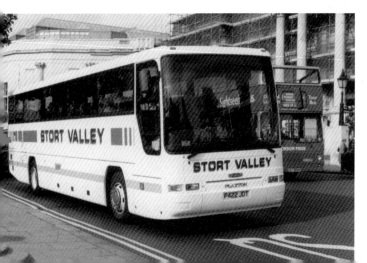

Until 1996 Stort Valley used a mix of coach types for their London Commuter services but these were displaced by Dennis Javelins with Plaxton bodywork. In late 1997, Stort Valley acquired the Hounslow-based Travellers operation inheriting thirteen coaches which have moved into the newly-opened base at Stanstead.
Paul Stockwell

SUFFOLK CC EDUCATION

Suffolk County Council Education Transport Trading Organisation, County Hall, Ipswich, Suffolk, IP4 1LJ

81	J81KBD	Mercedes-Benz 811D	Made-to-Measure	C24FL	1991	
101	H101GPV	Ford Transit VE6	Williams Deansgate	M14	1991	
102	H102GPV	Ford Transit VE6	Williams Deansgate	M14	1991	
131	H131EGV	Leyland-DAF 400	Leyland-DAF	M16	1991	
132	H132EGV	Leyland-DAF 400	Leyland-DAF	M16	1991	
133	H133EGV	Leyland-DAF 400	Leyland-DAF	M16	1991	
134	K134UDX	Leyland-DAF 400	Leyland-DAF	M16	1993	
135	K135UDX	Leyland-DAF 400	Leyland-DAF	M16	1993	
136	M136EBJ	LDV 400	Minibus Options	M16	1994	
137	M137EBJ	LDV 400	Minibus Options	M16	1994	
147	D266CBJ	Freight-Rover Sherpa	Freight-Rover	M16	1987	
148	D267CBJ	Freight-Rover Sherpa	Freight-Rover	M16	1987	
149	E465HDX	Freight-Rover Sherpa	Freight-Rover	M16	1988	
150	E466HDX	Freight-Rover Sherpa	Freight-Rover	M16L	1988	
157	D908MVU	Freight-Rover Sherpa	Dixon Lomas	M16L	1987	Ex High Suffolk, Bedfield, 1992
161	K161RGV	Leyland-DAF 400	....	M16L	1992	
162	L162XDX	Leyland-DAF 400	Minibus Options	M16L	1993	
163	L163XDX	Leyland-DAF 400	Minibus Options	M16L	1993	
164	L164XDX	Leyland-DAF 400	Minibus Options	M16L	1993	
165	L165XDX	Leyland-DAF 400	Minibus Options	M16L	1993	
166	M166EBJ	LDV 400	Minibus Options	M7L	1994	
167	N167HGV	LDV 400	Minibus Options	M16	1995	
168	N168HGV	LDV 400	Minibus Options	M16	1995	
169	N169HGV	LDV 400	Minibus Options	M12L	1995	
170	N170HGV	LDV 400	Minibus Options	M12L	1995	
171	N21LDX	LDV 400	Minibus Options	M12L	1996	
182	G782HVG	Renault Master T35	Coachwork-Walker	M14	1989	
183	G746HVG	Renault Master T35	Coachwork-Walker	M14	1989	
212	RGV690W	Bedford YMT	Duple Dominant II	C53F	1981	
213	RGV691W	Bedford YMT	Duple Dominant II	C53F	1981	
214	RGV692W	Bedford YMT	Duple Dominant II	C53F	1981	
215	RGV693W	Bedford YMT	Duple Dominant II	C53F	1981	
216	A620YJR	Bedford YMT	Duple Dominant IV Express	C53F	1983	Ex Gypsey Queen, Langley Park, 1987
231	YUT638Y	Bedford YNT	Plaxton Paramount 3200	C53F	1982	Ex Wainfleet, Nuneaton, 1987
232	C304NHD	Bedford YNT	Plaxton Paramount 3200 II	C53F	1986	Ex Brown, S. Kirkby, 1988
241	E501EFG	Dennis Javelin 12SDA1913	Duple 320	C53FT	1988	Ex Brighton & Hove, 1996
242	E502EFG	Dennis Javelin 12SDA1913	Duple 320	C53DTL	1988	Ex Brighton & Hove, 1996
251	VPR384X	DAF MB200DKTL600	Plaxton Supreme V	C53F	1982	Ex Kings, Stanway, 1989
252	SUH170Y	DAF MB200DKFL600	Plaxton Paramount 3200	C57F	1983	Ex Galloway, Harthill, 1992
261	B588NJF	DAF SB2300DHS585	Plaxton Paramount 3200	C53FL	1985	Ex Lewis, Pailton, 1990
262	C629HOK	DAF SB2300DHS585	Plaxton Paramount 3200 II	C53F	1985	Ex Meadway, Birmingham, 1992
265	A565WAV	DAF SB2300DHS585	Plaxton Paramount 3500	C53F	1984	Ex Relaince, Lutton, 1995
271	E111WAW	DAF SB2305DHDT585	Plaxton Paramount 3200 III	C57F	1987	Ex Elcock Reisen, Telford, 1993
272	E222WAW	DAF SB2305DHDT585	Plaxton Paramount 3200 III	C57F	1987	Ex Elcock Reisen, Telford, 1993
287	BRT787Y	Ford R1114	Duple Dominant IV	C53F	1983	
291	C151SRT	Ford R1115	Plaxton Paramount 3200 II	C53F	1985	
292	C152SRT	Ford R1115	Plaxton Paramount 3200 II	C53F	1985	
301	J301KDX	Ford Transit VE6	Williams Deansgate	M14L	1992	
302	J302KDX	Ford Transit VE6	Williams Deansgate	M14L	1992	
303	J303KDX	Ford Transit VE6	Williams Deansgate	M14L	1992	
331	H331FPV	Leyland-DAF 400	Leyland-DAF	M16	1991	
332	K332UDX	Leyland-DAF 400	Leyland-DAF	M16	1993	
333	L933YPV	Leyland-DAF 400	Leyland-DAF	M16	1994	
334	M334GGV	LDV 400	Minibus Options	M16	1996	
335	N347EKK	Ford Transit VE6	Ford	M14	1996	
343	E947FRT	Freight-Rover Sherpa	Steedrive	M16	1988	
362	K962UGV	Leyland-DAF 400	Minibus Options	M16	1993	
363	L363XDX	Leyland-DAF 400	Leyland-DAF	M16L	1994	
370	P143NDX	LDV Convoy	Minibus Options	M16	1996	
383	G783HVG	Renault Master T35	Coachwork-Walker	M16L	1989	

...	F871RFP	Dennis Javelin 12SDA1907	Duple 320	C53F	1989	Ex Pemico, Bermondsey, 1997
...	F872RFP	Dennis Javelin 12SDA1907	Duple 320	C53F	1989	Ex Pemico, Bermondsey, 1997
...	F874RFP	Dennis Javelin 12SDA1907	Duple 320	C53F	1989	Ex Pemico, Bermondsey, 1997
...	H31CFR	DAF SB2305DHTD585	Duple 340	C57F	1991	Ex Cass, Greasby, 1997
...	P211NDX	LDV Convoy	Minibus Options	M16	1996	
...	P212NDX	LDV Convoy	Minibus Options	M16	1996	

Previous registration:-
A565WAV   A262BTY, 8098NK

Livery:- Blue and white.

Depots:- Rougham Industrial Estate, Bury St Edmunds; Constantine Road Ipswich; Rotterdam Road Lowestoft plus various schools throughout the county.

Suffolk County Council provide many of their school journeys employing a fleet which the Education Department have forged into a commercial operation. The fleet is a mix of full-size coaches and minibuses. Seen here are two Plaxton Paramount-bodied DAF coaches. E222WAW, which was latterly with the Elcock Reisen fleet in Telford, is a 3200 example, and A565WAV, carries the higher 3500 body.
Colin Lloyd

SUPREME

Abridge Enterprises Ltd, 303 London Road, Hadleigh, Essex, SS7 2BN

VGD779R	Leyland Atlantean AN68A/1R	Roe	H43/33F	1975	Ex Graham, Paisley, 1982
OKW504R	Leyland Fleetline FE30AGR	MCW	H45/29F	1977	Ex Carterton Coaches, 1994
SDA620S	Leyland Fleetline FE30AGR	Park Royal	H43/33F	1977	Ex Carterton Coaches, 1994
BFR304R	Leyland Atlantean AN68A/1R	East Lancashire	H50/36F	1977	Ex Sheffield Omnibus, 1994
URF673S	Bristol VRT/SL3/501	Eastern Coach Works	H43/31F	1978	Ex Swallow, Rainham, 1994
BTU375S	Bristol VRT/SL3/501	Eastern Coach Works	H43/31F	1978	Ex Swallow, Rainham, 1994
PTD671S	Leyland National 11351A/1R		DP49F	1978	Ex White's Coaches, Heathfield, 1995
XRF24S	Leyland Atlantean AN68A/1R	East Lancashire	H45/27F	1978	Ex Sheffield Omnibus, 1994
OEM787S	Leyland Atlantean AN68A/1R	MCW	H43/32F	1978	Ex Sheffield Omnibus, 1994
CWU139T	Leyland Fleetline FE30AGR	Roe	H43/33F	1978	Ex Yorkshire Rider, 1995
ULS662T	Leyland Fleetline FE30AGR	Eastern Coach Works	H43/32F	1979	Ex Brentwood Coaches, 1997
GHB85W	Bristol VRT/SL3/6LXB	East Lancashire	H44/32F	1981	Ex Constable, Long Melford, 1995
HSK836	Volvo B10M-61	Plaxton P' 3500 III(1990)	C53F	1983	Ex The Kings Ferry, 1989
A319GLV	Leyland Olympian ONTL11/1R	Alexander RH	DPH40/23F	1983	Ex MTL (Merseybus), 1997
A320GLV	Leyland Olympian ONTL11/1R	Alexander RH	DPH40/23F	1983	Ex MTL (Merseybus), 1997
HSK845	Scania K113CRB	Jonckheere Deauville P599	C51FT	1989	Ex Swallow, Rainham, 1992
HSK844	Volvo B10M-46	Jonckheere Deauville P599	C37FT	1989	
HSK892	MAN 16.290	Jonckheere Deauville P599	C51FT	1990	Ex Dunn-Line, Nottingham, 1993
HSK857	LAG E180Z	LAG EOS 100	C53FT	1990	
HSK858	LAG E180Z	LAG EOS 100	C53FT	1990	
HSK860	LAG E180Z	LAG EOS 100	C53FT	1990	
HSK855	MAN 16.290	Jonckheere Deauville P599	C51FT	1990	
HSK856	MAN 16.290	Jonckheere Deauville P599	C51FT	1990	
HSK859	LAG E180Z	LAG EOS 100	C53FT	1990	
H10SUP	MAN 16.290	Jonckheere Deauville P599	C51FT	1991	
J2SUP	EOS E180Z	EOS 90	C53FT	1992	
J3SUP	EOS E180Z	EOS 90	C53FT	1992	
K4SUP	MAN 16.290	Jonckheere Deauville P599	C51FT	1993	
K5SUP	MAN 16.290	Jonckheere Deauville P599	C51FT	1993	
K6SUP	MAN 16.290	Jonckheere Deauville P599	C51FT	1993	
K707RNR	Volvo B10M-60	Caetano Algarve II	C49FT	1993	Ex Chartercoach, Dovercourt, 1994
K708PNR	Volvo B10M-60	Caetano Algarve II	C49FT	1993	Ex Chartercoach, Dovercourt, 1994
K459PNR	Toyota Coaster HDB30R	Caetano Optimo II	C18F	1993	Ex Chartercoach, Dovercourt, 1994
L67YJF	Toyota Hiace	Caetano	M11	1993	
L507KDA	Neoplan N122/3	Neoplan Skyliner	CH57/22CT	1994	Ex Harry Shaw, Coventry, 1997
L100SUP	Volvo B9M	Berkhof Excellence 2000	C37F	1994	
L200SUP	Scania K113CRB	Berkhof Excellence 2000	C51FT	1994	
L300SUP	Volvo B9M	Berkhof Excellence 2000	C37FT	1994	
M256TAK	Scania K113TRB	Irizar Century 12.37	C49FT	1995	
M257TAK	Scania K113TRB	Irizar Century 12.37	C49FT	1995	
M258TAK	Scania K113TRB	Irizar Century 12.37	C49FT	1995	
M259TAK	Scania K113TRB	Irizar Century 12.37	C49FT	1995	
M953UHK	LDV 400	LDV	M16	1995	
M24THJ	Volkswagen Transporter	Volkswagen	M6	1995	
N11RED	Neoplan N122/3	Neoplan Skyliner	CH53/20DT	1995	Ex Impact, Carlisle, 1997
N851DKU	Scania K113TRB	Irizar Century 12.37	C49FT	1996	
N852DKU	Scania K113TRB	Irizar Century 12.37	C49FT	1996	
N853DKU	Scania K113TRB	Irizar Century 12.37	C49FT	1996	
N854DKU	Scania K113TRB	Irizar Century 12.37	C49FT	1996	
N854DKU	Scania K113TRB	Irizar Century 12.37	C49FT	1996	
N680AHL	Scania K113TRB	Irizar Century 12.37	C51FT	1996	Ex A&R International, Bedfont, 1998
R290TLU	Neoplan N116	Neoplan Cityliner	C49FT	1998	

Previous registrations:-

HSK836	MRP840Y	HSK856	G370RNH	HSK860	G442NVV
HSK844	F919YNV	HSK857	G439NVV	HSK892	G169RBD
HSK845	F909YNV	HSK858	G438NVV	L507KDA	L41VRW, KOV2
HSK855	G369RNH	HSK859	G441NVV		

Opposite:- **LAG EOS integrally constructed coaches were available in several guises. LAG's independence ceased soon after this vehicle was built when Van Hool acquired the group and the vehicle is simply known as EOS. HSK860 circumnavigates Lambeth Bridge roundabout. H10SUP is now carried on this attractive Jonckheere Deauville. The vehicle is seen on a Supreme Holidays tour. Depots are at Stock Rd, Prittlewell and Refinery Rd, Parkstone.** *Colin Lloyd/Paul Stockwell.*

THORNS OF RAYLEIGH / APT TRAVEL

P A & A G Thorn, Unit 27 Rawreth Ind Est, Rawreth Lane, Rayleigh, Essex, SS6 9RL

DHJ255B	Bedford J2SZ10	Plaxton Embassy	C20F	1964	Ex Crown Bingo, Rayleigh, 1993
PTT92R	Bristol VRT/SL3/6LXB	Eastern Coach Works	H43/31F	1976	Ex Stagecoach Cambus, 1997
LHG445T	Bristol VRT/SL3/501	Eastern Coach Works	H43/31F	1979	Ex Ribble, 1993
UJI2347	DAF MB200DKL600	Plaxton Supreme IV	C57F	1979	Ex Bagust, Chislehurst, 1997
71FXO	Volvo B58-61	Plaxton Supreme IV	C57F	1980	Ex BJS, Great Wakering, 1995
JNJ510V	Bedford YMT	Plaxton Supreme IV	C53F	1980	Ex BJS, Great Wakering, 1996
YFC736	Bedford YNT	Duple Dominant	C53F	1981	Ex Mason, Perivale, 1997
BFV221Y	Leyland Atlantean AN68D/2R	East Lancashire	DPH45/32F	1983	Ex Ribble, 1997
HIL8435	Volvo B10M-61	Plaxton Paramount 3500	C51F	1984	Ex Libberton Travel, Edinburgh, 1998
B592XWW	Leyland Tiger TRCTL11/3RH	Plaxton Paramount 3200 II	C50FT	1985	Ex Stott, Milnsbridge, 1997
LIL2184	Kässbohrer Setra S215HD	Kässbohrer Tornado	C49FT	1985	Ex Watson Enterprises, Corringham, 1997
HIL7591	Volvo B10M-61	Plaxton Paramount 3500 III	C49FT	1987	Ex Libberton Travel, 1998
A12APT	DAF MB230LT615	Plaxton Paramount 3500 III	C53FT	1988	Ex Happy Days, Woodseaves, 1990
APT42S	Neoplan N122/3	Neoplan Skyliner	CH57/20CT	1988	Ex Selwyn, Runcorn, 1995
G300XAC	Neoplan N122/3	Neoplan Skyliner	CH57/20CT	1990	Ex Ebdon, Sidcup, 1996
M618YEH	Ford Transit	Ford	M8	1995	Ex private owner, 1997
N5APT	Dennis Javelin 12SDA2166	Neoplan Transliner	C50FT	1996	

Previous registrations:-

71FXO	EPC893V	HIL8435	A721BUX, SIJ4712, A922DUY
827APT	-	HIL7591	D270XRG
A12APT	E337EVH, APT42S	JNJ510V	BBB540V, WSV501
APT42S	E475YWJ, SEL23, E75DMA	LIL2184	7042EL
B592XWW	B103LJU, FIL3451, B369RJU, 82EV	UJI2347	KUR225V
DHJ255B	APT416B	YFC736	TGS924W

Livery:-Blue and grey or white with pink, lilac and maroon.

TOWLER COACHES

A C Towler, Church Road, Emneth, Norfolk, PE14 8AA

EJD510	Bedford SB	Duple	C33F	1952	Ex Grange, Westbury, 1969
RHS861W	Leyland Leopard PSU3/4R	Plaxton Supreme IV (1980)	C48F	1967	Ex Chalkwell, Sittingbourne, 1997
GNG710N	Bristol VRT/SL2/6G	Eastern Coach Works	H43/31F	1975	Ex The Bee Line, 1993
XDV607S	Bristol VRT/SL3/6LXB	Eastern Coach Works	H43/31F	1978	Ex Stagecoach Cambus, 1997
LVL806V	Bristol VRT/SL3/6LXB	Eastern Coach Works	H43/31F	1980	Ex RoadCar, 1997
RSE156W	Bedford YMT	Duple Dominant IV	C53F	1981	Ex Hawkes, Waunarlwydd, 1994
NPD690W	Bedford YNT	Plaxton Supreme IV	C53F	1981	Ex Safeguard, Guildford, 1986
PAY7W	Bedford YNT	Duple Dominant IV	C53F	1981	Ex Kinch, Mountsorrell, 1984
UFX629X	Bristol LHS6L	Plaxton Supreme V	C35F	1982	Ex Derby, 1987
TPM616X	Bedford YNT	Plaxton Supreme VI	C53F	1982	Ex Gastonia, Cranleigh, 1985
D217OOJ	Fright-Rover Sherpa	Carlyle	B18F	1987	Ex The Bee Line, 1992
E905LVE	Volkeswagen LT55	Optare City Pacer	B25F	1987	Ex Cambus, 1993
A16ATC	DAF SB2305DHTD585	Duple 320	C53F	1988	Ex Selwyn Hughes, Llanfair Caereinion, 1995
131HUO	Leyland Tiger TRCL10/3ARZM	Jonckheere Jubilee P50	C51FT	1988	Ex Gillespie, Kelty, 1992

Previous registrations:-

131HUO	E686NNH	EJD510	From new
A16ATC	E594LVH	RHS861W	JUA301E

Livery:- Cream, green and orange.

TRAVEL THE WRIGHT WAY

K C & B S Wright, 242, London Road, Brandon, Suffolk, IP27 0LY

XDP951T	Bedford YMT	Plaxton Supreme III	C53F	1978	Ex Buckland, Hurst, 1988
B88FVL	Bedford YNT	Plaxton Paramount 3200 II	C53F	1985	Ex Holloway, Scunthorpe, 1992
C116AFX	Bedford Venturer YNV	Plaxton Paramount 3200 II	C53F	1986	Ex Mitcham Belle, Mitcham, 1986
412CRU	Bedford YNT	Plaxton Paramount 3200 III	C53F	1987	Ex Johnson, Lough, 1990
D271HFX	Bedford Venturer YNV	Plaxton Paramount 3200 III	C53F	1987	Ex Ruffle, Castle Hedingham, 1996

Previous registration:-

412CRU   From new

Livery:- White, blue and red.

Thorns of Rayleigh trade as **APT Travel** and have acquired a number of appropriate index marks. Representing the fleet is Van Hool-bodied DAF SB3000 827APT. The vehicle, which has recently been sold, is seen entering Aldwych from Waterloo Bridge, in central London. *Colin Lloyd*

TRAVELRICH

R D & D F F Osborne, 51 Peter Bruff Avenue, Clacton-on-Sea, Essex, CO16 8UE

Depot:- Brunel Road, Gorse Industrial Estate, Clacton.

565EXV	Neoplan N116/3	Neoplan Cityliner	C48FT	1990	Ex The Kings Ferry, 1997
5765OZ	Neoplan N116/3	Neoplan Cityliner	C48FT	1992	Ex Dave Parry, Cheslyn Hay, 1996
L977MWB	Neoplan N116/3	Neoplan Cityliner	C48FT	1994	Ex Dave Parry, Cheslyn Hay, 1997

Previous registrations:-

565EXV	G338KWE, A14KFC, G382WKE, XIB1420
5765OZ	J21XHE

Livery:- Silver, blue and red.

All three vehicles in the Travelrich of Clacton fleet are Aüwaerter Neoplan N116 Cityliners in tri-axle form. Some European countries, including Britain, have lower maximum axle weight limits than elsewhere, therefore the use of tri-axle coaches spreads the axle weight allowing greater flexibility in their use. 5765OZ was taking a rest at South Mimms services when photographed in April 1997. From January 1999 the UK opt-out from the existing rules is expected to cease and 18-ton vehicles will be permitted when their journey covers more than one European country. *Colin Lloyd*

UPWELL & DISTRICT COACHES

A & D Hircock, Magnolia House, 69 School Road, Upwell,
Wisbech, Cambridgeshire, PE14 9EU

18	THX617M	AEC Reliance 6U3ZR	Duple Dominant	C49F	1973	Ex London Country, 1982
19	VMJ967S	AEC Reliance 6U3ZR	Plaxton Supreme III Express	C53F	1977	Ex Lewis, Greenwich, 1986
20	APM108T	AEC Reliance 6U2R	Plaxton Supreme IV Express	C53F	1979	Ex Embling, Guyhirn, 1988
21	EBM448T	AEC Reliance 6U3ZR	Plaxton Supreme IV Express	C57F	1979	Ex Andrew, Spalding, 1993
22	824CDM	Leyland Tiger TRCTL11/2R	Plaxton Paramount 3500	C48FT	1983	Ex Parish, Hawarden, 1991
23	YSU917	AEC Reliance 6U3ZR	Plaxton Viewmaster IV	C57F	1979	Ex Collins, Cliffe, 1995

Previous registrations:-

824CDM	KBM533Y		YSU917	YEW380T

Livery:- Blue, red and white.

The AEC Reliance continues in use with Upwell & District Coaches while the model is fast disappearing elsewhere. From an order for 150 with both Plaxton and Duple bodywork introduced by Green Line, Upwell's 20, APM108T is one of three with a Plaxton Supreme IV Express bodywork while number 18 is understood to be the sole example from the Duple-bodied batch still in PCV service. *Trevor Brookes*

VEAZEY

Veazey Coaches Ltd, Winwick Garage, Winwick, Cambridgeshire, PE17 5PX

MHP3V	Bedford YMT (Cummins)	Plaxton Supreme IV	C53F	1980	Ex Shaw, Bedworth, 1983
RLG428V	Bristol VRT/SL3/501	Eastern Coach Works	H43/31F	1980	Ex Partridge, Hadleigh, 1996
B733GWJ	Neoplan N122/3	Neoplan Skyliner	CH../..DT	19..	Ex ?, 1997
C756FMC	Mercedes-Benz L608D	Reeve Burgess	C21F	1986	
E752JAY	Toyota Coaster HB31R	Caetano Optimo	C21F	1988	
F368MUT	Dennis Javelin 8.5SDL1903	Plaxton Paramount 3200 III	C35F	1988	
G863VAY	Dennis Javelin 12SDA1916	Plaxton Paramount 3200 III	C53F	1989	
M263TAK	Scania K113CRB	Van Hool Alizée	C53FT	1994	

Livery:- Cream, caramel and orange

VICEROY

Viceroy of Essex Ltd, 12 Bridge Street, Saffron Walden, Essex, CB10 1BU

NVG194L	Bedford YRT	Willowbrook 001	B57F	1973	Ex Sworder, Walkern, 1997
794SKO	Bedford YMT	Duple Dominant	B61F	1978	Ex Sworder, Walkern, 1996
FDU5T	Bedford YMT	Plaxton Supreme IV	C53F	1979	Ex Moore, Saffron Walden, 1996
ECW65W	Bedford YMT	Plaxton Supreme IV	C53F	1980	Ex Moore, Saffron Walden, 1996
597AXF	Bova EL26/581	Bova Europa	C47FT	1982	Ex Moore, Saffron Walden, 1996
C141KGJ	Bedford Venturer YNV	Duple Laser 2	C57F	1986	Ex Moore, Saffron Walden, 1996
G23HKY	Scania K93CRB	Duple 320	C51FT	1989	Ex Moore, Saffron Walden, 1996
G329SVV	Leyland Tiger TRCL10/3ARZM	Plaxton Paramount 3200 III	C53F	1990	Ex Wainfleet, Nuneaton, 1997
H29CFR	DAF SB2305DHTD585	Duple 320	C57F	1991	Ex Jack Jackson, Blackpool, 1996
J480NJU	Toyota Coaster HDB30R	Caetano Optimo II	C21F	1992	Ex Moore, Saffron Walden, 1996
N990EAR	Mercedes-Benz 709D	Plaxton Beaver	B23F	1996	Ex Moore, Saffron Walden, 1996

Previous registrations:-

597AXF	VWX370X	794SKO	AKK175T

Livery:- White and two tone blue.

The latest vehicle in the Veazey fleet is M263TAK, a Scania K113CRB with a Van Hool Alizée body. It is seen leading a line of coaches at Wembley coach park when Swansea played Northampton.
Colin Lloyd

WARDS COACHES

E P Ward, 35 Crestlands, Alresford, Colchester, Essex, CO7 8AX

Depot:- Morses Lane Industrial Estate, Brightlingsea.

XRJ206S	Leyland Atlantean AN68A/1R	Northern Counties	H43/32F	1978	Ex GM Buses North, 1997
DWU297T	Bristol VRT/SL3/6LXB	Eastern Coach Works	H43/31F	1978	Ex Beestons, Hadleigh, 1995
XKX640X	Ford R1114	Plaxton Supreme IV	C53F	1981	Ex Grahams, Kelvedon, 1997
D893NHE	Freight-Rover Sherpa	Coachcraft	M16	1987	Ex Mott, Horley, 1997
E253CPU	Ford Transit VE6	Ford	M11	1988	Ex private owner, 1994
866VNU	DAF SB2305DHS585	Jonckheere Deauville P599	C51FT	1989	Ex Lucketts, Fareham, 1995
J916PEA	Ford Transit VE6	Ford	M14	1992	Ex private owner, 1997

Previous registration:-

866VNU   G470JNH, SJI8131

Livery:- Orange, red and beige.

WEBBS COACHES

W H Webb, Pools Lane, Highwood, Chelmsford, Essex, CM1 3QL

VPF322S	Bedford YMT	Plaxton Supreme III	C53F	1978	Ex Kemp, Clacton, 1991
986PVW	Bedford YLQ	Duple Dominant II	C45F	1979	Ex Brentwood Coaches, 1986
EHE228V	Bedford YMT	Duple Dominant II	C53F	1980	Ex LB Travel, Kettering, 1996
UTR705	Leyland Leopard PSU5C/4R	Duple Dominant IV	C50F	1982	Ex Jackson, Bicknacre, 1994
TIW2801	Volvo B10M-61	Plaxton Paramount 3200	C53F	1983	Ex County, Brentwood, 1996
KHF131	Volvo B10M-61	Duple Dominant IV	C51FT	1983	Ex Hambridge, Nuneaton, 1995
NAG463A	Volvo B10M-61	Jonckheere Jubilee P599	C49FT	1984	Ex Travel Line, Abbots Langley, 1997

Previous Registrations:-

986PVW	AUJ730T	NAG463A	A333YDT	UTR705	SHD330X
KHF131	A298RSU	TIW2801	FUA392Y, 2899RU		

Livery:- Cream, red and yellow.

Viceroy's **597AXF** is a **Bova Europa**, a model which was imported into Britian with two depths of side window. Here the deeper version is seen. *T K Brookes*

WEST'S COACHES LTD

West's Coaches Ltd, 198/200 High Road, Woodford Green, Essex, IG8 9EF

Depot:- Monkhams Garage, Buckhurst Way, Buckhurst Hill.

KGA56Y	Bova EL26/581	Bova Europa	C53F	1982	Ex Henry Crawford, Neilston, 1987
A15BUS	Bova EL28/581	Duple Calypso	C53F	1982	Ex North Somerset, Nailsea, 1985
A14BUS	Bova EL28/581	Duple Calypso	C53F	1984	Ex Antler, Rugeley, 1988
A10BUS	Volvo B10M-60	Plaxton Paramount 3200 III	C53F	1987	Ex Andrews, Trudoxhill, 1995
A12BUS	DAF SB2305DHS585	Caetano Algarve	C53F	1989	Ex Traject, Halifax, 1991
A13BUS	TAZ D3200	TAZ Dubrava	C53F	1989	
A16BUS	Volvo B10M-60	Plaxton Paramount 3500 III	C53F	1989	Ex Fishwick, Leyland, 1992
A18BUS	Volvo B10M-60	Plaxton Paramount 3500 III	C55F	1989	Ex Essex Coachways, Bow, 1994
A19BUS	DAF SB3000DKV601	Caetano Algarve	C49FT	1989	Ex Ace, Mansfield, 1993
H20BUS	Volvo B10M-60	Plaxton Paramount 3500 III	C53F	1991	Ex Camden, Sevenoaks, 1997
A17BUS	DAF SB2305DHS585	Caetano Algarve	C49FT	1992	Ex Browne, East Grinstead, 1996

Previous registrations:-

A10BUS	D267HFX, XEL55S, D569KJT	A16BUS	F972HGE
A12BUS	F233RJX	A17BUS	J516LRY
A13BUS	F788TBC	A18BUS	F813TMD
A14BUS	B127DHL	A19BUS	G949VBC
A15BUS	A321HFP	H20BUS	H840AHS

Livery:- White red and blue

West's of Woodford Green are based close to the Greater London border, but within Essex. In 1997 the company sold all its local service network to County Bus and Coach, since when it has concentrated on coaching work. The company retained many of the private index plates that include the BUS letters. Pictured here is A18BUS, a Volvo B10M with Plaxton Paramount 3500 bodywork. *Colin Lloyd*

WEST ROW COACH SERVICES

B J & D J Taylor-Balls, The Garage, West Row, Mildenhall, Suffolk, IP28 3NP

Depot:- Stock Corner, Beck Row, Mildenhall.

LAH893A	AEC Reliance 2U3RA	Plaxton Elite III (1974)	C51F	1963	Ex Ward, Alresford, 1996
JGV335V	Bedford YMT	Plaxton Supreme IV	C53F	1979	Ex Morley, West Row, 1985
VFK661X	Ford R1114	Plaxton Supreme IV	C53F	1981	Ex Mackenzie, West Row, 1997
TND418X	DAF MB200DKTL600	Plaxton Supreme V	C51F	1982	Ex Mackenzie, West Row, 1989
JIL2014	DAF MB200DKFL600	Van Hool Alizée	C48FT	1983	Ex Moss, Sheffield, 1987

Previous registrations:-

JIL2014	YTV165Y	LAH893A	6544FN

Livery:- Red, white and black.

WHINCOP

P S Whincop, The Garage, Peasenhall, Saxmundham, Suffolk, IP17 2HJ

UUX356S	Ford R1114	Plaxton Supreme III	C49F	1978	Ex Salopia, Whitchurch, 1983
WAD640S	Ford R1114	Plaxton Supreme III Express	C53F	1978	Ex Soames, Otley, 1988
YEX128S	Ford R1114	Plaxton Supreme III	C53F	1978	Ex Norfolk, Gt. Yarmouth, 1988
TPJ302S	Ford R1114	Duple Dominant II	C53F	1978	Ex Heaney, Enfield, 1981
EGV101T	Ford R1114	Plaxton Supreme III	C53F	1979	Ex Mike Boggis' Travel, Kirton, 1996
JJU442V	Volvo B58-56	Plaxton Supreme IV	C53F	1980	Ex Osborne, Tollesbury, 1994
JJU443V	Volvo B58-56	Plaxton Supreme IV	C53F	1980	Ex Osborne, Tollesbury, 1994
HYX418W	Ford R1114	Duple Dominant II	C53F	1981	Ex Super Simien, Canvey, 1996
VJT601X	DAF SB2005DHU585	Plaxton Supreme IV	C53F	1982	Ex Sanders, Holt, 1990
BRT786Y	Ford R1114	Duple Dominant IV	C53F	1983	Ex Suffolk CC, 1997
BRT788Y	Ford R1114	Duple Dominant IV	C53F	1983	Ex Suffolk CC, 1997
BRT789Y	Ford R1114	Duple Dominant IV	C53F	1983	Ex Suffolk CC, 1997
J624REG	Ford Transit VE6	Ford	M8	1982	Ex private owner, 1997

Livery:- Green and cream.

GO WHIPPET

Whippet Coaches Ltd, Cambridge Road, Fenstanton, Huntingdon,
Cambridgeshire, PE18 9JB

LEW971P	Leyland Atlantean AN68/2R	Roe	H43/34F	1976	
KJD271P	Scania BR111DH	MCW Metropolitan	H45/32F	1976	Ex London Transport, 1984
WKH424S	Scania BR111DH	MCW Metropolitan	H44/30F	1977	Ex Camms, Nottingham, 1989
WKH426S	Scania BR111DH	MCW Metropolitan	O44/30F	1977	Ex Camms, Nottingham, 1989
EAV811V	Leyland Atlantean AN68A/2R	Northern Counties	H47/36F	1980	
EAV812V	Volvo B58-56	Duple Dominant	B63F	1980	
FCY290W	Bedford YMQ	Duple Dominant	B45F	1981	Ex Hedingham & District, 1992
FCY292W	Bedford YMQ	Duple Dominant	B45F	1981	Ex Hedingham & District, 1992
FCY293W	Bedford YMQ	Duple Dominant	B53F	1981	Ex Hedingham & District, 1992
GYE265W	Leyland Titan TNLXB2RR	Leyland	H44/32F	1981	Ex Westlink, 1996
RDS82W	Volvo B58-56	Duple Dominant	DP53F	1980	Ex Skills, Nottingham, 1981
KYN283X	Leyland Titan TNLXB2RR	Leyland	H44/30F	1981	Ex Merseybus, 1993
KYN296X	Leyland Titan TNLXB2RR	Leyland	H44/30F	1981	Ex Merseybus, 1993
KYN300X	Leyland Titan TNLXB2RR	Leyland	H44/32F	1981	Ex Stagecoach Oxford, 1997
KYV346X	Leyland Titan TNLXB2RR	Leyland	H44/32F	1981	Ex Westlink, 1996
KYV422X	Leyland Titan TNLXB2RR	Leyland	H44/32F	1982	Ex Worth's, Enstone, 1996
REG870X	Volvo B58-56	Duple Dominant	B63F	1981	
VAV161X	Volvo B10M-61	Plaxton Supreme VI Express	C57F	1982	
EEW113Y	DAF MB200DKFL600	Plaxton Paramount 3200 E	C57F	1983	
FEW224Y	DAF MB200DKFL600	Plaxton Paramount 3200 E	C57F	1983	
FEW225Y	DAF MB200DKFL600	Plaxton Paramount 3200 E	C57F	1983	
FEW226Y	DAF MB200DKFL600	Plaxton Paramount 3200 E	C57F	1983	
FEW227Y	DAF MB200DKFL600	Plaxton Paramount 3200 E	C53F	1983	
A807REW	DAF MB200DKFL600	Duple Caribbean	C55F	1984	
A861SUL	Leyland Titan TNLXB2RR	Leyland	H44/32F	1983	Ex Westlink, 1996
A872SUL	Leyland Titan TNLXB2RR	Leyland	H44/32F	1983	Ex Westlink, 1996
A911SYE	Leyland Titan TNLXB2RR	Leyland	H44/32F	1983	Ex Westlink, 1996
GIL2968	Volvo B10M-61	Plaxton Paramount 3200 II	C57F	1985	Ex Reliance, Gravesend, 1991
D850AAV	Leyland Atlantean AN68/2L	Willowbrook	H49/33F	1980	
E441ADV	Volvo Citybus B10M-50	Alexander RV	DPH47/35F	1988	Ex Filer, Ilfracombe, 1991
E176OEW	Volvo Citybus B10M-50	Alexander RV	DPH47/35F	1988	
F693PAY	Volvo B10M-61	Plaxton Paramount 3200 III	C53F	1989	
F694PAY	Volvo B10M-61	Plaxton Paramount 3500 III	C53F	1989	
G823UMU	Volvo Citybus B10M-50	Northern Counties	DPH45/35F	1989	
G824UMU	Volvo Citybus B10M-50	Northern Counties	DPH45/35F	1989	
H303CAV	Volvo Citybus B10M-50	Northern Counties	DPH45/35F	1990	
PIW4798	CVE Omni	CVE	B24F	1991	Ex TRRL, Kent, 1994
J722KBC	Volvo B10M-60	Plaxton Premiére 350	C53F	1992	
J723KBC	Volvo B10M-60	Plaxton Premiére 350	C53F	1992	
J670LGA	Volvo B10M-60	Van Hool Alizée H	C49DT	1992	Ex Skills, Nottingham, 1997
J687LGA	Volvo B10M-60	Van Hool Alizée H	C49DT	1992	Ex Priory, Gosport, 1997
J688LGA	Volvo B10M-60	Van Hool Alizée H	C49DT	1992	Ex Skills, Nottingham, 1997
J669LGA	Volvo B10M-60	Van Hool Alizée H	C49DT	1992	Ex Shearings, 1997
J689LGA	Volvo B10M-60	Van Hool Alizée H	C49DT	1992	Ex Skills, Nottingham, 1997
M150EAV	OCC Omni	OCC	B24F	1995	
M589SDC	OCC Omni	OCC	B24F	1995	
N653EWJ	Volvo B10M-62	Van Hool Alizée HE	C53F	1996	
N654EWJ	Volvo B10M-62	Van Hool Alizée HE	C53F	1996	

Opposite, top:- **Go Whippet have replaced many of their Scania Metropolitans with Leyland Titans, all of which originated with London Buses. One of the earlier examples, KYN296X, shows the single door conversion which has been performed on all bar one of the fleet.** *Phillip Stephenson*
Opposite, bottom: - **Several of the newer coaches are employed on Go Whippet's express service to London, though J688LGA was working the Great Yarmouth service when photographed in Norwich. Latterly with a variety of operators these LGA-registered vehicles originated with Park's of Hamilton.** *Richard Godfrey*

After their displacement from front-line coach duties selected vehicles are often retained with Go Whippet for use on the longer rural services. Pictured arriving in Cambridge is FEW227Y, a Plaxton Paramount 3200 based on a DAF chassis. The bodies were fitted with power twin doors from new.
Phillip Stephenson

Previous registrations:-

GIL2968	B169WKO	J688LGA	J458HDS, LSK498
J669LGA	J459HDS, LSK499	J689LGA	J460HDS, LSK500
J670LGA	J456HDS, LSK496	PIW4798	H620OHN
J687LGA	J457HDS, LSK497		

Livery:- Two tone blue, cream and black.

Depots:-

Cambridge Road Fenstanton;

Railway Station Yard, Graffham,

FEN'S COACHES

Wiffen's Coaches Ltd, Sunnyside Garage, Finchingfield, Braintree, Essex, CM7 4JX

GSX115N	Bedford YRT	Alexander AY	B53F	1975	Ex Semmence, Wymondham, 1989
GSX118N	Bedford YRT	Alexander AY	B53F	1975	Ex Semmence, Wymondham, 1989
GSX119N	Bedford YRT	Alexander AY	B53F	1975	Ex Semmence, Wymondham, 1989
GSX121N	Bedford YRT	Alexander AY	B53F	1975	Ex Stan's, Great Totham, 1995,
C924DKR	Leyland Cub CU435	HTI Maxeta	B33F	1986	Ex Ruffle, Castle Hedingham, 1994
C464BHY	Ford Transit 190	Dormobile	B16F	1986	Ex Athelstan, Chippenham, 1990

WILTSHIRE

H L & R J Wiltshire, Sea Palling Service Station, Waxham Road, Sea Palling, Norwich, Norfolk, NR12 0UX

ORY707R	Bedford YMT	Plaxton Supreme III	C53F	1976	Ex Easton, Stratton Strawless, 1995
TJE995S	Bedford YMT	Plaxton Supreme III	C53F	1978	Ex Young, Rampton, 1982
3367PP	Bedford YMT	Plaxton Supreme IV	C53F	1979	Ex Travel the Wright Way, Brandon, 1997
BTH364V	AEC Reliance 6U3ZR	Duple Dominant II Express	C53F	1979	Ex Smith, Wouldham, 1995
C47WRT	Ford Transit 150	Ford	M8	1986	Ex private owner, 1992
GBZ4991	MCW Metroliner HR131/9	MCW	C53F	1986	Ex Roberts, Bridgend, 1997

Previous registration:-

3367PP   YJB331T, HR55, HFG366T   GBZ4991   D50OWJ

Livery: Blue and white

Windmill of Copford have recently added three double-deck vehicles to their fleet. Two of these are Eastern Coach Works-bodied Leyland Olympians that were new to Eastern National though latterly worked in south Wales. Pictured on rail-replacement duties isB690BPU.
Keith Grimes

WINDMILL COACHES

Windmill Coaches Ltd, 105 London Road, Copford, Colchester, Essex, CO6 1LH

A143AMO	MCW Metrobus 2 DR102/44	MCW	DPH39/27F	1984	Ex Reading Buses, 1997
B690BPU	Leyland Olympian ONCL10/1RV	Eastern Coach Works	CH45/28F	1985	Ex SWT, 1998
B696BPU	Leyland Olympian ONCL10/1RV	Eastern Coach Works	CH45/28F	1985	Ex SWT, 1998
C769WKS	Van Hool T815	Van Hool Alicron	C49FT	1986	Ex Staines Crusader, Clacton, 1997
C426VAY	Van Hool T815	Van Hool Acron	C48FT	1986	Ex Staines Crusader, Clacton, 1997
G421WFP	Bova FHD12.290	Bova Futura	C51FT	1990	Ex Staines Crusader, Clacton, 1997
H423EUT	Bova FHD12.290	Bova Futura	C53FT	1991	Ex Staines Crusader, Clacton, 1997
K424GHE	Bova FHD12.290	Bova Futura	C51FT	1993	Ex Staines Crusader, Clacton, 1997
L425OWF	Bova FHD12.340	Bova Futura	C51FT	1994	Ex Staines Crusader, Clacton, 1997

Named coaches:- B690BPU *Dylan Thomas*; B696BPU *Sir Harry Secombe*

Previous registrations:-

B690BPU	B690BPU, IIL1828	C426VAY	C830WKS, 196COY
B696BPU	B690BPU, IIL1829	C769WKS	TJF757, C384ADD, BAZ4772

Livery:- White, blue, red and yellow (double-decks); white, grey and orange (coaches)

Windmill Holidays have a quartet of Bova Futura coaches as well as a pair built integrally by Van Hool. H423EUT is seen entering Colchester bus station while engaged on feeder work for the Stena Line, at nearby Harwich. *Paul Stockwell.*

Index to vehicles

Reg	Operator	Reg	Operator	Reg	Operator	Reg	Operator
11PKN	Soames	841BMB	Brandons	A16ATC	Towler Coaches	A683KDV	Stagecoach Cambus
34DEW	Dews	856GKH	Lambert's	A16AWE	Eastons	A696OHJ	Eastern Counties
46AEW	Lodge's	866VNU	Wards	A16BUS	West's	A741TTW	Stephenson's
47HWT	Happy Wanderer	986PVW	Webbs	A17AWE	Eastons	A745JPB	Norfolk Green
70CLT	Arriva East Herts	987UYA	Goodwin's	A17BUS	West's	A776TYL	Leroy Coaches
71FXO	Thorns	1273LJ	Coach Services	A18AWE	Eastons	A784YGL	Beestons
91KC	Dolphin	1440PP	Galloway	A18BUS	West's	A807REW	Go Whippet
98TNO	Simonds	1482PP	Galloway	A19AWE	Eastons	A810LEL	Mike Boggis
100BGO	Coach Services	1754PP	Galloway	A19BUS	West's	A855UYM	Arriva Colchester
114RVX	Crusader	2086PP	Galloway	A20BCT	Bird's	A856UYM	Arriva Colchester
124CLT	Arriva East Herts	2328RU	County Coaches	A23FVT	Goldline	A858OVJ	Myall's
125LUP	Biss Bros	2508EL	Chenery	A33UGA	Semmence	A861SUL	Go Whippet
131ASV	Eastern Counties	2513PP	Galloway	A53NPP	Reynolds	A862UDM	Fargo Coachlines
131HUO	Towler Coaches	2629RU	County Coaches	A62OJX	Go-Dons	A872SUL	Go Whippet
149GJF	Semmence	2786RU	County Coaches	A65UEW	Shaws of Maxey	A911LUD	Ruffles
160EBK	Lodge's	3169RU	County Coaches	A66UEW	Shaws of Maxey	A911SYE	Go Whippet
166UMB	Simonds	3196DD	Embling	A110FDL	Arriva Southend	A926TEG	Collins
185CLT	Arriva East Herts	3367PP	Whiltshire	A122PAR	Hedingham	A987RFO	Reynolds
205CLT	Arriva East Herts	3990ME	Sanders	A124EPA	Arriva Southend	AAE655V	Eastern Counties
219GRA	Beestons	4092PP	Galloway	A129MFL	Leroy Coaches	AAL456A	D&H Harrod
222GRA	Beestons	4512UR	Simonds	A141EPA	Arriva Southend	AAL480A	D&H Harrod
224ENG	Simonds	4750WY	Eastern Counties	A143AMO	Windmill	AAP648T	Stephenson's
226LRB	Beestons	5019BT	Lambert's	A147RMJ	Goodwin's	AAS185W	Norfolk Green
227ASV	Mil-Ken	5048PP	Galloway	A154RUM	Kiddles	ABC330K	Dews
229LRB	Hedingham	5092EL	Chenery	A162KLK	Mikes Coaches	ABD71X	Eastern Counties
240FRH	Partridge	5189RU	County Coaches	A197RUR	BJS Travel	ABD72X	Eastern Counties
256JPA	Simonds	5281RU	County Coaches	A201YWP	Eastern Counties	ABD73X	Eastern Counties
259VYC	Sanders	530MUY	Arriva East Herts	A202LCL	Neave	ABD73X	Eastern Counties
271AKV	Beestons	530VPJ	Beestons	A202YWP	Eastern Counties	ABV881V	DMA Mini
299SAE	Jans Coaches	538ELX	Simonds	A203RUR	Cuttings	ACF877L	Partridge
354TRT	Sanders	5516PP	Galloway	A203YWP	Eastern Counties	ACG70V	Mike Boggis
361CLT	Arriva East Herts	556EHN	Cooks of Southend	A204YWP	Eastern Counties	ACM708X	Cedrick's
378BNG	Simonds	5611PP	Galloway	A205YWP	Eastern Counties	ACP832V	Lodge's
412CRU	Wright Way	5765OZ	Travelrich	A209YSF	Chariots	ADC366A	Chariots
434YAH	Semmence	5919RU	County Coaches	A221PBM	Chariots	ADC836A	Chariots
447HWT	Happy Wanderer	5946PP	Galloway	A246SVW	Arriva Southend	AEG984A	Beestons
453CLT	Arriva East Herts	6037PP	Galloway	A247SVW	Arriva Southend	AFJ759T	Galloway
454EAN	Brentwood Cs	6149KP	Eastern Counties	A248SVW	Arriva Southend	AFN297V	Goodwin's
460UEV	Simonds	6220WY	Eastern Counties	A249SVW	Arriva Southend	AJD24T	Neave
464CLT	Arriva East Herts	6539FN	Caroline Seagull	A250SVW	Arriva Colchester	AJD26T	Stephenson's
482SBJ	Simonds	6541FN	Caroline Seagull	A266BTY	Semmence	AJD959	Felix
4940VF	Simonds	6543FN	Caroline Seagull	A301KFP	Semmence	AJN825	Essex Buses
503EUC	Bure Valley	6544FN	Caroline Seagull	A319GLV	Supreme	ANX330X	Matthew Blue
522FN	Caroline Seagull	6545FN	Caroline Seagull	A319HFP	S M Travel	APA46B	Rules
523FN	Caroline Seagull	6546FN	Caroline Seagull	A320GLV	Supreme	APH511T	Neave
526FN	Caroline Seagull	6547FN	Caroline Seagull	A335VTU	Shaws of Maxey	APH520T	Ruffles
531FN	Caroline Seagull	711BHR	M & E Coaches	A431ESO	Dereham Coaches	APL777T	Goodwin's
535FN	Caroline Seagull	7236PW	Simonds	A479FBA	Mike Boggis	APM108T	Upwell & Dist
536FN	Caroline Seagull	7463RU	Cedrick's	A483JEX	Dolphin	APR855T	Dereham Coaches
537FN	Caroline Seagull	7694VC	Eastern Counties	A486FPV	Hedingham	APT42S	Thorns
538FN	Caroline Seagull	7947RU	County Coaches	A487FPV	Hedingham	APT813W	Hedingham
565EXV	Travelrich	8333UR	Simonds	A504HUT	Galloway	ARN291Y	NIBS
572XAE	Cunningham	8603PH	Chariots	A545TMA	Mil-Ken	ARN893Y	NIBS
597AXF	Viceroy	920ACH	Chenery	A561KWY	Stagecoach Cambus	ARN894Y	NIBS
610KWC	Brentwood Cs	9383MX	Simonds	A565WAV	Suffolk Education	AST155W	Eastern Counties
625DAO	Brandons	9803RU	County Coaches	A583MEH	Semmence	ATH777V	Cuttings
687DEW	Dews	9983PW	Simonds	A600NWC	Chariots	ATL312X	Sanders
759KFC	Partridge	A10BUS	West's	A620YJR	Suffolk Education	ATV11B	Beestons
794SKO	Viceroy	A12APT	Thorns	A646LEX	Dolphin	AUD460R	Ford's
799XWC	Cooks of Southend	A12BUS	West's	A647LEX	Dolphin	AUD461R	Hedingham
820KPO	Ford's	A13BUS	West's	A660KUM	Essex Buses	AUK47K	Buzz
824CDM	Upwell & Dist	A14BUS	West's	A665KUM	Essex Buses	AUP714S	NIBS
840FAY	Goodwin's	A15BUS	West's	A681KDV	Stagecoach Cambus	AYG850S	Essex Buses

Reg	Operator	Reg	Operator	Reg	Operator	Reg	Operator
B4FEN	Fenn	B812XNK	Soames	BRT787Y	Suffolk Education	C373CTP	Soames
B23XKK	Coach Services	B857XYR	Arriva Colchester	BRT788Y	Whincop	C374WBF	Dolphin
B42ECV	Beestons	B858XRY	Arriva Colchester	BRT789Y	Whincop	C381WBF	Dolphin
B44DNY	Leroy Coaches	B859XYR	Arriva Colchester	BTH364V	Whiltshire	C393FBO	Lewis's
B45DNY	Peelings	B860XYR	Arriva Colchester	BTU375S	Supreme	C398BUV	Arriva East Herts
B82NDX	Ipswich	B861XYR	Arriva Colchester	BTX39V	Morley's	C404LRP	Kings
B83SWX	Arriva Southend	B862XYR	Lewis's	BUF260C	Paynes of Paxton	C407HJN	Essex Buses
B84SWX	Arriva Southend	B869XYR	Lewis's	BVG218T	Eastern Counties	C408HJN	Essex Buses
B85SWX	Arriva Southend	B873XFL	Felix	BVG219T	Eastern Counties	C409HJN	Essex Buses
B88FVL	Wright Way	B884AJX	Amber Bus	BVG220T	Eastern Counties	C410HJN	Essex Buses
B91UBM	Norfolk Green	B885WNB	Cunningham	BVG222T	Eastern Counties	C412HJN	Essex Buses
B94PLU	Reynolds	B895YAV	Collins	BVG223T	Eastern Counties	C413DUM	Cuttings
B97PLU	Caroline Seagull	B897AGJ	Jacksons Cs	BVG224T	Eastern Counties	C413HJN	Essex Buses
B100XTW	Arriva Southend	B906OPJ	Norfolk Green	BVG225T	Eastern Counties	C414HJN	Essex Buses
B104JAB	Eastern Counties	B910YAV	Collins	BVP812V	Arriva Southend	C415HJN	Essex Buses
B109LPH	Cedrick's	B916SPR	Soames	BVP821V	Beestons	C416HJN	Essex Buses
B114LDX	Ipswich	B948ASU	Beestons	BWK9T	Sanders	C417HJN	Essex Buses
B115LDX	Ipswich	BAJ998T	Blue Diamond	BXI3079	Semmence	C418HJN	Essex Buses
B116DTG	Lewis's	BAR103X	Hedingham	BYW391V	Associated Cs	C419HJN	Essex Buses
B116LDX	Ipswich	BAZ6527	Golden Boy	BYX170V	Arriva East Herts	C421HJN	Essex Buses
B122UAH	Collins	BAZ6877	M & E Coaches	BYX175V	Arriva East Herts	C426DML	Paynes of Paxton
B124BOO	Hedingham	BAZ7349	Biss Bros	BYX266V	Arriva East Herts	C426VAY	Windmill
B136AAV	Reynolds	BAZ7384	Arriva East Herts	BYX301V	Arriva Colchester	C430BHY	Flying Banana
B156PPW	Dolphin	BBM34A	Buckland	C25KAV	Kenzies	C431BHY	Flying Banana
B162AKH	Cedrick's	BBM34A	Whincop	C27OFL	Kings	C463SJU	Goldline
B183BLG	Arriva Southend	BBM53A	Galloway	C28RFL	Kenzies	C463SRT	Leroy Coaches
B184BLG	Arriva Southend	BCL216T	Eastern Counties	C41HHJ	Arriva Colchester	C464BHY	Whiffens
B185BLG	Arriva Southend	BDZ5198	Jacksons Cs	C42LEW	Collins	C485BHY	Essex Buses
B189BLG	Arriva Southend	BEA344Y	Rayleigh	C46DUR	Galloway	C485BHY	Stephenson's
B201GNL	Flying Banana	BEG438T	Mil-Ken	C47WRT	Whiltshire	C486BHY	Essex Buses
B204GNL	Flying Banana	BEP963V	Essex Buses	C54VJU	S M Travel	C489BHY	Essex Buses
B220JPH	Morley's	BEV105X	Hedingham	C72HDT	Semmence	C493BHY	Essex Buses
B223OJU	Sanders	BEV542S	CI Coachlines	C106SDX	Ipswich	C493KGP	Reynolds
B240RBA	Dolphin	BEW49T	Embling	C107HGL	Essex Buses	C504DYM	Crown
B248WUL	Arriva East Herts	BFL497Y	Collins	C116AFX	Wright Way	C511BFB	Essex Buses
B258GWJ	Norfolk Green	BFL503V	Lambert's	C120SRB	Chenery	C629HOK	Suffolk Education
B273AMG	Hedingham	BFL504V	Shaws of Maxey	C130HJN	Essex Buses	C629XVU	Myall's
B345RVF	Coach Services	BFR304R	Supreme	C130PPE	Colchester Coaches	C638KDS	Brandons
B387UEX	Beestons	BFV221Y	Thorns	C133PPE	Amber Bus	C647YKE	Ruffles
B389DCA	Matthew Blue	BGS304X	Coach Services	C141KFL	Ford's	C658KVW	Ford's
B405DWG	Chelmsford Taxi	BGY584T	Mil-Ken	C141KGJ	Viceroy	C667DVG	Eastons
B420NJF	Flying Banana	BGY585T	Mil-Ken	C141LOO	Blue Diamond	C678ECV	Essex Buses
B423CMC	Fargo Coachlines	BHJ368S	Hedingham	C151SRT	Suffolk Education	C682VLJ	Dolphin
B500YUR	Norfolk Green	BHK710X	Hedingham	C152SRT	Suffolk Education	C695ECV	Essex Buses
B512JJR	Semmence	BIL4419	NIBS	C176EMU	Dereham Coaches	C698ECV	Essex Buses
B513JJR	Semmence	BIL4539	NIBS	C204HJN	Stephenson's	C711BEX	Eastern Counties
B529GNV	D-Way Travel	BIL4710	NIBS	C212HJN	Stephenson's	C711GEV	Essex Buses
B531GNV	D-Way Travel	BIL6538	NIBS	C212PCD	Eastern Counties	C717BEX	Eastern Counties
B544PAH	Dolphin	BIL7894	NIBS	C217HJN	Essex Buses	C718NHJ	Kings
B568BOK	Eastern Counties	BIL8430	Sanders	C230HCV	Essex Buses	C722NNN	Ipswich
B588NJF	Suffolk Education	BIL8949	Sanders	C238HNO	Fargo Coachlines	C738CUC	County Travel
B592XWW	Thorns	BIL9406	NIBS	C245OFE	Jacksons Cs	C756BEX	Stephenson's
B6200DX	Reynolds	BJS327Y	BJS Travel	C247OFE	Collins	C756FMC	Veazey
B650JSS	Dereham Coaches	BJS98Y	BJS Travel	C253SPC	Stephenson's	C764NRC	J Amos
B660OVU	Leroy Coaches	BKE835T	Cedrick's	C254SPC	Arriva East Herts	C769WKS	Windmill
B671DVL	Jans Coaches	BKE838T	Embling	C255SPC	Arriva East Herts	C782BWY	Chariots
B689BPU	Essex Buses	BKE839T	Stephenson's	C260GOF	Mike Boggis	C791PEM	Bakerbus
B690BPU	Windmill	BKR835Y	Stephenson's	C260SPC	Arriva East Herts	C801FYA	S & P Coach
B691BPU	Essex Buses	BLJ721Y	Reynolds	C263SPC	Stephenson's	C802FMC	Leroy Coaches
B694BPU	Cedrick's	BMA646S	Norfolk Green	C265SPC	Arriva East Herts	C810FMC	Peelings
B694BPU	Stephenson's	BMB20M	Brandons	C288VLF	Neave	C815FMC	Coach Services
B696BPU	Windmill	BNG444Y	Chenery	C304NHD	Suffolk Education	C822XCJ	Myall's
B696WAR	Essex Buses	BNO672T	Essex Buses	C315DRH	Flying Banana	C840SSB	Bure Valley
B697WAR	Essex Buses	BNO676T	Essex Buses	C318DRH	Dolphin	C874CYX	Arriva East Herts
B698BPU	Essex Buses	BNO679T	Essex Buses	C319DRH	Dolphin	C876CYX	Arriva East Herts
B699BPU	Essex Buses	BNO700T	Hedingham	C330PEW	Ruffles	C891BEX	Eastern Counties
B711EOF	Beestons	BNO703T	Heddingham	C333HHB	Enterprise	C902JOF	Leroy Coaches
B714HVO	Ipswich	BRC836T	Heddingham	C348RPE	Dolphin	C924DKR	Whiffens
B733GWJ	Veazey	BRC839T	Heddingham	C357FBO	Spratts	C932EWW	Eastons
B800TNE	Dolphin	BRT786Y	Whincop	C367BUV	Arriva East Herts	C964GCV	M & E Coaches

The East Anglia Bus Handbook

Reg	Operator	Reg	Operator	Reg	Operator	Reg	Operator
C979HOX	Fourways	D140NDT	Goldline	D636CNP	Matthew Blue	E40OAH	Eastern Counties
C989KUK	Leroy Coaches	D145WCC	Peter Goodward	D654DFL	Collins	E41OAH	Eastern Counties
C995ERO	Ford's	D164TCX	Jans Coaches	D683YTN	Bakerbus	E41SBO	Go-Dons
C995ERO	Lodge's	D174LNA	Dolphin	D685JVF	Kings	E42OAH	Eastern Counties
CAH885Y	Ambassador Travel	D177MOV	Goldline	D703NUH	Flagfinders	E46MMT	Neal's Travel
CAH886Y	Ambassador Travel	D202NON	Crown	D753JUB	Collins	E48RVG	Eastern Counties
CAZ2819	Golden Boy	D203NON	Rules	D755DLO	Essex Buses	E48YDO	Collins
CAZ6829	Kiddles	D211LWX	Chambers	D758LEX	Eastern Counties	E49RVG	Eastern Counties
CBE882X	Semmence	D212LWX	Chambers	D764KWT	Essex Buses	E79HVX	Hedingham
CBV10S	Leroy Coaches	D212PPU	Stephenson's	D774PTU	Collins	E85AVO	County Travel
CBV308S	Brentwood Cs	D215YHK	BJS Travel	D781SGB	Burtons	E92VWA	Jans Coaches
CCF669	Chambers	D217OOJ	Towler Coaches	D797KWR	Collins	E99ODH	Spratts
CDO999V	Belle Coaches	D225PPU	Stephenson's	D822LVS	DMA Mini	E101VWA	NIBS
CDT322T	Jacksons Cs	D227OOJ	Flying Banana	D823UBH	Sanders	E105GOO	Crusader
CEV89T	Hedingham	D228PPU	Essex Buses	D832DPF	Cuttings	E106GOO	Crusader
CFM356S	Beestons	D230PPU	Essex Buses	D849OJA	Dolphin	E107GOO	Crusader
CFR297V	Happy Wanderer	D231PPU	Essex Buses	D850AAV	Go Whippet	E107JPL	Essexbus
CFX319T	Caroline Seagull	D233PPU	Essex Buses	D855OJA	Brandons	E108GOO	Crusader
CHK312X	Ford's	D234PPU	Essex Buses	D858CKV	First Choice	E111WAW	Suffolk Education
CJH115V	Hedingham	D256HFX	Dereham Coaches	D866TFJ	Eastons	E114KDX	Ipswich
CJH121V	Brentwood Cs	D266CBJ	Suffolk Education	D868VKE	Amber Bus	E115KDX	Ipswich
CJH123V	M & E Coaches	D267CBJ	Suffolk Education	D893NHE	Wards	E116KDX	Ipswich
CJH141V	Hedingham	D267OOJ	Collins	D908MVU	Suffolk Education	E117KDX	Ipswich
CJH143V	Hedingham	D271HFX	Wright Way	D913EHM	S & P Coach	E125AAL	Clintona
CJH144V	Eastern Counties	D272HFX	Coach Services	D939HMU	Soames	E134PLJ	Sanders
CJS447	Spratts	D279XCX	Shaws of Maxey	D952CDX	Dolphin	E140FLD	Reynolds
CKM140Y	Semmence	D298XCX	Shaws of Maxey	D967CVV	Dolphin	E158NEG	Dolphin
CKM141Y	Semmence	D328UTU	Burtons	DAL771J	Rules	E160NEG	Dolphin
CKX392T	Ford's	D343CPB	Jans Coaches	DAR118T	Essex Buses	E168FLK	DMA Mini
CLB779Y	Reynolds	D345JUM	Crown	DAR121T	Essex Buses	E174CDS	Eastons
CPT731S	Hedingham	D345WPE	Hedingham	DAR129T	Essex Buses	E176OEW	Go Whippet
CPU125X	Hedingham	D352OAK	Felix	DAZ4303	Belle Coaches	E190YWE	Clintona
CRO689L	Beestons	D356KVA	Paynes of Paxton	DAZ4304	Belle Coaches	E201PWY	Eastern Counties
CSK282	Anglian Coaches	D369JUM	Enterprise	DBH452X	Hedingham	E202PWY	Eastern Counties
CSV253	Paynes of Paxton	D408OSJ	Chenery	DBU889	Felix	E205EPB	Chariots
CSV303	Eastern Counties	D408XEV	Chariots	DCA31S	Associated Cs	E206SVG	Dolphin
CSV524	Eastern Counties	D40MAG	Arriva East Herts	DDX741T	Arriva East Herts	E212FLD	Beestons
CSV992	Eastern Counties	D411OSJ	Chenery	DEL192T	Chariots	E221LER	Beestons
CTN635V	Essex Buses	D420HPO	Crown	DEW130Y	Dews	E222WAW	Suffolk Education
CUL83V	Arriva East Herts	D429SKD	Leroy Coaches	DEX229T	Eastern Counties	E222YTU	Ruffles
CUL92V	Morley's	D441CEW	Sanders	DEX230T	Eastern Counties	E233WKW	Galloway
CUL100V	Arriva East Herts	D447PGH	Sanders	DHE695V	Sanders	E237VOM	Flying Banana
CUT465	Dews	D468ALR	Eastons	DHJ255B	Thorns	E245RBE	Crusader
CVA108V	Sanders	D501NWG	Norfolk Green	DIB3122	Euroview	E253CPU	Wards
CVE12V	Kenzies	D505NWG	Norfolk Green	DKE350Y	Fourways	E256PEL	Go-Dons
CVF28T	Eastern Counties	D510PPU	Essex Buses	DNG232T	NIBS	E278YPS	Dereham Coaches
CVF29T	Eastern Counties	D511NWG	Norfolk Green	DNG236T	Eastern Counties	E280HRY	Soames
CVF30T	Eastern Counties	D511PPU	Essex Buses	DNK431T	Partridge	E290OMG	Biss Bros
CVF31T	Eastern Counties	D512PPU	Essex Buses	DNK576Y	Ruffles	E296VOM	Arriva East Herts
CWF738T	Burtons	D519FYL	Lodge's	DPO567W	Flagfinders	E305BWL	Stagecoach Cambus
CWG769V	Burtons	D531NDA	Blue Diamond	DPW781T	Eastern Counties	E306BWL	Stagecoach Cambus
CWU139T	Supreme	D532FAE	Eastern Counties	DRT681T	CI Coachlines	E309DMA	Gretton's
CWU150T	Embling	D532NDA	Blue Diamond	DSK107	Ford's	E317OMG	Fourways
CXI8635	Chariots	D534KGL	Essex Buses	DSK648	Simonds	E331LHN	First Choice
D30BEW	Kenzies	D537FAE	Eastern Counties	DSU105	Partridge	E352NEG	Arriva East Herts
D39KAX	S M Travel	D540FAE	Stephenson's	DSU116	Simonds	E353NEG	Arriva East Herts
D43RWC	Arriva Colchester	D541FAE	Eastern Counties	DSU733	Biss Bros	E354NEG	Arriva East Herts
D45OKH	Arriva East Herts	D544FAE	Eastern Counties	DTG366V	Arriva East Herts	E364KKV	Brandons
D66ONS	Ford's	D547FAE	Stephenson's	DTG367V	Arriva East Herts	E377FVX	Cooks of Southend
D68VJC	Burtons	D555HNW	S M Travel	DTG372V	Arriva East Herts	E400HWC	Essex Buses
D70TLV	Flying Banana	D557MVR	Shaws of Maxey	DWJ566V	Burtons	E401HWC	Essex Buses
D71HRU	County Coaches	D560CJF	Kiddles	DWJ567V	Burtons	E417MOU	Chariots
D80APC	Reynolds	D576VBV	Hedingham	DWK410T	Dews	E422BMY	Goodwin's
D103DAJ	Norfolk Green	D584MVR	Hedingham	DWU293T	Essexbus	E441ADV	Go Whippet
D129SHE	Sanders	D600MVR	Hedingham	DWU294T	Hedingham	E448TYG	Arriva East Herts
D136XVW	Hedingham	D601RGJ	Sanders	DWU297T	Wards	E457BOO	BJS Travel
D137SWE	Matthew Blue	D604RGJ	Sanders	DWU298T	Essex Buses	E463NVT	Mikes Coaches
D137XVW	Hedingham	D606AFR	Eastern Counties	DWY166T	Beestons	E465CGM	Eastern Counties
D138WCC	Amber Bus	D624KJT	Sanders	E23EFW	Grahams	E465HDX	Suffolk Education
D139AFH	Paynes of Paxton	D628JPW	Dolphin	E32MCE	Soames	E466HDX	Suffolk Education

Reg	Operator	Reg	Operator	Reg	Operator	Reg	Operator
E467CGM	Norfolk Green	EJD510	Towler Coaches	F171SMT	Stagecoach Cambus	F426MJN	Essex Buses
E467MRE	Reynolds	ELP554T	Shaws of Maxey	F171WFL	Paynes of Paxton	F427MJN	Essex Buses
E470CGM	Eastern Counties	ENM10T	Neave	F172WFL	Paynes of Paxton	F428DUG	Soames
E472CGM	Eastern Counties	EON825V	Arriva Southend	F173CKW	Clintona	F428MJN	Essex Buses
E473CGM	Eastern Counties	EPH212V	Beestons	F213NST	Associated Cs	F429MJN	Essex Buses
E476CGM	Eastern Counties	EPH27V	Semmence	F224AKG	S M Travel	F436DUG	Soames
E478CGM	Norfolk Green	EPM126V	Rules	F225RJX	Shaws of Maxey	F448CAH	Dolphin
E500LFL	Stagecoach Cambus	EPW928Y	Caroline Seagull	F226RJX	Shaws of Maxey	F464NRT	Hedingham
E501EFG	Suffolk Education	ESU238	Greys of Ely	F239PAC	Clintona	F464SJD	Burtons
E501LFL	Stagecoach Cambus	ESU307	Greys of Ely	F243RRT	Chambers	F467UVW	Arriva Southend
E502EFG	Suffolk Education	ESU308	Greys of Ely	F245MTW	Arriva Colchester	F470BOH	Crown
E502LFL	Stagecoach Cambus	ESU320	Greys of Ely	F245MVW	Essex Buses	F476OFJ	Beestons
E502NMD	DMA Mini	ESU350	Greys of Ely	F246HNE	Chambers	F477OFJ	Beestons
E515MME	First Choice	ESU369	Greys of Ely	F246MTW	Arriva Colchester	F484WFX	Shaws of Maxey
E518PWR	BJS Travel	ESU378	Greys of Ely	F246MVW	Essex Buses	F491DNY	Galloway
E519PWR	Enterprise	ESU389	Greys of Ely	F250NJN	Essex Buses	F506NJE	Stagecoach Cambus
E554UWF	Leroy Coaches	ESU394	Greys of Ely	F251NJN	Essex Buses	F507NJE	Stagecoach Cambus
E564BNK	Arriva East Herts	ESU629	Greys of Ely	F254RHK	Essex Buses	F508NJE	Stagecoach Cambus
E565BNK	Arriva East Herts	ESU910	Andrews Coaches	F255RHK	Essex Buses	F509NJE	Stagecoach Cambus
E597WAH	Belle Coaches	ESU912	Andrews Coaches	F256RHK	Essex Buses	F510NJE	Stagecoach Cambus
E613UPW	Dolphin	ESU914	Andrews Coaches	F257RHK	Essex Buses	F511NJE	Stagecoach Cambus
E633SEL	Chambers	ETC760B	Go-Dons	F258NUT	Cooks of Southend	F512NJE	Stagecoach Cambus
E644UVG	Dolphin	ETM238T	Mil-Ken	F258RHK	Essex Buses	F513NJE	Stagecoach Cambus
E667UND	Semmence	EUB552Y	Semmence	F259OFP	Shaws of Maxey	F514NJE	Stagecoach Cambus
E667YDT	Arriva East Herts	EWR166T	Beestons	F260RHK	Essex Buses	F515NJE	Stagecoach Cambus
E668UNE	Hedingham	EWR651Y	Essex Buses	F289PAC	Clintona	F516NJE	Stagecoach Cambus
E690UND	Dolphin	EWR652Y	Essex Buses	F301RMH	Felix	F517NJE	Stagecoach Cambus
E699GNH	Leroy Coaches	EWR653Y	Essex Buses	F303RMH	Jacksons Cs	F523UVW	Arriva Southend
E700EHJ	Stephenson's	EWW213T	Hedingham	F310EVG	Beestons	F533DVG	Dolphin
E701TNG	Eastern Counties	EWW946Y	Essex Buses	F310OVW	Harris Bus	F551TMH	Coach Services
E702TNG	Eastern Counties	EX6566	Hedingham	F312EJO	Stagecoach Cambus	F562KNM	DMA Mini
E703UND	Dolphin	EYE336V	Arriva Colchester	F313YOL	DMA Mini	F569MCH	Spratts
E705GNH	Bakerbus	EYH693V	Ford's	F321SMD	Jacksons Cs	F572SMG	Arriva Southend
E710JJN	County Coaches	F22HGG	Soames	F327COV	Caroline Seagull	F572UPB	Arriva Southend
E743OEW	Felix	F29SBL	Leroy Coaches	F337JTN	Go-Dons	F573SMG	Arriva Southend
E752JAY	Veazey	F34TJN	Eastern Counties	F342VEF	Essexbus	F574SMG	Arriva Southend
E758JAY	Go-Dons	F39EEG	Soames	F353VRN	S M Travel	F575SMG	Arriva Southend
E786MEU	Grahams	F50ACL	Chambers	F356BWU	Eastons	F576SMG	Arriva Southend
E816UKW	Ruffles	F51ACL	Chambers	F367CHE	Arriva East Herts	F579SMG	Arriva Southend
E827EUT	Gretton's	F61SMC	Arriva East Herts	F368MUT	Veazey	F580RTL	Rules
E832EUT	Coach Services	F62SMC	Arriva East Herts	F385XVN	Chelmsford Taxi	F589HUS	Fargo Coachlines
E838NHP	Dereham Coaches	F63SMC	Arriva East Herts	F399KKM	Dolphin	F613HGO	Kings
E853PEX	Eastern Counties	F72SMC	Buzz	F401XWR	Norfolk Green	F613XWY	Eastern Counties
E856ENR	Grahams	F73SMC	Buzz	F402LTW	Essex Buses	F614XWY	Eastern Counties
E856GFV	Felix	F76SMC	Buzz	F403LTW	Essex Buses	F616CWJ	NIBS
E861TNG	Lewis's	F77CJC	S M Travel	F404LTW	Essex Buses	F620HWE	Matthew Blue
E874DTT	Beestons	F77SMC	Buzz	F405LTW	Essex Buses	F626SAY	Leroy Coaches
E888KYW	Arriva East Herts	F78SMC	Buzz	F406LTW	Essex Buses	F635SAY	Go-Dons
E889KYW	Arriva East Herts	F79SMC	Buzz	F407LTW	Essex Buses	F647JHO	Greys of Ely
E905LVE	Towler Coaches	F81ODX	Ipswich	F408LTW	Essex Buses	F651OHD	Neal's Travel
E933GPV	Associated Cs	F82WBD	Fargo Coachlines	F409CEW	Dolphin	F652OHD	Neal's Travel
E935RWR	Dolphin	F94CBD	Beestons	F409LTW	Essex Buses	F661RVX	DMA Mini
E940CJN	Biss Bros	F101AVG	Eastern Counties	F410MNO	Essex Buses	F677BBD	Crown
E947FRT	Suffolk Education	F102AVG	Eastern Counties	F411MNO	Essex Buses	F678AWW	Buzz
E954ANO	Associated Cs	F102CCL	Burtons	F412MNO	Essex Buses	F688KWC	Flagfinders
E964EHK	Crown	F103AVG	Eastern Counties	F413MNO	Essex Buses	F693PAY	Go Whippet
E966VKY	Lewis's	F104AVG	Eastern Counties	F414MNO	Essex Buses	F694PAY	Go Whippet
EAC878T	Sanders	F105AVG	Eastern Counties	F415MWC	Essex Buses	F694XMS	Eastern Counties
EAV811V	Go Whippet	F106CCL	Ambassador Travel	F416MWC	Essex Buses	F695XMS	Eastern Counties
EAV812V	Go Whippet	F115JGS	Arriva East Herts	F417MWC	Essex Buses	F696XMS	Eastern Counties
EBM448T	Upwell & Dist	F118OGS	Chelmsford Taxi	F418MWC	Essex Buses	F697PAY	BJS Travel
ECU772W	Collins	F145SPV	Hedingham	F419MWC	Essex Buses	F697XMS	Eastern Counties
ECW65W	Viceroy	F146SPV	Hedingham	F420MJN	Essex Buses	F698XMS	Eastern Counties
EDR793	County Coaches	F147SPV	Hedingham	F421MJN	Essex Buses	F699XMS	Eastern Counties
EEW113Y	Go Whippet	F148SPV	Hedingham	F421RRY	Ruffles	F700OPA	Crown
EGS158T	Chenery	F150LTW	Hedingham	F422MJN	Essex Buses	F700XMS	Eastern Counties
EGV101T	Whincop	F151NPU	Hedingham	F423MJN	Essex Buses	F703XMS	Eastern Counties
EGV719T	Belle Coaches	F154DKV	Arriva East Herts	F424MJN	Essex Buses	F704XMS	Eastern Counties
EHE228V	Webbs	F167SMT	Stagecoach Cambus	F425MJN	Essex Buses	F705XMS	Eastern Counties
EHE234V	Eastern Counties	F168SMT	Stagecoach Cambus	F425UVW	Arriva Southend	F708ENE	Coach Services

Reg	Operator	Reg	Operator	Reg	Operator	Reg	Operator
F709ENE	Coach Services	FIL4169	Beestons	G407DPD	Semmence	G904KPW	Dolphin
F713CWJ	Arriva East Herts	FIL4344	Beestons	G421WFP	Windmill	G905KPW	Dolphin
F714CWJ	Arriva East Herts	FIL4345	Beestons	G432SNN	Chariots	G918UPP	Arriva East Herts
F715CWJ	Arriva East Herts	FIL4741	Beestons	G434ART	Galloway	G919UPP	Arriva East Herts
F715UBX	Goldline	FIL4743	Beestons	G441PWW	Biss Bros	G922DVX	Clintona
F716PFP	Neave	FIL6002	Eurosun Cs	G442WLL	Crown	G924WGS	Arriva East Herts
F718CWJ	Arriva East Herts	FIL7253	Buzz	G453SGB	Eastern Counties	G925WGS	Arriva East Herts
F719CWJ	Arriva East Herts	FIL8613	Beestons	G454PGO	Matthew Blue	G926WGS	Arriva East Herts
F728ENE	Matthew Blue	FIL8614	Beestons	G456KNG	Eastern Counties	G927WGS	Arriva East Herts
F743TWC	Reynolds	FIL8615	Beestons	G457KNG	Eastern Counties	G928WGS	Arriva East Herts
F752SPU	Associated Cs	FIL8693	Sanders	G458KNG	Eastern Counties	G929WGS	Arriva East Herts
F769OBY	Leroy Coaches	FIW5447	Peter Goodward	G468JNH	Beestons	G930WGS	Arriva East Herts
F770CKM	DMA Mini	FNJ993V	Fargo Coachlines	G469LVG	Caroline Seagull	G931WGS	Arriva East Herts
F771DKW	Carter's Coaches	FNR100V	Shaws of Maxey	G470LVG	Caroline Seagull	G932WGS	Arriva East Herts
F779LNB	Chambers	FRP907T	Beestons	G501VRV	Coach Services	G947PFD	DMA Mini
F781GNA	Hedingham	FRP911T	Stephenson's	G512MNG	Ambassador Travel	G954KJX	Pullman
F795JKX	Arriva East Herts	FSU637	Felix	G515MWA	Paynes of Paxton	G959KJX	Shaws of Maxey
F796JKX	Arriva East Herts	FSU826	Carter's Coaches	G525LWU	Stagecoach Cambus	G965VBC	Dolphin
F799NPP	Cuttings	FTO551V	Sanders	G531EAD	Matthew Blue	G973LRP	Beestons
F800RHK	Essex Buses	FTO557V	Sanders	G533BRK	Chelmsford Taxi	G976KJX	Kings
F801RHK	Essex Buses	FUJ903V	Dereham Coaches	G541AGV	Happy Wanderer	G994JKY	Clintona
F802RHK	Essex Buses	FVS893Y	Leroy Coaches	G545JOG	Arriva East Herts	G996DVX	Clintona
F803RHK	Essex Buses	G21CSG	First Choice	G553CRF	Gretton's	GAL967	Gretton's
F804RHK	Essex Buses	G21KAH	Dolphin	G569YJF	Chelmsford Taxi	GAZ3137	Carter's Coaches
F840BPW	Dolphin	G23HKY	Viceroy	G621YMG	Arriva East Herts	GAZ4381	Stagecoach Cambus
F871RFP	Suffolk Education	G24CSG	First Choice	G622EDC	Chelmsford Taxi	GAZ4382	Stagecoach Cambus
F872RFP	Suffolk Education	G27XBK	Leroy Coaches	G624WPB	Norfolk Green	GBF79N	Stephenson's
F874RFP	Suffolk Education	G32HKY	Grahams	G636CAF	Kirby's Rayleigh	GBH506T	Dereham Coaches
F878TNH	Rayleigh	G40KAH	Dolphin	G643YVS	Biss Bros	GBU1V	Arriva East Herts
F880TNH	Beestons	G40SAV	Kenzies	G644YVS	Eastern Counties	GBU4V	Arriva East Herts
F882FWJ	Chelmsford Taxi	G49HDW	Semmence	G645YVS	Eastern Counties	GBU5V	Arriva East Herts
F882RFP	D&H Harrod	G52GEX	Eastern Counties	G646YVS	Eastern Counties	GBU8V	Arriva East Herts
F883RFP	D&H Harrod	G53GEX	Eastern Counties	G647YVS	Eastern Counties	GBU9V	Arriva East Herts
F884PYM	Chelmsford Taxi	G54GEX	Eastern Counties	G651PKO	Chelmsford Taxi	GBZ4991	Whiltshire
F893CCL	Dolphin	G55GEX	Eastern Counties	G670RAV	Dolphin	GDG241V	Reynolds
F898KHJ	Felix	G95VFP	Colchester Coaches	G695LNV	Dolphin	GDZ435	Freestones
F963CEG	Reynolds	G105APC	Chariots	G706JAH	Eastern Counties	GDZ481	Freestones
F964XEW	Dolphin	G106APC	Paynes of Paxton	G707JAH	Eastern Counties	GDZ540	Freestones
F967XEW	Dolphin	G107HNG	Ambassador Travel	G708JAH	Eastern Counties	GDZ541	Freestones
F993MTW	Kirby's Rayleigh	G108HNG	Ambassador Travel	G709JAH	Eastern Counties	GDZ571	Freestones
F995UME	Beestons	G109HNG	Ambassador Travel	G710JAH	Eastern Counties	GDZ623	Freestones
F996UME	Beestons	G111HNG	Ambassador Travel	G716WDU	Clintona	GDZ760	Freestones
FAZ3942	Dereham Coaches	G118VDX	Ipswich	G718NWY	Soames	GDZ967	Freestones
FBJ713T	Rules	G119VDX	Ipswich	G731PGA	Clintona	GDZ9097	Freestones
FCY287W	Hedingham	G120VDX	Ipswich	G743DSG	S M Travel	GEG963W	Neave
FCY287W	Hedingham	G121VDX	Ipswich	G746HVG	Suffolk Education	GEX790Y	Ford's
FCY288W	Hedingham	G122VDX	Ipswich	G760VRT	Chambers	GFH6V	Sanders
FCY289W	Hedingham	G123VDX	Ipswich	G782HVG	Suffolk Education	GGD847X	Fargo Coachlines
FCY290W	Go Whippet	G124UKJ	Chelmsford Taxi	G783HVG	Suffolk Education	GGM84W	Hedingham
FCY292W	Go Whippet	G124VDX	Ipswich	G801VJU	Chelmsford Taxi	GGM89W	Eastern Counties
FCY293W	Go Whippet	G154XJF	Neal's Travel	G801VJU	Chelmsford Taxi	GGM90W	Eastern Counties
FDU5T	Viceroy	G163TNM	Chariots	G805RNC	Grahams	GGM104W	Brentwood Cs
FDX230T	Simonds	G167RBD	Dereham Coaches	G807SKP	Chelmsford Taxi	GGM106W	Brentwood Cs
FDZ5347	Kiddles	G167RBD	Ruffles	G823UMU	Go Whippet	GGM107W	Eastern Counties
FDZ984	Peter Goodward	G189HPW	Dolphin	G824UMU	Go Whippet	GGM108W	Hedingham
FEH1Y	Eastern Counties	G221VDX	Ipswich	G833RDS	Eastern Counties	GGM109W	Stephenson's
FEV115Y	Hedingham	G222VDX	Ipswich	G834RDS	Eastern Counties	GHB85W	Supreme
FEW224Y	Go Whippet	G223VDX	Ipswich	G842VAY	Myall's	GHB86W	C&G Coach
FEW225Y	Go Whippet	G224VDX	Ipswich	G851VAY	Semmence	GHM797N	NIBS
FEW226Y	Go Whippet	G228PGU	Fargo Coachlines	G852VAY	Semmence	GHM803N	NIBS
FEW227Y	Go Whippet	G289UFB	Anglian Coaches	G854VAY	Ford's	GHV3N	Brandons
FHJ565	Beestons	G294OTV	Goldline	G855KKY	Chambers	GHV13N	Brandons
FHS768X	Peter Goodward	G300JEP	Sanders	G855VGS	Chelmsford Taxi	GHV23N	Brandons
FIL2296	Lambert's	G300XAC	Thorns	G863VAY	Veazey	GHV29N	S & M Coaches
FIL4033	Beestons	G329SVV	Viceroy	G864XDX	Chambers	GHV43N	S & M Coaches
FIL4034	Beestons	G342PKR	Chelmsford Taxi	G878SKE	Mike Boggis	GHV97N	Brandons
FIL4164	Beestons	G350GCK	Norfolk Green	G885VNA	Grahams	GIJ4797	Mil-Ken
FIL4165	Beestons	G391MAG	Dolphin	G897MTH	Goldline	GIL2968	Go Whippet
FIL4166	Beestons	G395OWB	Eastern Counties	G901BLP	DMA Mini	GIL3244	Embling
FIL4168	Norfolk Green	G396VMD	DMA Mini	G903KPW	Dolphin	GJF274N	C&G Coach

Reg	Operator	Reg	Operator	Reg	Operator	Reg	Operator
GJF286N	Gretton's	H132EGV	Suffolk Education	H335LAN	Eastern Counties	H394MAR	Essex Buses
GJF302N	Gretton's	H133EGV	Suffolk Education	H335LJN	Essex Buses	H394OHK	Essex Buses
GJG750D	Arriva East Herts	H144NVW	Fargo Coachlines	H336LJN	Essex Buses	H395MAR	Essex Buses
GJI832	Lewis's	H157DJU	Semmence	H337LJN	Essex Buses	H395OHK	Essex Buses
GKE441Y	Stephenson's	H160HJN	Hedingham	H338LJN	Essex Buses	H396OHK	Essex Buses
GND492N	Peter Goodward	H170DVM	Chariots	H339LJN	Essex Buses	H397OHK	Essex Buses
GNG710N	Towler Coaches	H172DVM	Chariots	H341LJN	Essex Buses	H398OHK	Essex Buses
GNK781T	Rules	H175DJF	Cuttings	H342LJN	Essex Buses	H407GAV	Stagecoach Cambus
GNM235N	Caroline Seagull	H176DVM	Chariots	H343LJN	Essex Buses	H411BVR	Eastern Counties
GNN221N	Ambassador Travel	H177DVM	Chariots	H344LJN	Essex Buses	H411CJF	Ford's
GOE264V	Sanders	H177EJU	Matthew Blue	H345LJN	Essex Buses	H423EUT	Windmill
GOI1294	Galloway	H180HPV	Ipswich	H346LJN	Essex Buses	H425DVM	Dolphin
GRA842V	Eastern Counties	H182DVM	Spratts	H347LJN	Essex Buses	H430KOV	Embling
GRA843V	Eastern Counties	H184CNS	Eastons	H348LJN	Essex Buses	H435GVL	Boon's
GRA845V	Eastern Counties	H194TYC	Go-Dons	H349LJN	Essex Buses	H473CEG	Stagecoach Cambus
GRA846V	Eastern Counties	H204DVM	Chambers	H350PNO	Arriva East Herts	H474CEG	Stagecoach Cambus
GRA847V	Eastern Counties	H210BKM	Chelmsford Taxi	H351LJN	Essex Buses	H475CEG	Stagecoach Cambus
GRP260D	Buckland	H224BKM	Chelmsford Taxi	H352LJN	Essex Buses	H487BND	Dolphin
GRT500V	Kiddles	H225BKM	Chelmsford Taxi	H353LJN	Essex Buses	H515YCX	Shaws of Maxey
GRT520V	Coach Services	H225EDX	Ipswich	H353MIJ	Burtons	H521YCX	Leroy Coaches
GSC660X	Dews	H226EDX	Ipswich	H354LJN	Essex Buses	H566MPD	Arriva Southend
GSC661X	Dews	H227BKM	Chelmsford Taxi	H355LJN	Essex Buses	H567MPD	Arriva Southend
GSC662X	Dews	H227EDX	Ipswich	H356HPA	Chelmsford Taxi	H601OVW	Essex Buses
GSC664X	Dews	H228BKM	Chelmsford Taxi	H356LJN	Essex Buses	H602OVW	Essex Buses
GSC665X	Dews	H239ANE	Clintona	H357LJN	Essex Buses	H603OVW	Essex Buses
GSC855T	Stephenson's	H251GEV	Arriva East Herts	H358LJN	Essex Buses	H604OVW	Essex Buses
GSC856T	Eastern Counties	H252GEV	Arriva East Herts	H359LJN	Essex Buses	H605OVW	Essex Buses
GSV905	Mikes Coaches	H253GEV	Arriva East Herts	H361LJN	Essex Buses	H606OVW	Essex Buses
GSX115N	Whiffens	H254GEV	Arriva East Herts	H362LJN	Essex Buses	H607OVW	Essex Buses
GSX118N	Whiffens	H255GEV	Arriva East Herts	H363LJN	Essex Buses	H608OVW	Essex Buses
GSX119N	Whiffens	H256GEV	Arriva East Herts	H364LJN	Essex Buses	H609OVW	Essex Buses
GSX121N	Whiffens	H257GEV	Arriva East Herts	H365LJN	Essex Buses	H611RAH	Eastern Counties
GTX758W	Essexbus	H258GEV	Arriva East Herts	H366LJN	Essex Buses	H612RAH	Eastern Counties
GTX759W	Essexbus	H258LNR	Chelmsford Taxi	H367LJN	Essex Buses	H614RAH	Eastern Counties
GUG132N	NIBS	H259LNR	Chelmsford Taxi	H368OHK	Essex Buses	H615RAH	Eastern Counties
GUP743C	Kenzies	H262GEV	Arriva Southend	H369OHK	Essex Buses	H616RAH	Eastern Counties
GVF777Y	Dolphin	H263GEV	Arriva Southend	H370GRY	Biss Bros	H617RAH	Eastern Counties
GVS948Y	Hedingham	H264GEV	Arriva Southend	H370OHK	Essex Buses	H618RAH	Eastern Counties
GVW894T	Hedingham	H265GEV	Arriva Southend	H371OHK	Essex Buses	H619RAH	Eastern Counties
GWO111W	Semmence	H271CEW	Embling	H372OHK	Essex Buses	H620RAH	Eastern Counties
GWV926V	Buzz	H277DPS	Dereham Coaches	H372PHK	Arriva Southend	H633GUD	Go-Dons
GYE265W	Go Whippet	H283TAH	Neal's Travel	H373OHK	Essex Buses	H642UWR	Stagecoach Cambus
GYE491W	Arriva East Herts	H301LPU	Essex Buses	H374OHK	Essex Buses	H643GRO	Arriva East Herts
GYE537W	Arriva East Herts	H302LPU	Essex Buses	H375OHK	Essex Buses	H643UWR	Stagecoach Cambus
GYE544W	Arriva East Herts	H303CAV	Go Whippet	H376OHK	Essex Buses	H645UWR	Hedingham
GYE573W	Arriva East Herts	H303LPU	Essex Buses	H377OHK	Essex Buses	H649UWR	Stagecoach Cambus
H4FEN	Fenn	H304LPU	Essex Buses	H378OHK	Essex Buses	H652UWR	Stagecoach Cambus
H10SUP	Supreme	H305LPU	Essex Buses	H379OHK	Essex Buses	H653UWR	Stagecoach Cambus
H20BUS	West's	H306LPU	Essex Buses	H380OHK	Essex Buses	H691HRT	Eastern Counties
H29CFR	Viceroy	H307LJN	Essex Buses	H381OHK	Essex Buses	H692HLC	Chelmsford Taxi
H31CFR	Suffolk Education	H308LJN	Essex Buses	H382OHK	Essex Buses	H709UKY	Chelmsford Taxi
H47MJN	Arriva Colchester	H310LJN	Essex Buses	H383OHK	Essex Buses	H714MKV	Chelmsford Taxi
H48MJN	Hedingham	H311LJN	Essex Buses	H384OHK	Essex Buses	H721VWU	Gretton's
H48NDU	Hedingham	H312LJN	Essex Buses	H385OHK	Essex Buses	H729UKY	Chelmsford Taxi
H49MJN	Arriva Colchester	H313LJN	Essex Buses	H386OHK	Essex Buses	H743LHN	Chelmsford Taxi
H62PDW	Chenery	H314LJN	Essex Buses	H387OHK	Essex Buses	H744LHN	Chelmsford Taxi
H63BKM	Clintona	H315LJN	Essex Buses	H388MAR	Essex Buses	H745LHN	Chelmsford Taxi
H63PDW	Chenery	H317LJN	Essex Buses	H388OHK	Essex Buses	H830YGA	Ford's
H84RUX	Neal's Travel	H319LJN	Essex Buses	H389MAR	Essex Buses	H836EKL	Chelmsford Taxi
H91YNL	Chelmsford Taxi	H321LJN	Essex Buses	H389OHK	Essex Buses	H845AHS	Arriva Southend
H101GPV	Suffolk Education	H322LJN	Essex Buses	H390MAR	Essex Buses	H846OHB	Chelmsford Taxi
H101KVX	Eastern Counties	H324LJN	Essex Buses	H390OHK	Essex Buses	H862VCL	Chelmsford Taxi
H102GPV	Suffolk Education	H326LJN	Essex Buses	H391CFT	Neal's Travel	H881AVK	Cedrick's
H102KVX	Eastern Counties	H327LJN	Essex Buses	H391MAR	Essex Buses	H903AHS	Arriva East Herts
H103KVX	Eastern Counties	H329LJN	Essex Buses	H391OHK	Essex Buses	H909SKW	First Choice
H104KVX	Eastern Counties	H330LJN	Essex Buses	H392CFT	Grahams	H933GFA	Chelmsford Taxi
H113DVM	Sanders	H331FPV	Suffolk Education	H392MAR	Essex Buses	H935DRJ	Dereham Coaches
H120KWC	Clintona	H331LJN	Essex Buses	H392OHK	Essex Buses	H982KVX	Fargo Coachlines
H123WFM	Arriva Colchester	H332LJN	Essex Buses	H393MAR	Essex Buses	H984XYH	Chelmsford Taxi
H131EGV	Suffolk Education	H334LJN	Essex Buses	H393OHK	Essex Buses	H994DKL	Chelmsford Taxi

Reg	Operator	Reg	Operator	Reg	Operator	Reg	Operator
HAH238V	Eastern Counties	HSK836	Supreme	J308WHJ	Arriva East Herts	J722KBC	Go Whippet
HAH239V	Eastern Counties	HSK844	Supreme	J309WHJ	Arriva East Herts	J723KBC	Go Whippet
HAH240V	Eastern Counties	HSK845	Supreme	J310WHJ	Arriva East Herts	J724KBC	Hedingham
HAL241V	Avro & Elm Park	HSK855	Supreme	J311WHJ	Arriva East Herts	J734CWT	Hedingham
HBH411Y	Morley's	HSK856	Supreme	J312WHJ	Arriva East Herts	J739CWT	Stagecoach Cambus
HCL927Y	Ambassador Travel	HSK857	Supreme	J313WHJ	Arriva East Herts	J740CWT	Stagecoach Cambus
HCL957Y	Ambassador Travel	HSK858	Supreme	J314XVX	Arriva East Herts	J741CWT	Stagecoach Cambus
HDW873N	D-Way Travel	HSK859	Supreme	J315XVX	Arriva East Herts	J742CWT	Stagecoach Cambus
HDX907N	Go-Dons	HSK860	Supreme	J316XVX	Arriva East Herts	J743CWT	Stagecoach Cambus
HDZ8354	Arriva East Herts	HSK892	Supreme	J317XVX	Arriva East Herts	J744CWT	Stagecoach Cambus
HEW174Y	Shaws of Maxey	HSV192	Andrews Coaches	J318LNL	Matthew Blue	J762ONK	Beestons
HEX47Y	Ambassador Travel	HSV193	Andrews Coaches	J388RRX	Ruffles	J764ONK	Felix
HEX52Y	Ambassador Travel	HSV197	Andrews Coaches	J392BNG	Belle Coaches	J765ONK	Beestons
HEX118Y	Eastern Counties	HTC729N	S & P Coach	J401XVX	Arriva East Herts	J805DWW	Stagecoach Cambus
HEX119Y	Eastern Counties	HTU154N	Embling	J402XVX	Arriva East Herts	J806DWW	Stagecoach Cambus
HEX211Y	Sanders	HUP766T	Grahams	J403XVX	Arriva East Herts	J807DWW	Stagecoach Cambus
HFL14W	Kenzies	HUX82V	Sanders	J404WDA	Eastern Counties	J832RNK	Neal's Travel
HFL950N	Shaws of Maxey	HWJ933W	Cedrick's	J404XVX	Arriva East Herts	J916PEA	Wards
HGA637T	Beestons	HWJ934W	Cedrick's	J408TEW	Stagecoach Cambus	J926CYL	Arriva East Herts
HGG997T	Sanders	HWY701	Brentwood Cs	J409TEW	Stagecoach Cambus	J927CYL	Arriva East Herts
HHJ372Y	Eastern Counties	HYX418W	Whincop	J427HDS	Shaws of Maxey	J928CYL	Arriva East Herts
HHJ375Y	Essex Buses	IAZ6387	Amber Bus	J438HDS	Ambassador Travel	J933WHJ	Arriva East Herts
HHJ376Y	Essex Buses	IAZ6394	Peter Goodward	J480NJU	Viceroy	J934WHJ	Arriva East Herts
HHJ381Y	Eastern Counties	IUI2733	CI Coachlines	J530FCL	Eastern Counties	J935WHJ	Arriva East Herts
HHJ382Y	Eastern Counties	IUI2734	CI Coachlines	J582WVX	Harris Bus	J936WHJ	Arriva East Herts
HIB644	Simonds	IUI2735	CI Coachlines	J583WVX	Harris Bus	J937WHJ	Arriva East Herts
HIJ6931	Fargo Coachlines	IUI3589	CI Coachlines	J601WHJ	Arriva East Herts	J938WHJ	Arriva East Herts
HIL2325	Brandons	J2SUP	Supreme	J603WHJ	Arriva East Herts	J960DWX	Stagecoach Cambus
HIL2391	Brentwood Cs	J3SUP	Supreme	J604WHJ	Arriva East Herts	J961DWX	Stagecoach Cambus
HIL2392	Brentwood Cs	J4TCC	Stort Valley	J605WHJ	Arriva East Herts	J962DWX	Stagecoach Cambus
HIL2921	Brandons	J7BBC	Biss Bros	J606WHJ	Arriva East Herts	J992AKY	Chelmsford Taxi
HIL2922	Brandons	J7FTG	Sanders	J607WHJ	Arriva East Herts	J996XKU	Chelmsford Taxi
HIL2923	S M Travel	J8BBC	Biss Bros	J608WHJ	Arriva East Herts	J998MKL	Chelmsford Taxi
HIL3087	DMA Mini	J8FTG	Sanders	J609WHJ	Arriva East Herts	JA5515	Brentwood Cs
HIL4346	Stephenson's	J20GSM	Belle Coaches	J610UTW	Essex Buses	JAG406N	Gretton's
HIL4349	Stephenson's	J31KLR	Eastern Counties	J610WHJ	Arriva East Herts	JAH241V	Eastern Counties
HIL6244	Cedrick's	J37KLR	Eastern Counties	J611UTW	Essex Buses	JAH242V	Eastern Counties
HIL6327	Mil-Ken	J42PAV	Kenzies	J611WHJ	Arriva East Herts	JAH243V	Eastern Counties
HIL6328	Mil-Ken	J51GCX	Harris Bus	J612UTW	Essex Buses	JAH552D	Stagecoach Cambus
HIL6919	Spratts	J52GCX	Harris Bus	J612WHJ	Arriva East Herts	JAH553D	Stagecoach Cambus
HIL7391	Spratts	J56GCX	Arriva East Herts	J613UTW	Essex Buses	JAR484Y	J Amos
HIL7394	Spratts	J64BJN	Arriva East Herts	J614UTW	Essex Buses	JAR495V	Hedingham
HIL7477	Spratts	J65BJN	Arriva East Herts	J615UTW	Essex Buses	JAZ3562	Mil-Ken
HIL7478	Spratts	J78SNK	Neal's Travel	J616UTW	Essex Buses	JAZ6847	Mil-Ken
HIL7479	Spratts	J81KBD	Suffolk Education	J617UTW	Essex Buses	JAZ6914	Mil-Ken
HIL7591	Thorns	J97BWG	Chelmsford Taxi	J618UTW	Essex Buses	JAZ6917	Mil-Ken
HIL7618	Chenery	J110LKO	Chelmsford Taxi	J619UTW	Essex Buses	JAZ6918	Mil-Ken
HIL8130	Myall's	J142LKC	Goldline	J620UTW	Essex Buses	JAZ6948	Mil-Ken
HIL8221	Brentwood Cs	J160LPV	Ipswich	J621BVG	Eastern Counties	JAZ7815	Mil-Ken
HIL8435	Thorns	J213XKY	Pullman	J621UTW	Essex Buses	JAZ8291	Mil-Ken
HIL9272	Brentwood Cs	J218NRT	Ipswich	J622BVG	Eastern Counties	JAZ8315	Mil-Ken
HIL9275	Brentwood Cs	J220HDS	Felix	J622UTW	Essex Buses	JAZ9860	Chambers
HIW1175	Bure Valley	J222SJS	Euroview	J623BVG	Eastern Counties	JAZ9861	Chambers
HIW233	Happy Wanderer	J228JDX	Ipswich	J623UTW	Essex Buses	JBO75W	Arriva East Herts
HIW471	Happy Wanderer	J233XKY	Embling	J624BVG	Eastern Counties	JBO80W	Arriva East Herts
HIW9901	Happy Wanderer	J234XKY	Spratts	J624REG	Whincop	JBY804	Kenzies
HJB455W	Hedingham	J275TVU	Gretton's	J624UTW	Essex Buses	JBZ3250	Chariots
HJB456W	Hedingham	J276NNC	Galloway	J625BVG	Eastern Counties	JDB932V	Bird's
HJB459W	Hedingham	J282GMF	Chelmsford Taxi	J625UTW	Essex Buses	JDB934V	Andrews Coaches
HJB464W	Hedingham	J295TWK	Hedingham	J626UTW	Essex Buses	JDB948V	Bird's
HJI3932	Stephenson's	J301KDX	Suffolk Education	J627UTW	Essex Buses	JDG322V	Neave
HKG65N	Cunningham	J301WHJ	Arriva East Herts	J628UTW	Essex Buses	JDN506L	Sanders
HMB672X	Bird's	J302KDX	Suffolk Education	J629UTW	Essex Buses	JEV245Y	Ford's
HNM201Y	Amber Bus	J302WHJ	Arriva East Herts	J630UTW	Essex Buses	JEV706N	Fenn
HOI7624	M & E Coaches	J303KDX	Suffolk Education	J652DVG	Caroline Seagull	JFA450V	Belle Coaches
HOI7624	S & P Coach	J303WHJ	Arriva East Herts	J669LGA	Go Whippet	JFR397N	Morley's
HRT530N	J Amos	J304WHJ	Arriva East Herts	J670LGA	Go Whippet	JGA189N	Go-Dons
HSB312Y	Stephenson's	J305WHJ	Arriva East Herts	J687LGA	Go Whippet	JGU938V	Sanders
HSB906Y	Bird's	J306WHJ	Arriva East Herts	J688LGA	Go Whippet	JGV321V	Stephenson's
HSD77V	Embling	J307WHJ	Arriva East Herts	J689LGA	Go Whippet	JGV335V	West Row

Reg	Operator	Reg	Operator	Reg	Operator	Reg	Operator
JGV336V	Semmence	K100LCT	Ipswich	K642GVX	Essex Buses	K965HUB	Stagecoach Cambus
JGV929	Simonds	K101VJU	Belle Coaches	K643GVX	Essex Buses	K966GWR	Golden Boy
JHJ142V	Essex Buses	K103VJT	Chambers	K644GVX	Essex Buses	K966HUB	Stagecoach Cambus
JHJ147V	Essex Buses	K112YFL	Jans Coaches	K645GVX	Essex Buses	K967HUB	Stagecoach Cambus
JHJ150V	Essex Buses	K124TCP	Arriva East Herts	K646GVX	Essex Buses	K968HUB	Stagecoach Cambus
JHK495N	Arriva Colchester	K129OCT	Boon's	K651EEV	Cooks of Southend	K969HUB	Stagecoach Cambus
JIL2014	West Row	K134UDX	Suffolk Education	K707FNO	Arriva East Herts	K96GEV	Jacksons Cs
JIL2015	Coach Services	K135UDX	Suffolk Education	K707RNR	Supreme	K970HUB	Stagecoach Cambus
JIL2146	Carter's Coaches	K142PLP	Felix	K708FNO	Arriva East Herts	K971HUB	Stagecoach Cambus
JIL2194	Arriva Colchester	K144PLP	Ruffles	K708PNR	Supreme	K972HUB	Stagecoach Cambus
JIL2195	Arriva Colchester	K146PLP	Ruffles	K709FNO	Arriva East Herts	K973HUB	Stagecoach Cambus
JIL3580	Partridge	K161RGV	Suffolk Education	K710FNO	Arriva East Herts	K974HUB	Stagecoach Cambus
JIL3968	Coach Services	K171CAV	Stagecoach Cambus	K710RNR	Rayleigh	K975KUB	Stagecoach Cambus
JIL5623	Hedingham	K172CAV	Stagecoach Cambus	K711FNO	Arriva East Herts	KAC1	Dolphin
JIL7540	Leroy Coaches	K173CAV	Stagecoach Cambus	K712FNO	Arriva East Herts	KAU574V	Sanders
JIW3696	Arriva East Herts	K174CAV	Stagecoach Cambus	K731JAH	Eastern Counties	KAU575V	Sanders
JIW3889	Leroy Coaches	K175CAV	Stagecoach Cambus	K732JAH	Eastern Counties	KBC2V	Hedingham
JIW7131	Peter Goodward	K176CAV	Stagecoach Cambus	K733JAH	Eastern Counties	KBH860V	Biss Bros
JJG1P	Peter Goodward	K177CAV	Stagecoach Cambus	K734JAH	Eastern Counties	KBH861V	Buzz
JJT436N	Beestons	K198EVW	Hedingham	K735JAH	Eastern Counties	KBJ831	Brentwood Cs
JJT445N	Beestons	K219PPV	Ipswich	K736JAH	Eastern Counties	KBV211S	Kiddles
JJU442V	Whincop	K317EJV	Clintona	K737JAH	Eastern Counties	KCJ677Y	County Travel
JJU443V	Whincop	K318CVX	Arriva East Herts	K738JAH	Eastern Counties	KEH976N	S M Travel
JKV413V	Neave	K319CVX	Arriva East Herts	K739JAH	Eastern Counties	KEL95	Brentwood Cs
JKV414V	Hedingham	K320CVX	Arriva East Herts	K740JAH	Eastern Counties	KEP829X	Eastern Counties
JKV420V	Semmence	K321CVX	Arriva East Herts	K741JAH	Eastern Counties	KFX675	S M Travel
JKV422V	Semmence	K322CVX	Arriva East Herts	K742JAH	Eastern Counties	KGA56Y	West's
JKW277W	Burtons	K323CVX	Arriva East Herts	K743JAH	Eastern Counties	KGS483Y	Bure Valley
JMJ144V	Blue Diamond	K327EJV	Neal's Travel	K744JAH	Eastern Counties	KGS489Y	Hedingham
JNJ510V	Thorns	K329KVG	Galloway	K750UJO	Pullman	KHB29W	Andrews Coaches
JNK551N	Sanders	K332UDX	Suffolk Education	K752UJO	Pullman	KHB35W	Fargo Coachlines
JOX467P	Ambassador Travel	K341EYT	Chelmsford Taxi	K760JVX	Arriva East Herts	KHD832V	Galloway
JPE605V	Rules	K344BOK	Pullman	K761JVX	Arriva East Herts	KHF131	Webbs
JPL185K	Stort Valley	K379DBL	Eastern Counties	K762JVX	Arriva East Herts	KIA891	Simonds
JPV221N	Dews	K390KUA	Stagecoach Cambus	K805DJN	Essex Buses	KIB5227	Rules
JSC883E	Boon's	K391KUA	Stagecoach Cambus	K806DJN	Essex Buses	KIB7256	NIBS
JSC890E	Caroline Seagull	K392BVS	Felix	K807DJN	Essex Buses	KIW7813	DMA Mini
JSK951	Partridge	K392KUA	Stagecoach Cambus	K808DJN	Essex Buses	KJI6029	Beestons
JTD392P	Arriva Southend	K393KUA	Stagecoach Cambus	K809DJN	Essex Buses	KJN299	Freestones
JTD396P	Arriva Southend	K396KHJ	Essex Buses	K810DJN	Essex Buses	KKK887V	Brentwood Cs
JTM106V	County Coaches	K397KHJ	Essex Buses	K811DJN	Essex Buses	KKV701V	Euroview
JTY926P	Eastern Counties	K398KHJ	Essex Buses	K816HUM	Chambers	KNG999L	Fourways
JUM178N	Norfolk Green	K405FHJ	Arriva East Herts	K832FEE	Neal's Travel	KNK539V	Neave
JUS774N	Go-Dons	K406FHJ	Arriva East Herts	K841EKW	Reynolds	KNP1X	Associated Cs
JVE370P	Embling	K407FHJ	Arriva East Herts	K861NST	Coach Services	KNR310V	Semmence
JWT757V	Hedingham	K408FHJ	Arriva East Herts	K901CVW	Essex Buses	KOF663	Leroy Coaches
JWT762V	Eastern Counties	K409FHJ	Arriva East Herts	K902CVW	Essex Buses	KON340P	Beestons
JWV271W	Hedingham	K410FHJ	Arriva East Herts	K903CVW	Essex Buses	KOO787V	Essex Buses
JXI6133	Felix	K411FHJ	Arriva East Herts	K904CVW	Essex Buses	KOO789V	Essex Buses
JYC855	Brentwood Cs	K412FHJ	Arriva East Herts	K905CVW	Essex Buses	KOO790V	Essex Buses
K2HWT	Happy Wanderer	K413FHJ	Arriva East Herts	K906CVW	Essex Buses	KOO794V	Essex Buses
K4SUP	Supreme	K414FHJ	Arriva East Herts	K907CVW	Essex Buses	KOU796P	M & E Coaches
K5SUP	Supreme	K424GHE	Windmill	K908CVW	Essex Buses	KPJ248W	Arriva East Herts
K6SUP	Supreme	K442BMO	Lodge's	K908RGE	Cedrick's	KPJ268W	Colchester Coaches
K11BOO	Boon's	K459PNR	Supreme	K909CVW	Essex Buses	KPJ269W	Greys of Ely
K13BYS	Kirby's Rayleigh	K45DFA	Chelmsford Taxi	K910CVW	Essex Buses	KPJ289W	Colchester Coaches
K15FTG	Dereham Coaches	K545ORH	Arriva East Herts	K911CVW	Essex Buses	KSU369	Boon's
K17WEB	Go-Dons	K546ORH	Arriva East Herts	K911RGE	Stagecoach Cambus	KSU412	Anglian Coaches
K26HCL	Eastern Counties	K555KGM	Fargo Coachlines	K912CVW	Essex Buses	KSU470	CI Coachlines
K27HCL	Eastern Counties	K631GVX	Essex Buses	K912RGE	Stagecoach Cambus	KSU850P	Go-Dons
K28HCL	Eastern Counties	K632GVX	Essex Buses	K913CVW	Essex Buses	KUC154P	S & M Coaches
K29HCL	Eastern Counties	K633GVX	Essex Buses	K914CVW	Essex Buses	KUC217P	Brandons
K30GGY	Goldline	K634GVX	Essex Buses	K915CVW	Essex Buses	KUC941P	S & M Coaches
K49TER	Kenzies	K635GVX	Essex Buses	K916CVW	Essex Buses	KVF245V	Stagecoach Cambus
K51TER	Kenzies	K636GVX	Essex Buses	K917CVW	Essex Buses	KVF246V	Stagecoach Cambus
K52TER	Kenzies	K637GVX	Essex Buses	K919TBC	Galloway	KVF250V	Stagecoach Cambus
K62KEX	Eastern Counties	K638GVX	Essex Buses	K936GWR	Chambers	KVG602V	Eastern Counties
K63KEX	Eastern Counties	K639GVX	Essex Buses	K962UGV	Suffolk Education	KVG604V	Eastern Counties
K95GEV	Harris Bus	K640GVX	Essex Buses	K963HUB	Stagecoach Cambus	KVG607V	Eastern Counties
K97GEV	Harris Bus	K641GVX	Essex Buses	K964HUB	Stagecoach Cambus	KVG609V	Eastern Counties

Reg	Operator	Reg	Operator	Reg	Operator	Reg	Operator
KYN283X	Go Whippet	L299KKW	Burtons	L738NMU	Jacksons Cs	LIL9457	Belle Coaches
KYN296X	Go Whippet	L300SUP	Supreme	L768XLK	Buzz	LIL9458	Belle Coaches
KYN300X	Go Whippet	L304PWR	Essex Buses	L801KNO	Arriva East Herts	LIL9713	Belle Coaches
KYO625X	Arriva East Herts	L337HFU	Ruffles	L801MEV	Essex Buses	LIL9714	Belle Coaches
KYV346X	Go Whippet	L343RWF	Biss Bros	L802KNO	Arriva East Herts	LIL9715	Belle Coaches
KYV422X	Go Whippet	L345MKU	Bakerbus	L802MEV	Essex Buses	LIL9716	Belle Coaches
KYV649X	Arriva East Herts	L347MKU	Bakerbus	L803KNO	Arriva East Herts	LIL9717	Belle Coaches
KYV782X	Arriva East Herts	L34VBX	Goldline	L803OPU	Essex Buses	LIL9718	Belle Coaches
L3CED	Cedrick's	L363XDX	Suffolk Education	L804KNO	Arriva East Herts	LIW1933	C&G Coach
L3LWR	Enterprise	L399LHE	Fargo Coachlines	L804OPU	Essex Buses	LJI477	Ford's
L4WMS	Goldline	L415NHJ	Arriva East Herts	L805OPU	Essex Buses	LJI1613	Leroy Coaches
L46CNY	Soames	L425OWF	Windmill	L805OVX	Arriva East Herts	LMS151W	Brentwood Cs
L54REW	Simonds	L452UEB	Myall's	L806OPU	Essex Buses	LMS152W	Brentwood Cs
L56REW	Kenzies	L469DOA	Clintona	L807OPU	Eastern Counties	LMS155W	Brentwood Cs
L57REW	Kenzies	L470DOA	Clintona	L808OPU	Essex Buses	LMS166W	Brentwood Cs
L67UNG	Ambassador Travel	L471DOA	Clintona	L809OPU	Essex Buses	LNU581W	Sanders
L67YJF	Supreme	L472DOA	Clintona	L810OPU	Essex Buses	LPB217P	Associated Cs
L68UNG	Ambassador Travel	L475GOV	Harris Bus	L811OPU	Essex Buses	LPV111P	Buckland
L69UNG	Ambassador Travel	L476GOV	Harris Bus	L812OPU	Essex Buses	LRA801P	Hedingham
L71UNG	Ambassador Travel	L484JFU	Neal's Travel	L813OPU	Essex Buses	LRU822	Stort Valley
L73UNG	Ambassador Travel	L501MOO	Arriva East Herts	L814OPU	Essex Buses	LSK643	Peelings
L74UNG	Ambassador Travel	L501VHU	Eastern Counties	L815OPU	Essex Buses	LSU113	Crusader
L93OAR	Harris Bus	L502VHU	Eastern Counties	L816OPU	Essex Buses	LTG272X	Anglian Coaches
L98PTW	Harris Bus	L507KDA	Supreme	L817OPU	Essex Buses	LTG274X	Anglian Coaches
L100SUP	Supreme	L520CAY	Flagfinders	L818OPU	Essex Buses	LUA283V	Beestons
L101PWR	Eastern Counties	L531XUT	Coach Services	L819OPU	Essex Buses	LUA288V	S & M Coaches
L102PWR	Eastern Counties	L601MWC	Eastern Counties	L820OPU	Essex Buses	LUA289V	Hedingham
L103PWR	Eastern Counties	L613LVX	Arriva East Herts	L821OPU	Essex Buses	LUA716V	Essex Buses
L104PWR	Eastern Counties	L614LVX	Arriva East Herts	L822OPU	Essex Buses	LUA717V	Essex Buses
L105PWR	Eastern Counties	L631WLD	Ruffles	L832MWT	Ipswich	LUA718V	Eastern Counties
L106PWR	Eastern Counties	L634ANX	Fargo Coachlines	L890UVE	NIBS	LUA719V	Eastern Counties
L109PVW	Crusader	L637ANX	Fargo Coachlines	L891UVE	NIBS	LUM154V	Beestons
L110PVW	Crusader	L647MEV	Essex Buses	L919ABJ	Ruffles	LVH481P	Embling
L111PVW	Crusader	L648MEV	Essex Buses	L933YPV	Suffolk Education	LVL806V	Towler Coaches
L112PVW	Crusader	L649MEV	Essex Buses	L938ORC	Ambassador Travel	LVS228P	Neave
L161ADX	Ipswich	L650MEV	Essex Buses	L960VFL	Greys of Ely	LVS426V	Bure Valley
L162ADX	Ipswich	L651MEV	Essex Buses	L966FLJ	Shaws of Maxey	LVV124P	Fenn
L162XDX	Suffolk Education	L652MEV	Essex Buses	L967OFL	Myall's	LVY520T	DMA Mini
L163XDX	Suffolk Education	L653MEV	Essex Buses	L977MWB	Travelrich	LWU469V	Essex Buses
L164XDX	Suffolk Education	L654MEV	Essex Buses	L978UAH	Ambassador Travel	LWU472V	Eastern Counties
L165XDX	Suffolk Education	L655MEV	Essex Buses	L979UAH	Ambassador Travel	LXR958	Brandons
L169ADX	Ipswich	L655MFL	Stagecoach Cambus	LAH817A	Sanders	M2SOB	Simonds
L181ADX	Ipswich	L656MEV	Essex Buses	LAH893A	West Row	M3ERH	Galloway
L182ADX	Ipswich	L656MFL	Stagecoach Cambus	LDA637W	Amber Bus	M3SOB	Simonds
L183APV	Ipswich	L657MFL	Stagecoach Cambus	LDV398P	Beestons	M4CNG	C&G Coach
L184APV	Ipswich	L658MFL	Stagecoach Cambus	LEW16W	Kenzies	M4FEN	Fenn
L185PRF	Coach Services	L659ADS	Dereham Coaches	LEW971P	Go Whippet	M4WMS	Goldline
L198SCM	Felix	L659ADS	Soames	LGV34	Partridge	M7SLC	Lodge's
L200SUP	Supreme	L659MFL	Stagecoach Cambus	LHG440T	Beestons	M8CED	Cedrick's
L202HYE	Hedingham	L660MFL	Stagecoach Cambus	LHG441T	Greys of Ely	M23JDW	Ambassador Travel
L203HYE	Hedingham	L661MFL	Stagecoach Cambus	LHG445T	Thorns	M24THJ	Supreme
L207RNO	Hedingham	L662MFL	Stagecoach Cambus	LHK589Y	Kirby's Rayleigh	M34KAX	Ambassador Travel
L208RNO	Hedingham	L663MFL	Stagecoach Cambus	LHU662L	Partridge	M35KAX	Ambassador Travel
L21AHA	Essex Buses	L664MFL	Stagecoach Cambus	LIB226	Simonds	M40TGM	Burtons
L232FRX	Golden Boy	L665MFL	Stagecoach Cambus	LIB1474	C&G Coach	M41EPV	Ipswich
L245PAH	Eastern Counties	L667MFL	Stagecoach Cambus	LIB1745	C&G Coach	M42EPV	Ipswich
L246PAH	Eastern Counties	L668MFL	Stagecoach Cambus	LIB2006	Lewis's	M52WEV	Harris Bus
L247PAH	Eastern Counties	L668MFL	Fargo Coachlines	LIB8340	C&G Coach	M61WEB	Kenzies
L248PAH	Eastern Counties	L669MFL	Stagecoach Cambus	LIL2184	Thorns	M61WER	Biss Bros
L249PAH	Eastern Counties	L691XLK	Goldline	LIL2493	Sanders	M63WEB	Kenzies
L250PAH	Eastern Counties	L705CNR	Lodge's	LIL2592	Lodge's	M64WEB	Kenzies
L251PAH	Eastern Counties	L713OVX	Arriva East Herts	LIL2697	Embling	M65WEB	Kenzies
L252PAH	Eastern Counties	L714OVX	Arriva East Herts	LIL2816	Embling	M67WEB	Kenzies
L253PAH	Eastern Counties	L715OVX	Arriva East Herts	LIL5870	Paynes of Paxton	M68XVF	Eastern Counties
L254PAH	Eastern Counties	L716OVX	Arriva East Herts	LIL7230	Brentwood Cs	M69XVF	Eastern Counties
L255PAH	Eastern Counties	L717OVX	Arriva East Herts	LIL9452	Belle Coaches	M107RRJ	Eastern Counties
L256PAH	Eastern Counties	L718OVX	Arriva East Herts	LIL9453	Belle Coaches	M107UWY	Hedingham
L257PAH	Eastern Counties	L720OVX	Arriva East Herts	LIL9454	Belle Coaches	M121SKY	Biss Bros
L258PAH	Eastern Counties	L723PHK	Arriva East Herts	LIL9455	Belle Coaches	M131SKY	Biss Bros
L259PAH	Eastern Counties	L724PHK	Arriva East Herts	LIL9456	Belle Coaches	M136EBJ	Suffolk Education

Almost half of Brandons' fleet comprises double-deck vehicles. While most are Daimler Fleetlines new to London Buses, two double-deck coaches are also present. One of these is a Kässbohrer Setra Imperial and the other is LXR958, an integral Van Hool Astromega. The vehicle is seen with a Mercedes-Benz sign, though normally a MAN engine is fitted. *Colin Lloyd*

M137EBJ	Suffolk Education	M310VET	Fargo Coachlines	M379YEX	Eastern Counties	M618YEH	Thorns
M140AVG	D-Way Travel	M312VET	Belle Coaches	M380YEX	Eastern Counties	M635UCT	Golden Boy
M150EAV	Go Whippet	M313VET	Boon's	M381KVR	Eastern Counties	M640EPV	Ipswich
M166EBJ	Suffolk Education	M321VET	Ambassador Travel	M384KVR	Flying Banana	M649RCP	Harris Bus
M166VJN	Essex Buses	M325VET	Ambassador Travel	M384WET	Biss Bros	M657VJN	Essex Buses
M173YGF	Dolphin	M330KRY	Ambassador Travel	M391KVR	Felix	M658VJN	Essex Buses
M201VWW	Eastern Counties	M331KRY	Ambassador Travel	M440AVG	Dereham Coaches	M659VJN	Essex Buses
M202VWW	Eastern Counties	M332KRY	Ambassador Travel	M441CVG	Lambert's	M660VJN	Essex Buses
M203VWW	Eastern Counties	M334GGV	Suffolk Education	M486HBC	Ford's	M661VJN	Essex Buses
M210VEV	Hedingham	M341MRU	Simonds	M501XWC	Harris Bus	M662VJN	Essex Buses
M211WHJ	Hedingham	M345UVX	Grahams	M502XWC	Harris Bus	M663VJN	Essex Buses
M212WHJ	Hedingham	M360XEX	Eastern Counties	M503XWC	Harris Bus	M664VJN	Essex Buses
M213EDX	Ipswich	M361XEX	Eastern Counties	M504XWC	Harris Bus	M665VJN	Essex Buses
M214EDX	Ipswich	M362XEX	Eastern Counties	M513MFX	Soames	M667VJN	Essex Buses
M215EDX	Ipswich	M363XEX	Eastern Counties	M515NCG	Harris Bus	M668VJN	Essex Buses
M216EDX	Ipswich	M364XEX	Eastern Counties	M517NCG	Hedingham	M669VJN	Essex Buses
M242AEX	Eastern Counties	M365UML	Clintona	M519NCG	Harris Bus	M670VJN	Essex Buses
M244TAK	Euroview	M365XEX	Eastern Counties	M534NCG	Shaws of Maxey	M671VJN	Essex Buses
M256TAK	Supreme	M366XEX	Eastern Counties	M561TJL	Myall's	M672VJN	Essex Buses
M257LNR	Chelmsford Taxi	M367XEX	Eastern Counties	M571XKY	Hedingham	M673VJN	Essex Buses
M257TAK	Supreme	M368XEX	Eastern Counties	M577VSF	Myall's	M674VJN	Essex Buses
M258TAK	Supreme	M369XEX	Eastern Counties	M584ANG	Eastern Counties	M675VJN	Essex Buses
M259TAK	Supreme	M370XEX	Eastern Counties	M585ANG	Eastern Counties	M676VJN	Essex Buses
M261KWK	Hedingham	M371XEX	Eastern Counties	M586ANG	Eastern Counties	M707HBC	Go-Dons
M262KWK	Hedingham	M372XEX	Eastern Counties	M587ANG	Eastern Counties	M719UTW	Arriva East Herts
M263TAK	Veazey	M373VER	Neal's Travel	M588ANG	Eastern Counties	M720UTW	Arriva East Herts
M266VPU	Arriva East Herts	M373XEX	Eastern Counties	M589ANG	Eastern Counties	M721UTW	Arriva East Herts
M267VPU	Arriva East Herts	M374XEX	Eastern Counties	M589SDC	Go Whippet	M725UTW	Arriva East Herts
M268VPU	Arriva East Herts	M375YEX	Eastern Counties	M590ANG	Eastern Counties	M726UTW	Arriva East Herts
M269VPU	Arriva East Herts	M376YEX	Eastern Counties	M591ANG	Eastern Counties	M727UTW	Arriva East Herts
M306VET	Fargo Coachlines	M377YEX	Eastern Counties	M592ANG	Eastern Counties	M728UTW	Arriva East Herts
M307VET	Fargo Coachlines	M378YEX	Eastern Counties	M593ANG	Eastern Counties	M729UTW	Arriva East Herts

OTW116K is believed to be the first Kässbohrer Setra integral coach imported into Britain, entering service in 1971. The S130 model displays lines of the 100 series which are less familiar in Britain, though still common in its home country of Germany where the latest deliveries from the Ulm factory are mainly the highly impressive 300 series. *Colin Lloyd*

M730AOO	Arriva East Herts	M924TEV	Essex Buses	MBE616R	Fargo Coachlines	MIL4682	Beestons
M731AOO	Arriva East Herts	M925TEV	Essex Buses	MBT674T	Cooks of Southend	MIL5015	Chambers
M732AOO	Arriva East Herts	M926TEV	Essex Buses	MBZ7140	Stephenson's	MIL5733	Embling
M733AOO	Arriva East Herts	M927TEV	Essex Buses	MCL555V	Chenery	MIL7163	Collins
M734AOO	Arriva East Herts	M928TEV	Essex Buses	MDS860V	Eastern Counties	MIL7164	Collins
M735AOO	Arriva East Herts	M929TEV	Essex Buses	MDS868V	Eastern Counties	MIL7165	Collins
M736AOO	Arriva East Herts	M930TEV	Essex Buses	MDX668V	Belle Coaches	MIL9423	Lambert's
M737AOO	Arriva East Herts	M931TEV	Essex Buses	MEB626	Embling	MIW3561	Sanders
M738AOO	Arriva East Herts	M932TEV	Essex Buses	MEV83V	Arriva Colchester	MIW5802	Bure Valley
M738OKK	Clintona	M933TEV	Essex Buses	MEV84V	Arriva Colchester	MJA749W	County Travel
M741KJU	Ambassador Travel	M934TEV	Essex Buses	MEV85V	Arriva Colchester	MJB481	Lodge's
M742KJU	Ambassador Travel	M935TEV	Essex Buses	MEV86V	Arriva Colchester	MJI1306	Jacksons Cs
M743KJU	Ambassador Travel	M936TEV	Essex Buses	MEV87V	Arriva Colchester	MJI2374	Jacksons Cs
M759PVM	Beestons	M937TEV	Essex Buses	MFA719V	Stephenson's	MJI2550	Jacksons Cs
M761JPA	Arriva Southend	M938TEV	Essex Buses	MFN44R	Flagfinders	MJI3376	Jacksons Cs
M762JPA	Arriva Southend	M939TEV	Essex Buses	MFN45R	Fargo Coachlines	MJI4487	Anglian Coaches
M763JPA	Arriva Southend	M940TEV	Essex Buses	MGR672P	Hedingham	MJI4690	Mil-Ken
M764JPA	Arriva Southend	M941TEV	Essex Buses	MHJ731V	Eastern Counties	MKK458P	Hedingham
M808WWR	Stagecoach Cambus	M942TEV	Essex Buses	MHP3V	Veazey	MLK677L	Brandons
M809WWR	Stagecoach Cambus	M943TEV	Essex Buses	MHX49X	D-Way Travel	MMJ538V	Andrews Coaches
M810WWR	Stagecoach Cambus	M951LYR	Arriva East Herts	MIB1366	Flagfinders	MMJ547V	Sanders
M830RCP	Galloway	M953UHK	Supreme	MIB3378	Peelings	MNK427V	Fourways
M832CVG	Lambert's	M971CVG	Sanders	MIB9067	Sanders	MNK429V	Fourways
M853WEB	Neal's Travel	M975WWR	Stagecoach Cambus	MIL1030	C&G Coach	MNM40V	Sanders
M883XVG	Eastern Counties	M976WWR	Stagecoach Cambus	MIL1032	C&G Coach	MOD569P	Hedingham
M884XVG	Eastern Counties	M977WWR	Stagecoach Cambus	MIL1658	Mil-Ken	MPJ210L	Arriva Southend
M918TEV	Essex Buses	M978WWR	Stagecoach Cambus	MIL1803	Mil-Ken	MRB802P	Hedingham
M919TEV	Essex Buses	M979VWY	Stagecoach Cambus	MIL2886	Cedrick's	MRJ8W	Hedingham
M920TEV	Essex Buses	M988NAA	Hedingham	MIL3728	Beestons	MRJ9W	Hedingham
M921TEV	Essex Buses	MAU142P	NIBS	MIL4420	Beestons	MRJ231W	Arriva Southend
M922TEV	Essex Buses	MAZ6740	Flagfinders	MIL4421	Beestons	MRJ232W	Arriva Southend
M923TEV	Eastern Counties	MBC39V	Fourways	MIL4681	Beestons	MRJ233W	Arriva Southend

Reg	Operator	Reg	Operator	Reg	Operator	Reg	Operator
MRJ234W	Arriva Southend	N345CJA	Eastern Counties	N617VSS	Stagecoach Cambus	N887FVF	Eastern Counties
MRJ235W	Arriva Southend	N346CJA	Eastern Counties	N618APU	Essex Buses	N907GHJ	Buzz
MRJ236W	Arriva Southend	N347EKK	Suffolk Education	N618GAH	Eastern Counties	N940RBC	Ambassador Travel
MRJ237W	Arriva Southend	N350YFL	Stagecoach Cambus	N618VSS	Stagecoach Cambus	N944CPU	Essex Buses
MRJ238W	Arriva Southend	N351YFL	Stagecoach Cambus	N619APU	Eastern Counties	N945CPU	Essex Buses
MRJ239W	Arriva Southend	N352YFL	Stagecoach Cambus	N619GAH	Eastern Counties	N946CPU	Essex Buses
MRJ240W	Arriva Southend	N369GPU	Lodge's	N619VSS	Stagecoach Cambus	N947CPU	Essex Buses
MRJ241W	Arriva Southend	N375EAK	Neal's Travel	N620GAH	Eastern Counties	N948CPU	Essex Buses
MRJ242W	Arriva Southend	N375EHJ	Chelmsford Taxi	N620VSS	Stagecoach Cambus	N949CPU	Essex Buses
MRR808K	S & M Coaches	N376EAK	Neal's Travel	N621GAH	Eastern Counties	N950CPU	Essex Buses
MRT9P	Ipswich	N419WJL	Neal's Travel	N622GAH	Eastern Counties	N950RBC	Ambassador Travel
MSJ385P	Andrews Coaches	N420WJL	Clintona	N623GAH	Eastern Counties	N951CPU	Essex Buses
MSU916	Chenery	N445XVA	Stagecoach Cambus	N624GAH	Eastern Counties	N952CPU	Essex Buses
MSU917	Chenery	N446XVA	Stagecoach Cambus	N625GAH	Eastern Counties	N952KBJ	Chambers
MUD535W	Coach Services	N447XVA	Stagecoach Cambus	N626GAH	Eastern Counties	N953CPU	Essex Buses
MUH281X	Arriva Southend	N448XVA	Stagecoach Cambus	N627GAH	Eastern Counties	N954CPU	Essex Buses
MUH283X	Arriva Southend	N449XVA	Stagecoach Cambus	N628GAH	Eastern Counties	N955CPU	Essex Buses
MUH285X	Arriva Southend	N450XVA	Stagecoach Cambus	N641VSS	Stagecoach Cambus	N956CPU	Essex Buses
MUH286X	Arriva Southend	N451XVA	Stagecoach Cambus	N642VSS	Stagecoach Cambus	N957CPU	Essex Buses
MVK538R	Boon's	N452XVA	Stagecoach Cambus	N643VSS	Stagecoach Cambus	N958CPU	Essex Buses
MXI8204	Cedrick's	N473LCL	Dolphin	N644VSS	Stagecoach Cambus	N959CPU	Essex Buses
N2JWE	Embling	N505CVW	Harris Bus	N653EWJ	Go Whippet	N960CPU	Essex Buses
N4CNG	C&G Coach	N518XER	Stagecoach Cambus	N654EWJ	Go Whippet	N961CPU	Essex Buses
N4WMS	Goldline	N519XER	Stagecoach Cambus	N662HBY	S M Travel	N962CPU	Essex Buses
N5APT	Thorns	N520XER	Stagecoach Cambus	N665JGV	Galloway	N963CPU	Essex Buses
N5HGB	Boon's	N551LUA	Arriva East Herts	N668YAV	Dolphin	N964CPU	Essex Buses
N10DEW	Dews	N552LUA	Arriva East Herts	N680AHL	Supreme	N965CPU	Essex Buses
N11NJS	Sanders	N571AWJ	Flagfinders	N701CPU	Essex Buses	N966CPU	Essex Buses
N11RED	Supreme	N581BDT	Coach Stop	N705TPK	Arriva Southend	N967CPU	Essex Buses
N14CNG	C&G Coach	N589WND	Flying Banana	N706TPK	Arriva Southend	N968CPU	Essex Buses
N20TCC	Stort Valley	N592WND	Eastern Counties	N707TPK	Arriva Southend	N969CPU	Essex Buses
N21LDX	Suffolk Education	N600TCC	Stort Valley	N708TPK	Arriva Southend	N970CPU	Essex Buses
N25COO	Harris Bus	N601APU	Essex Buses	N709TPK	Arriva Southend	N971CPU	Essex Buses
N33SCS	Sanders	N601EEV	Harris Bus	N70TCC	Stort Valley	N972CPU	Essex Buses
N44SCS	Sanders	N602APU	Essex Buses	N739AVW	Arriva East Herts	N973EHJ	Essex Buses
N60TCC	Stort Valley	N602EEV	Harris Bus	N740AVW	Arriva East Herts	N974EHJ	Essex Buses
N63MDW	Sanders	N603APU	Essex Buses	N741AVW	Arriva East Herts	N975EHJ	Essex Buses
N65MDW	Sanders	N603EEV	Harris Bus	N742AVW	Arriva East Herts	N976EHJ	Essex Buses
N68GPU	Buzz	N604APU	Essex Buses	N743ANW	Arriva East Herts	N977EHJ	Essex Buses
N68MDW	Sanders	N604EEV	Harris Bus	N743NAY	Coach Stop	N978EHJ	Essex Buses
N68WEW	Kenzies	N605APU	Essex Buses	N744AVW	Arriva East Herts	N979EHJ	Essex Buses
N69WEW	Kenzies	N605GAH	Eastern Counties	N770BWF	Embling	N980EHJ	Essex Buses
N71MDW	Sanders	N606APU	Essex Buses	N781OGA	Goldline	N981EHJ	Essex Buses
N71WEW	Kenzies	N606GAH	Eastern Counties	N783OGA	Clintona	N982EHJ	Essex Buses
N73WEW	Kenzies	N607APU	Essex Buses	N783WEF	Felix	N983EHJ	Essex Buses
N74WEW	Kenzies	N607GAH	Eastern Counties	N796PDS	Myall's	N984EHJ	Essex Buses
N75JDX	County Travel	N608APU	Essex Buses	N811CSC	NIBS	N985EHJ	Essex Buses
N75WEW	Kenzies	N608GAH	Eastern Counties	N820DKU	Boon's	N986EHJ	Essex Buses
N75WSB	Cooks of Southend	N609APU	Essex Buses	N822DKU	Ambassador Travel	N987EHJ	Essex Buses
N80TCC	Stort Valley	N609GAH	Eastern Counties	N823APU	Essex Buses	N988FWT	Simonds
N105BPU	Chelmsford Taxi	N610APU	Essex Buses	N823DKU	Ambassador Travel	N990EAR	Viceroy
N115FHK	Crusader	N610GAH	Eastern Counties	N824APU	Essex Buses	N991FWT	Galloway
N116FHK	Crusader	N611APU	Essex Buses	N824DKU	Ambassador Travel	N992FWT	Galloway
N117FHK	Crusader	N611GAH	Eastern Counties	N825APU	Essex Buses	N993JRT	Felix
N118FHK	Crusader	N612APU	Essex Buses	N826APU	Essex Buses	N999RWC	Chenery
N119FHK	Crusader	N612GAH	Eastern Counties	N827APU	Essex Buses	NAG463A	Webbs
N157CMM	Clintona	N613APU	Essex Buses	N828APU	Essex Buses	NAU924W	Collins
N167BCE	Greys of Ely	N613GAH	Eastern Counties	N829APU	Essex Buses	NBJ462P	Dews
N167HGV	Suffolk Education	N613VSS	Stagecoach Cambus	N830APU	Essex Buses	NBU707	Chenery
N168HGV	Suffolk Education	N614APU	Essex Buses	N844DKU	Cunningham	NBX862	Anglian Coaches
N169HGV	Suffolk Education	N614GAH	Eastern Counties	N851CPU	Essex Buses	NCD553M	Hedingham
N170HGV	Suffolk Education	N614VSS	Stagecoach Cambus	N851DKU	Supreme	NCD563M	S M Travel
N210FWA	Biss Bros	N615APU	Essex Buses	N852CPU	Essex Buses	NCF888	Beestons
N211YJE	Myall's	N615GAH	Eastern Counties	N852DKU	Supreme	NCK980J	Eastern Counties
N212KBJ	Galloway	N615VSS	Stagecoach Cambus	N853CPU	Essex Buses	NDF158P	D&H Harrod
N241EWC	Hedingham	N616APU	Essex Buses	N853DKU	Supreme	NDL652R	NIBS
N245NNR	County Coaches	N616GAH	Eastern Counties	N854CPU	Essex Buses	NDP38R	Morley's
N249GOO	Ruffles	N616VSS	Stagecoach Cambus	N854DKU	Supreme	NEH724W	Stephenson's
N275DWY	Dereham Coaches	N617APU	Essex Buses	N854DKU	Supreme	NEH726W	Stephenson's
N316VNT	Harris Bus	N617GAH	Eastern Counties	N878ENK	Rayleigh	NEL119P	Amber Bus

Despite attempts for some twenty years, Mercedes-Benz have had only marginal success in marketing full-size coaches in the UK market. There have been various attemps to match the O303 underframe with coachwork familiar to British tastes. Seen here is a particularly rare compbination, an O303 with Jonckheere Jubilee P50 bodywork from the early 1980s which operated, until recently, by Biss Brothers as its 125LUP.

Reg	Operator	Reg	Operator	Reg	Operator	Reg	Operator
NER610M	Morley's	NIW6510	Arriva Colchester	OCK995K	Eastern Counties	OJI4756	Belle Coaches
NFP110W	Eastons	NIW6511	Arriva Colchester	OCN902R	DMA Mini	OJI4758	Belle Coaches
NFP115W	Lambert's	NIW6512	Arriva Colchester	OCU769R	Gretton's	OJN357P	Arriva East Herts
NFX446P	Hedingham	NJI5892	Gretton's	OCY913R	Leroy Coaches	OKW504R	Supreme
NHJ714	Cooks of Southend	NJI9241	Belle Coaches	ODL175R	Caroline Seagull	OKY84R	S M Travel
NIB4968	Collins	NJI9242	Belle Coaches	ODL176R	Caroline Seagull	OKY89R	Gretton's
NIJ2384	Eurosun Cs	NJI9243	Belle Coaches	ODU254P	Morley's	ONN279M	Ambassador Travel
NIL2266	Cedrick's	NJI9244	Belle Coaches	ODX102W	Buckland	OPL215R	Rayleigh
NIL3952	Eastern Counties	NJI9245	Belle Coaches	ODX608W	Caroline Seagull	ORY707R	Whiltshire
NIL3953	Eastern Counties	NJP35P	Flagfinders	OEG289P	Brandons	OSE739W	Mikes Coaches
NIL3954	Eastern Counties	NKY161	Go-Dons	OEH930W	Blue Diamond	OSG51V	Eastern Counties
NIL3955	Eastern Counties	NLH288	Coach Services	OEM787S	Supreme	OSG55V	Eastern Counties
NIL3956	Eastern Counties	NMC873	Kirby's Rayleigh	OFB965R	Stagecoach Cambus	OSG55V	Stephenson's
NIL3957	Eastern Counties	NNO61P	Essexbus	OGR647	Sanders	OSG67V	Stephenson's
NIL3958	Eastern Counties	NNO63P	Boon's	OGV364P	Rules	OSG74V	Eastern Counties
NIL3959	Eastern Counties	NNO66P	Boon's	OGV374P	Partridge	OSM95M	Dews
NIL3960	Eastern Counties	NOC409R	Rayleigh	OHE274X	Arriva Colchester	OSR192R	Jacksons Cs
NIL3961	Eastern Counties	NPD690W	Towler Coaches	OHE280X	Arriva Colchester	OSR194R	Jacksons Cs
NIL3962	Eastern Counties	NPU979M	Hedingham	OHE282X	D&H Harrod	OSU314	Semmence
NIL3963	Eastern Counties	NPV308W	Belle Coaches	OIB3517	Bakerbus	OSU894	Eurosun Cs
NIL3964	Eastern Counties	NPV309W	Belle Coaches	OIB5401	Stephenson's	OSV517	C&G Coach
NIL3965	Eastern Counties	NRR36W	Lambert's	OIB5402	Stephenson's	OTG551	Anglian Coaches
NIL3966	Eastern Counties	NRY22W	Spratts	OIL6275	Mil-Ken	OTO547M	Fourways
NIL3967	Eastern Counties	NRY333W	Neave	OJD167R	S & M Coaches	OTW116K	Kirby's Rayleigh
NIL4810	Reynolds	NSJ19R	Morley's	OJD192R	Morley's	OUC38R	S & M Coaches
NIL5673	Pullman	NSJ21R	Morley's	OJD195R	Stephenson's	OUC100R	C&G Coach
NIL7951	Flagfinders	NTU183L	Bird's	OJD198R	S & M Coaches	OWV819	Stort Valley
NIW1639	County Coaches	NUF990W	Semmence	OJD232R	Morley's	OXI2381	Mikes Coaches
NIW3646	Caroline Seagull	NUM339V	Essex Buses	OJD383R	S & M Coaches	OXK395	Anglian Coaches
NIW4122	Go-Dons	NVG194L	Viceroy	OJI1681	Stephenson's	P1AWE	Eastons
NIW6507	Arriva Colchester	NXL847	Brentwood Cs	OJI2830	Stephenson's	P4CNG	C&G Coach
NIW6508	Arriva Colchester	OAL631M	Ambassador Travel	OJI4627	Belle Coaches	P5FEN	Fenn
NIW6509	Arriva Colchester	OAY153P	Bure Valley	OJI4754	Belle Coaches	P22TCC	Stort Valley

Reg	Operator	Reg	Operator	Reg	Operator	Reg	Operator
P34KWA	Sanders	P329HVX	Arriva East Herts	P430HVX	Arriva East Herts	P545EFL	Stagecoach Cambus
P35KWA	Sanders	P329NHJ	Harris Bus	P430JDT	Neal's Travel	P545RNG	Eastern Counties
P55TCC	Stort Valley	P330HVX	Arriva East Herts	P431HVX	Arriva East Herts	P546EFL	Stagecoach Cambus
P76OEW	Kenzies	P330NHJ	Harris Bus	P433NEX	Eastern Counties	P546RNG	Eastern Counties
P77OEW	Kenzies	P330RVG	Eastern Counties	P434NEX	Eastern Counties	P547EFL	Stagecoach Cambus
P77SCS	Sanders	P331HVX	Arriva East Herts	P435NEX	Eastern Counties	P547RNG	Eastern Counties
P78OEW	Kenzies	P331NHJ	Harris Bus	P436NEX	Eastern Counties	P548EFL	Stagecoach Cambus
P79OEW	Kenzies	P332HVX	Arriva East Herts	P437NEX	Eastern Counties	P548RNG	Eastern Counties
P88TCC	Stort Valley	P332NHJ	Harris Bus	P437OVW	Biss Bros	P549EFL	Stagecoach Cambus
P99TCC	Stort Valley	P333HBC	Harris Bus	P438NEX	Eastern Counties	P549RNG	Eastern Counties
P105GHE	Ambassador Travel	P333TCC	Stort Valley	P438OVW	Biss Bros	P550EFL	Stagecoach Cambus
P111ABC	Kings	P334HVX	Arriva East Herts	P439NEX	Eastern Counties	P550RNG	Eastern Counties
P112GHE	Cunningham	P334NHJ	Harris Bus	P440NEX	Eastern Counties	P551EFL	Stagecoach Cambus
P113GHE	Euroview	P335ROO	Harris Bus	P441NEX	Eastern Counties	P552EFL	Stagecoach Cambus
P120KNO	Crusader	P336ROO	Harris Bus	P442NEX	Eastern Counties	P553EFL	Stagecoach Cambus
P130PPV	Ipswich	P337ROO	Harris Bus	P443NEX	Eastern Counties	P554EFL	Stagecoach Cambus
P131PPV	Ipswich	P338ROO	Harris Bus	P443SWX	Ipswich	P556EFL	Stagecoach Cambus
P132PPV	Ipswich	P339ROO	Harris Bus	P445NEX	Eastern Counties	P557EFL	Stagecoach Cambus
P134RBX	Goldline	P340ROO	Harris Bus	P446NEX	Eastern Counties	P558EFL	Stagecoach Cambus
P143NDX	Suffolk Education	P341ROO	Harris Bus	P447NEX	Eastern Counties	P559EFL	Stagecoach Cambus
P145GHE	Fargo Coachlines	P342ROO	Harris Bus	P448NEX	Eastern Counties	P561EFL	Stagecoach Cambus
P173NAK	Burtons	P343ROO	Harris Bus	P449NEX	Eastern Counties	P562EFL	Stagecoach Cambus
P190SGV	Ipswich	P344ROO	Harris Bus	P450NEX	Eastern Counties	P563EFL	Stagecoach Cambus
P191SGV	Ipswich	P345ROO	Harris Bus	P451RPW	Eastern Counties	P564EFL	Stagecoach Cambus
P192SGV	Ipswich	P346ROO	Harris Bus	P452RPW	Eastern Counties	P565EFL	Stagecoach Cambus
P194SGV	Ipswich	P347ROO	Harris Bus	P453RPW	Eastern Counties	P566EFL	Stagecoach Cambus
P195SGV	Ipswich	P348ROO	Harris Bus	P466JWB	Coach Stop	P567EFL	Stagecoach Cambus
P196SGV	Ipswich	P349ROO	Harris Bus	P478DPE	Arriva Southend	P568EFL	Stagecoach Cambus
P211NDX	Suffolk Education	P350ROO	Harris Bus	P481DPE	Arriva Southend	P569EFL	Stagecoach Cambus
P212NDX	Suffolk Education	P351ROO	Harris Bus	P482DPE	Arriva Southend	P570EFL	Stagecoach Cambus
P256FPK	Arriva Southend	P352ROO	Harris Bus	P501MNO	Essex Buses	P571EFL	Stagecoach Cambus
P257FPK	Arriva Southend	P353ROO	Harris Bus	P502MNO	Essex Buses	P572EFL	Stagecoach Cambus
P258FPK	Arriva Southend	P364APM	Stagecoach Cambus	P503MNO	Essex Buses	P573EFL	Stagecoach Cambus
P258NVG	Dolphin	P401HPU	Essex Buses	P504MNO	Essex Buses	P574EFL	Stagecoach Cambus
P259FPK	Arriva Southend	P402HPU	Essex Buses	P505MNO	Essex Buses	P575EFL	Stagecoach Cambus
P260FPK	Arriva Southend	P403HPU	Essex Buses	P506MNO	Essex Buses	P576EFL	Stagecoach Cambus
P261FPK	Arriva Southend	P404HPU	Essex Buses	P507MNO	Essex Buses	P577EFL	Stagecoach Cambus
P262FPK	Arriva Southend	P405HPU	Essex Buses	P508MNO	Essex Buses	P578EFL	Stagecoach Cambus
P263FPK	Arriva Southend	P406HPU	Essex Buses	P509MNO	Essex Buses	P579EFL	Stagecoach Cambus
P264FPK	Arriva Southend	P407HPU	Essex Buses	P510MNO	Essex Buses	P585HME	Clintona
P265FPK	Arriva Southend	P408HPU	Essex Buses	P511MNO	Essex Buses	P586HME	Clintona
P266FPK	Arriva Southend	P409HPU	Essex Buses	P512MNO	Essex Buses	P675LWA	Clintona
P267FPK	Arriva Southend	P410HPU	Essex Buses	P513MNO	Essex Buses	P676LWA	Clintona
P309PBJ	Galloway	P411MDT	Ambassador Travel	P526EFL	Stagecoach Cambus	P678HPU	Essex Buses
P315EFL	Stagecoach Cambus	P412MDT	Ambassador Travel	P527EFL	Stagecoach Cambus	P679HPU	Essex Buses
P316EFL	Stagecoach Cambus	P413MDT	Ambassador Travel	P528EFL	Stagecoach Cambus	P680HPU	Essex Buses
P317EFL	Stagecoach Cambus	P413TNG	Dereham Coaches	P529EFL	Stagecoach Cambus	P681HND	Flying Banana
P317KTW	Harris Bus	P416ACT	Neal's Travel	P530CLJ	Hedingham	P681HPU	Essex Buses
P318EFL	Stagecoach Cambus	P416HVX	Arriva East Herts	P530EFL	Stagecoach Cambus	P682HND	Flying Banana
P318KTW	Harris Bus	P417HVX	Arriva East Herts	P531CLJ	Simonds	P682HPU	Essex Buses
P319EFL	Stagecoach Cambus	P418HVX	Arriva East Herts	P531EFL	Stagecoach Cambus	P692HND	Flying Banana
P320EFL	Stagecoach Cambus	P419HVX	Arriva East Herts	P532EFL	Stagecoach Cambus	P692XVL	Coach Stop
P320KAR	Harris Bus	P420HVX	Arriva East Herts	P533EFL	Stagecoach Cambus	P693HND	Flying Banana
P321EFL	Stagecoach Cambus	P421HVX	Arriva East Herts	P534EFL	Stagecoach Cambus	P700TCC	Stort Valley
P321KAR	Harris Bus	P421JDT	Stort Valley	P535EFL	Stagecoach Cambus	P701NHJ	Harris Bus
P322EFL	Stagecoach Cambus	P422HVX	Arriva East Herts	P536EFL	Stagecoach Cambus	P701PWC	Essex Buses
P322KAR	Harris Bus	P422JDT	Stort Valley	P537EFL	Stagecoach Cambus	P702HPU	Essex Buses
P323EFL	Stagecoach Cambus	P423HVX	Arriva East Herts	P538EFL	Stagecoach Cambus	P702NHJ	Harris Bus
P323KAR	Harris Bus	P423JDT	Stort Valley	P539EFL	Stagecoach Cambus	P702PWC	Essex Buses
P324EFL	Stagecoach Cambus	P424HVX	Arriva East Herts	P540EFL	Stagecoach Cambus	P703HPU	Essex Buses
P324HVX	Arriva East Herts	P424JDT	Stort Valley	P541EFL	Stagecoach Cambus	P703NHJ	Harris Bus
P324NHJ	Harris Bus	P425HVX	Arriva East Herts	P541RNG	Eastern Counties	P703PWC	Essex Buses
P325HVX	Arriva East Herts	P425JDT	Stort Valley	P542EFL	Stagecoach Cambus	P704HPU	Essex Buses
P325NHJ	Harris Bus	P426HVX	Arriva East Herts	P542RNG	Eastern Counties	P704PWC	Essex Buses
P326HVX	Arriva East Herts	P426JDT	Stort Valley	P542SCL	Sanders	P705HPU	Essex Buses
P326NHJ	Harris Bus	P427HVX	Arriva East Herts	P543EFL	Stagecoach Cambus	P705PWC	Essex Buses
P327HVX	Arriva East Herts	P427JDT	Stort Valley	P543RNG	Eastern Counties	P706HPU	Essex Buses
P327NHJ	Harris Bus	P428HVX	Arriva East Herts	P543SCL	Sanders	P706PWC	Essex Buses
P328HVX	Arriva East Herts	P428JDT	Stort Valley	P544EFL	Stagecoach Cambus	P707HPU	Essex Buses
P328NHJ	Harris Bus	P429HVX	Arriva East Herts	P544RNG	Eastern Counties	P707PWC	Essex Buses

Reg	Operator	Reg	Operator	Reg	Operator	Reg	Operator
P708HPU	Essex Buses	PJI5526	Beestons	R3AWE	Eastons	R373DJN	Harris Bus
P708PWC	Essex Buses	PJI5637	Sanders	R3BOY	Golden Boy	R374DJN	Harris Bus
P709HPU	Essex Buses	PJI6079	DMA Mini	R4CNG	C&G Coach	R375DJN	Harris Bus
P710HPU	Essex Buses	PJI6391	Beestons	R4FEN	Fenn	R376DJN	Harris Bus
P711HPU	Essex Buses	PJI7229	Anglian Coaches	R60BCL	Burtons	R377DJN	Harris Bus
P731NVG	Eastern Counties	PJI7348	Sanders	R70BCL	Burtons	R378DJN	Harris Bus
P732NVG	Eastern Counties	PJI7727	County Coaches	R80BCL	Burtons	R379DJN	Harris Bus
P733NVG	Eastern Counties	PJI8327	Sanders	R90BCL	Burtons	R380DJN	Harris Bus
P734NVG	Eastern Counties	PJJ18S	Jans Coaches	R101HEV	Crusader	R411VPU	Essex Buses
P750HTW	Biss Bros	PJT518W	DMA Mini	R102HEV	Crusader	R412VPU	Essex Buses
P751HTW	Biss Bros	PKE809M	Ford's	R103HEV	Crusader	R413VPU	Essex Buses
P753RWU	Arriva East Herts	PKG735R	Freestones	R104HEV	Crusader	R414VPU	Essex Buses
P754RWU	Arriva East Herts	PNB806W	Happy Wanderer	.R121HEV	Crusader	R415VPU	Essex Buses
P767PCL	Sanders	PNH183	Brandons	R122HEV	Crusader	R416COO	Arriva East Herts
P768JCL	Sanders	PNU133R	D&H Harrod	R123HEV	Crusader	R416VPU	Essex Buses
P800TCC	Stort Valley	PNW314W	Happy Wanderer	R124HEV	Crusader	R417COO	Arriva East Herts
P806REX	Eastern Counties	PPG3R	Belle Coaches	R129XWF	Stort Valley	R417VPU	Essex Buses
P807REX	Eastern Counties	PPG7R	Beestons	R133SBJ	Ipswich	R418COO	Arriva East Herts
P808REX	Eastern Counties	PPY238	Chenery	R134SBJ	Ipswich	R418VPU	Essex Buses
P809REX	Eastern Counties	PRA12R	Jacksons Cs	R165GNW	Arriva East Herts	R419COO	Arriva East Herts
P810REX	Eastern Counties	PRC848X	Eastern Counties	R169GNW	Arriva East Herts	R419VPU	Essex Buses
P811REX	Eastern Counties	PRC850X	Eastern Counties	R170GNW	Arriva East Herts	R420COO	Arriva East Herts
P812REX	Eastern Counties	PRC851X	Eastern Counties	R179TKU	Stort Valley	R421COO	Arriva East Herts
P813REX	Eastern Counties	PRC852X	Eastern Counties	R185DDX	Ipswich	R422COO	Arriva East Herts
P814REX	Eastern Counties	PRC853X	Eastern Counties	R186DDX	Ipswich	R423COO	Arriva East Herts
P815REX	Eastern Counties	PRC854X	Eastern Counties	R187DDX	Ipswich	R424COO	Arriva East Herts
P816REX	Eastern Counties	PRC855X	Eastern Counties	R189DDX	Ipswich	R425COO	Arriva East Herts
P817REX	Eastern Counties	PRC857X	Eastern Counties	R197DDX	Ipswich	R426COO	Arriva East Herts
P818REX	Eastern Counties	PRE205R	Embling	R201VPU	Arriva East Herts	R427COO	Arriva East Herts
P819REX	Eastern Counties	PRG124J	Ford's	R202VPU	Arriva East Herts	R428COO	Arriva East Herts
P820SCL	Eastern Counties	PRG127J	Ford's	R203VPU	Arriva East Herts	R429COO	Arriva East Herts
P821SCL	Eastern Counties	PRG134J	Ford's	R204VPU	Arriva East Herts	R430COO	Arriva East Herts
P822SCL	Eastern Counties	PRG138J	Ford's	R205VPU	Arriva East Herts	R431COO	Arriva East Herts
P833HVX	Arriva East Herts	PRT700W	Belle Coaches	R206VPU	Arriva East Herts	R441PCK	Grahams
P844OAH	Eastern Counties	PTD671S	Supreme	R207VPU	Arriva East Herts	R447YDT	Cunningham
P865VTJ	Arriva East Herts	PTF751L	Norfolk Green	R208VPU	Arriva East Herts	R448YDT	Fargo Coachlines
P888MUL	Beestons	PTT92R	Thorns	R209VPU	Arriva East Herts	R449YDT	Fargo Coachlines
P926NNO	Ruffles	PTV583X	Norfolk Green	R233SEF	Soames	R453FCE	Stagecoach Cambus
P939HVX	Arriva East Herts	PTV587X	Norfolk Green	R252KWY	Biss Bros	R454FCE	Stagecoach Cambus
P969HWF	Coach Stop	PTV588X	Norfolk Green	R255FBJ	Galloway	R455FCE	Stagecoach Cambus
P970HWF	Coach Stop	PTV597X	Semmence	R256FBJ	Galloway	R456FCE	Stagecoach Cambus
PAY7W	Towler Coaches	PUM148W	Eastern Counties	R267THL	Flagfinders	R458BNG	Eastern Counties
PBB760	Coach Services	PUU970	Biss Bros	R268TEG	Dews	R459BNG	Eastern Counties
PBC648W	D&H Harrod	PVF377	Sanders	R281THL	Neal's Travel	R460BNG	Eastern Counties
PCE637R	Myall's	PVG24W	Eastern Counties	R290TLU	Supreme	R461BNG	Eastern Counties
PCL251W	Eastern Counties	PVG25W	Eastern Counties	R353LER	Stagecoach Cambus	R462BNG	Eastern Counties
PCL252W	Eastern Counties	PVG26W	Eastern Counties	R354LER	Stagecoach Cambus	R463CAH	Eastern Counties
PCL253W	Eastern Counties	PVG27W	Eastern Counties	R354XVX	Harris Bus	R464CAH	Eastern Counties
PCL254W	Eastern Counties	PVV312	Semmence	R355LER	Stagecoach Cambus	R465CAH	Eastern Counties
PCL255W	Eastern Counties	PVV313	Semmence	R355XVX	Harris Bus	R466CAH	Eastern Counties
PCL257W	Eastern Counties	PWR446W	Cedrick's	R356LER	Stagecoach Cambus	R467CAH	Eastern Counties
PEB2R	Kenzies	PWY37W	Stagecoach Cambus	R356XVX	Harris Bus	R468CAH	Eastern Counties
PEX610W	Eastern Counties	PWY39W	Hedingham	R357XVX	Harris Bus	R469CAH	Eastern Counties
PEX615W	Eastern Counties	PWY42W	Eastern Counties	R358XVX	Harris Bus	R470CAH	Eastern Counties
PEX617W	Eastern Counties	PWY43W	Hedingham	R359XVX	Harris Bus	R471CAH	Eastern Counties
PFL963R	Shaws of Maxey	PWY44W	Essex Buses	R360DJN	Harris Bus	R472CAH	Eastern Counties
PFL964R	Shaws of Maxey	PWY45W	Stagecoach Cambus	R361DJN	Harris Bus	R473CAH	Eastern Counties
PFL965R	Shaws of Maxey	PWY46W	Hedingham	R362DJN	Harris Bus	R474CAH	Eastern Counties
PHH408R	Leroy Coaches	PWY47W	Stagecoach Cambus	R363DJN	Harris Bus	R475CAH	Eastern Counties
PHK387R	Hedingham	PWY49W	Stagecoach Cambus	R364DJN	Harris Bus	R476CAH	Eastern Counties
PIJ3379	Ambassador Travel	PWY50W	Stagecoach Cambus	R365DJN	Harris Bus	R477CAH	Eastern Counties
PIJ4317	Ambassador Travel	Q287HNR	Stephenson's	R365JVA	Stagecoach Cambus	R478CAH	Eastern Counties
PIJ8513	Ambassador Travel	Q290FDF	Leroy Coaches	R366DJN	Harris Bus	R486AVG	Simonds
PIW4789	Associated Cs	Q475MEV	Arriva Southend	R366JVA	Stagecoach Cambus	R580JVA	Stagecoach Cambus
PIW4795	Mikes Coaches	Q476MEV	Arriva Southend	R367DJN	Harris Bus	R581JVA	Stagecoach Cambus
PIW4798	Go Whippet	Q552MEV	Arriva Southend	R368DJN	Harris Bus	R582JVA	Stagecoach Cambus
PJB614R	Leroy Coaches	Q553MEV	Arriva Southend	R369DJN	Harris Bus	R583JVA	Stagecoach Cambus
PJE999J	Kenzies	Q554MEV	Arriva Southend	R370DJN	Harris Bus	R584JVA	Stagecoach Cambus
PJI3745	Arriva Southend	Q856MEV	Leroy Coaches	R371DJN	Harris Bus	R585JVA	Stagecoach Cambus
PJI4712	Beestons	R2JWE	Embling	R372DJN	Harris Bus	R586JVA	Stagecoach Cambus

Reg	Operator	Reg	Operator	Reg	Operator	Reg	Operator
R687ACL	Freestones	RDX20R	Ipswich	SDX29R	Ipswich	SPV555	Chenery
R712DJN	Essex Buses	REG870X	Go Whippet	SDX30R	Ipswich	SPW92N	Boon's
R713DJN	Essex Buses	REV188R	Hedingham	SDX31R	Ipswich	SRP816N	Ford's
R714DJN	Essex Buses	RFS585V	Beestons	SDX32R	Ipswich	SSU331	Boon's
R715DJN	Essex Buses	RFS586V	Beestons	SDX33R	Ipswich	STW21W	Essex Buses
R716DJN	Essex Buses	RFS588V	Beestons	SDX34R	Ipswich	STW22W	Essex Buses
R717DJN	Essex Buses	RGS598R	Spratts	SDX35R	Ipswich	STW23W	Essex Buses
R718DJN	Essex Buses	RGV111	Beestons	SEL118R	S & M Coaches	STW24W	Stagecoach Cambus
R718TRV	Neal's Travel	RGV284N	Hedingham	SFC2T	Sanders	STW27W	Essex Buses
R719DJN	Essex Buses	RGV684W	CI Coachlines	SFF160M	Avro & Elm Park	STW28W	Essex Buses
R719TRV	Neal's Travel	RGV690W	Suffolk Education	SFL373R	Stagecoach Cambus	STW30W	Hedingham
R720DJN	Essex Buses	RGV691W	Suffolk Education	SGF965	Sanders	STW36W	Essex Buses
R721DJN	Essex Buses	RGV692W	Suffolk Education	SGR780V	Hedingham	STW37W	Essex Buses
R877SDT	Coach Stop	RGV693W	Suffolk Education	SGS497W	Arriva East Herts	STW38W	Essex Buses
R940VPU	Arriva East Herts	RHB234Y	Eurosun Cs	SHL882S	Enterprise	SUB789W	Essex Buses
R941VPU	Arriva East Herts	RHS861W	Towler Coaches	SIA488	Simonds	SUB790W	Stagecoach Cambus
R942VPU	Arriva East Herts	RHT505S	Stephenson's	SIB3276	Bakerbus	SUB791W	Hedingham
R943VPU	Arriva East Herts	RIB3929	Lewis's	SIB3277	Bakerbus	SUB792W	Stagecoach Cambus
R944VPU	Arriva East Herts	RIB8031	County Travel	SIB6176	Ruffles	SUB793W	Stagecoach Cambus
R945VPU	Arriva East Herts	RIW4037	Carter's Coaches	SIB7359	Stort Valley	SUB795W	Stagecoach Cambus
R946VPU	Arriva East Herts	RIW4038	Carter's Coaches	SIB7517	Cuttings	SUH170Y	Suffolk Education
R947VPU	Arriva East Herts	RIW9057	Kiddles	SIB8528	Gretton's	SUP685R	Hedingham
R948VPU	Arriva East Herts	RIW9456	Kiddles	SIJ82	Simonds	SVF896G	Pullman
R949VPU	Arriva East Herts	RJI1632	Sanders	SIW8306	Rayleigh	SVM182W	Amber Bus
R950VPU	Arriva East Herts	RJI1682	Mikes Coaches	SJI1615	Sanders	SVW274K	Essexbus
R951VPU	Arriva East Herts	RJI4078	Leroy Coaches	SJI1616	Sanders	SWO70N	J Amos
R952VPU	Arriva East Herts	RJI4576	Bakerbus	SJI1617	Sanders	SWW143R	Beestons
R953VPU	Arriva East Herts	RJI4577	Bakerbus	SJI1618	Sanders	TAH271W	Eastern Counties
R954VPU	Arriva East Herts	RJI5721	Semmence	SJI1619	Sanders	TAH272W	Eastern Counties
R956RFP	Chelmsford Taxi	RJI5723	Semmence	SJI1620	Sanders	TAH273W	Eastern Counties
R957RFP	Chelmsford Taxi	RJI6859	Gretton's	SJI1621	Sanders	TAH275W	Eastern Counties
R958RFP	Chelmsford Taxi	RJI7972	Beestons	SJI1622	Sanders	TAH276W	Eastern Counties
R959RFP	Chelmsford Taxi	RJI7973	Beestons	SJI1623	Sanders	TAZ4517	Semmence
R972CJS	Spratts	RJI8604	Sanders	SJI1624	Sanders	TAZ4518	Semmence
R980GUB	Coach Stop	RJI8607	Sanders	SJI1625	Sanders	TBD619N	Dews
RAH258W	Eastern Counties	RJI8614	Sanders	SJI1626	Sanders	TBJ545W	Soames
RAH259W	Eastern Counties	RJR869Y	Enterprise	SJI1627	Sanders	TBM626W	Ruffles
RAH260W	Hedingham	RJR869Y	Peelings	SJI1628	Sanders	TBW451P	Hedingham
RAH261W	Eastern Counties	RLG428V	Veazey	SJI1629	Sanders	TCF496	Simonds
RAH262W	Eastern Counties	RNC478	Gretton's	SJI1630	Sanders	TCS352J	Simonds
RAH263W	Eastern Counties	RNK317W	Amber Bus	SJI2953	Gretton's	TDL127S	Caroline Seagull
RAH264W	Stagecoach Cambus	RNN982N	Ambassador Travel	SJI4423	DMA Mini	TDL420S	Caroline Seagull
RAH266W	Eastern Counties	RNN984N	Ambassador Travel	SJI4424	Beestons	TDT32S	Ford's
RAH267W	Eastern Counties	RPW189R	Eastern Counties	SJI4425	Beestons	TDX120W	Ipswich
RAH269W	Eastern Counties	RRB118R	Ambassador Travel	SJI4426	Beestons	TDX124W	Ipswich
RAH270W	Eastern Counties	RRB120R	Ambassador Travel	SJI4427	Beestons	TE7870	Buckland
RAX624R	Norfolk Green	RRP857R	Ford's	SJI4429	Beestons	TET748S	Go-Dons
RAY160W	Leroy Coaches	RRT100W	Sanders	SJI4430	Beestons	TEX402R	Eastern Counties
RAY742R	Cooks of Southend	RRT535R	Felix	SJI4431	Beestons	TGX704M	S & M Coaches
RAZ2228	Cuttings	RRW900W	Eurosun Cs	SJI5629	Sanders	TGX892M	NIBS
RBU183R	Beestons	RSD978R	Morley's	SJI7477	Mikes Coaches	THE383Y	County Travel
RBZ2562	Robinson	RSE156W	Towler Coaches	SJI8098	Beestons	THM705M	NIBS
RBZ2563	Robinson	RSU883	Avro & Elm Park	SJI8130	Eurosun Cs	THM707M	Brandons
RBZ2564	Robinson	RUT684W	Beestons	SJI9319	Beestons	THX225S	Enterprise
RBZ2565	Robinson	RVW88W	Arriva Colchester	SJI9320	Beestons	THX285S	Stort Valley
RBZ2566	Robinson	RVW89W	Arriva Colchester	SJI9321	Beestons	THX617M	Upwell & Dist
RBZ2959	Robinson	RVW90W	Arriva Colchester	SJI9333	Bakerbus	TIA5599	Chenery
RBZ2960	Robinson	RWC41W	Hedingham	SJI9334	Bakerbus	TIA5819	M & E Coaches
RBZ2961	Robinson	RYG664R	Gretton's	SJI9335	Bakerbus	TIW2801	Webbs
RBZ2962	Robinson	RYG684	Chenery	SKG901S	Leroy Coaches	TJE995S	Whiltshire
RCH487R	Norfolk Green	RYL710R	Cooks of Southend	SLK886	Simonds	TJE996S	Carter's Coaches
RCS754	Spratts	RYL728R	Neave	SMR381Y	Peelings	TJI1670	Ruffles
RDA670R	Ambassador Travel	SAH379R	Bird's	SMU721N	NIBS	TJI1685	Ruffles
RDC103R	Leroy Coaches	SAO411R	Rayleigh	SMU729N	NIBS	TJI1686	Neal's Travel
RDC113R	Chariots	SDA620S	Supreme	SMW56Y	Ford's	TJI1688	Hedingham
RDC114R	Chariots	SDX22R	Ipswich	SNJ591R	Hedingham	TJI3132	Partridge
RDS82W	Go Whippet	SDX23R	Ipswich	SNT925H	Sanders	TJI3133	Partridge
RDV903	Sanders	SDX24R	Ipswich	SPA192R	Morley's	TJI4267	Carter's Coaches
RDX18R	Ipswich	SDX25R	Ipswich	SPU443W	S & M Coaches	TJI4268	Carter's Coaches
RDX19R	Ipswich	SDX27R	Ipswich	SPU898W	Hedingham	TJI4821	Stephenson's

VJT601X, from Whincop of Peasenhall fleet, is a Plaxton Supreme-bodied DAF while almost all of the other coaches in the fleet are based on Ford chassis . *T K Brookes*

TJI4824	Stephenson's	TPU69R	Arriva Colchester	ULS646T	S M Travel	UWW3X	Stagecoach Cambus
TJI5401	Ambassador Travel	TPU71R	Arriva Colchester	ULS662T	Supreme	UWW4X	Stagecoach Cambus
TJI5402	Ambassador Travel	TPU74R	Arriva Colchester	ULS671T	Brentwood Cs	UWW8X	Stagecoach Cambus
TJI5403	Ambassador Travel	TPU75R	Arriva Colchester	ULS675T	Brentwood Cs	VAE507T	Norfolk Green
TJI6277	Mikes Coaches	TPU86R	Arriva Colchester	UNK11W	Neave	VAH277X	Eastern Counties
TJI6306	Cedrick's	TSU611	Boon's	UNO100W	Hedingham	VAH278X	Stagecoach Cambus
TJI6707	Gretton's	TUB1M	Rayleigh	UNW928R	Brentwood Cs	VAH279X	Stagecoach Cambus
TJI7515	Simonds	TVG397	Simonds	UPV337	Chenery	VAH280X	Stagecoach Cambus
TJI7519	Associated Cs	TVN330X	Lambert's	URF666S	Stephenson's	VAH281X	Eastern Counties
TJN502R	Essex Buses	TVU716X	Leroy Coaches	URF673S	Supreme	VAH282X	Eastern Counties
TKJ769X	Beestons	TWR465W	Stephenson's	URP943W	Stagecoach Cambus	VAR899S	Essex Buses
TKV18W	Semmence	TXI8748	Flagfinders	USU677	Avro & Elm Park	VAV161X	Go Whippet
TMA329R	Leroy Coaches	TXI8756	Go-Dons	USV802	Caroline Seagull	VBH97S	Leroy Coaches
TND134X	Beestons	TXI8762	Beestons	USV807	S & P Coach	VBH605S	Neave
TND418X	West Row	TYE707S	Leroy Coaches	UTR705	Webbs	VEJ561V	S & P Coach
TNH870R	Stephenson's	TYE708S	Spratts	UTV221S	Embling	VEX283X	Eastern Counties
TOD657R	Beestons	UAR591W	Essex Buses	UUB402	Simonds	VEX284X	Eastern Counties
TPA666X	Galloway	UAR593W	Essex Buses	UUB403	Simonds	VEX285X	Eastern Counties
TPD101X	Arriva East Herts	UAR596W	Essex Buses	UUB404	Simonds	VEX286X	Eastern Counties
TPD102X	Arriva East Herts	UAR599W	Essex Buses	UUF110J	Embling	VEX287X	Eastern Counties
TPD104X	Arriva East Herts	UAR930M	S & P Coach	UUF332J	Partridge	VEX288X	Eastern Counties
TPD107X	Arriva East Herts	UAV457X	Morley's	UUX356S	Whincop	VEX289X	Stagecoach Cambus
TPD109X	Arriva East Herts	UDW142S	Bure Valley	UVE593K	Reynolds	VEX290X	Eastern Counties
TPD110X	Arriva East Herts	UEB782K	Morley's	UVF624X	Eastern Counties	VEX291X	Stagecoach Cambus
TPD115X	Arriva East Herts	UFC422K	S & M Coaches	UVF625X	Eastern Counties	VEX292X	Eastern Counties
TPD117X	Arriva East Herts	UFT914T	Kiddles	UVF628X	Eastern Counties	VEX293X	Stagecoach Cambus
TPD123X	Arriva East Herts	UFX360L	Dews	UVG846	Anglian Coaches	VEX294X	Eastern Counties
TPE155S	Fargo Coachlines	UFX629X	Towler Coaches	UVO123S	Ambassador Travel	VEX295X	Stagecoach Cambus
TPJ302S	Whincop	UHH267	Andrews Coaches	UVX4S	Hedingham	VEX296X	Stagecoach Cambus
TPJ780M	Leroy Coaches	UHJ797Y	Kiddles	UVX5S	Hedingham	VEX297X	Eastern Counties
TPM616X	Towler Coaches	UHJ969Y	Neave	UVX6S	Hedingham	VEX298X	Stagecoach Cambus
TPU67R	Arriva Colchester	UJI2347	Thorns	UVX7S	Hedingham	VEX299X	Stagecoach Cambus
TPU67R	Beestons	UJN159V	County Coaches	UWA93S	Beestons	VEX300X	Stagecoach Cambus
TPU68R	Arriva Colchester	ULR923X	County Travel	UWV860R	Stort Valley	VEX301X	Stagecoach Cambus

VEX302X	Eastern Counties	WNO115K	Kirby's Rayleigh	XIB2453	Ruffles	YEV328S	Essex Buses
VEX303X	Stagecoach Cambus	WNO479	Essex Buses	XJO46	Simonds	YEX128S	Whincop
VEX304X	Stagecoach Cambus	WNO480	Essex Buses	XJX795V	Fourways	YFC736	Thorns
VFK661X	West Row	WNP332V	Cuttings	XKX640X	Wards	YGC295W	Lewis's
VFT935T	J Amos	WNT377Y	DMA Mini	XLF611	Mil-Ken	YJE3T	Kenzies
VG7	Dolphin	WNU27Y	Fourways	XMA194M	Bird's	YJE9T	Sanders
VGD779R	Supreme	WOA521	Sanders	XMW279W	Goodwin's	YMJ545S	Robinson
VHB672S	Stephenson's	WOD142X	Coach Services	XNG203S	Eastern Counties	YMJ555S	Lodge's
VHB677S	Stephenson's	WOI2658	Brandons	XNG205S	Eastern Counties	YNJ214	Cooks of Southend
VHB678S	Stephenson's	WOI607	Ipswich	XNG770S	Eastern Counties	YNO77S	Arriva Colchester
VJT601X	Whincop	WOO903W	Hedingham	XNM820S	Lodge's	YNO78S	Arriva Colchester
VKC832V	Sanders	WPH130Y	Arriva East Herts	XNM824S	Eastern Counties	YNO80S	Arriva Colchester
VKC833V	Sanders	WPH135Y	Hedingham	XNR997Y	Semmence	YNO81S	Arriva Colchester
VKN836X	Beestons	WPW199S	Eastern Counties	XNV882S	Ford's	YNO82S	Arriva Colchester
VLT12	Arriva East Herts	WSU225	Boon's	XPP282X	Carter's Coaches	YOI949	Golden Boy
VLT88	Arriva East Herts	WSU483	Greys of Ely	XPW877X	Hedingham	YOI1214	Golden Boy
VMJ967S	Upwell & Dist	WSU484	Greys of Ely	XRF24S	Supreme	YOI2642	Golden Boy
VNK49W	Lewis's	WSU485	Greys of Ely	XRJ206S	Wards	YOI2805	Golden Boy
VNO732S	Essex Buses	WSV503	Sanders	XRN718R	Amber Bus	YOI5475	Golden Boy
VOD590S	Hedingham	WSV555	Beestons	XRR613M	Ambassador Travel	YOI5997	Golden Boy
VOD603S	S & P Coach	WTG357T	Partridge	XRR622M	Ambassador Travel	YOI7079	Golden Boy
VOI3252	Jans Coaches	WTH949T	Essex Buses	XRR629M	Ambassador Travel	YOI7145	Golden Boy
VPF322S	Webbs	WTH958T	Essex Buses	XRT931X	Ipswich	YOI7353	Golden Boy
VPR384X	Suffolk Education	WUL261N	Beestons	XRT932X	Ipswich	YOI7374	Golden Boy
VRC605Y	Norfolk Green	WVY596	Kirby's Rayleigh	XRT947X	Ipswich	YOI7725	Golden Boy
VRC608Y	Norfolk Green	WWC820	Cooks of Southend	XRW506S	Gretton's	YOI7744	Golden Boy
VRC609Y	Norfolk Green	WWY118S	Eastern Counties	XSU913	Burtons	YOI7757	Golden Boy
VRU204S	D-Way Travel	WWY122S	Eastern Counties	XTE221V	Arriva Southend	YOI8271	Golden Boy
VRY841	Simonds	WWY123S	Eastern Counties	XTE222V	Arriva Southend	YPB829T	Carter's Coaches
VTH941T	Essex Buses	WWY126S	Beestons	XTE223V	Arriva Southend	YPD104Y	D&H Harrod
VUN678	Gretton's	WXC732	Brentwood Cs	XTE224V	Arriva Southend	YPD105Y	D&H Harrod
VVY670	Peter Goodward	WXI9253	Sanders	XTE225V	Arriva Southend	YPD111Y	Carter's Coaches
VWL817	Mil-Ken	WYV48T	Morley's	XTE226V	Arriva Southend	YRT240	Happy Wanderer
VWX361X	Kirby's Rayleigh	XBD556W	Mil-Ken	XTE227V	Arriva Southend	YSK331	Enterprise
WAD640S	Whincop	XBJ876	Semmence	XTE228V	Arriva Southend	YSU917	Upwell & Dist
WAH592S	Norfolk Green	XBL333	Chenery	XTE229V	Arriva Southend	YUJ318T	Mil-Ken
WAW353Y	Soames	XCF297	Semmence	XTE230V	Arriva Southend	YUT638Y	Suffolk Education
WAY456X	Semmence	XCF447	Brentwood Cs	XUN344V	DMA Mini	YVF158	Simonds
WCE95T	Dews	XCG264V	Simonds	XUP692	Brentwood Cs	YVJ677	Sanders
WDB551S	Anglian Coaches	XCM495W	County Travel	XUX540T	DMA Mini	YWE503M	Partridge
WDX663X	Simonds	XDP951T	Wright Way	XUY402R	Bird's	YWF512T	Enterprise
WED984S	D-Way Travel	XDV607S	Towler Coaches	XVA545T	Simonds	YXI3049	Golden Boy
WFO866T	Galloway	XEH254M	Biss Bros	XVE8T	Kenzies	YXI3057	Golden Boy
WGE37S	Avro & Elm Park	XEW322T	Shaws of Maxey	XYK761T	Essex Buses	YXI8897	Golden Boy
WGR66R	Ford's	XEW323T	Shaws of Maxey	YAE518V	Stephenson's	YXI9253	Golden Boy
WIB1160	Carter's Coaches	XEW324T	Shaws of Maxey	YBF682S	Fargo Coachlines	YXI9255	Embling
WJI1722	Simonds	XFC777R	Embling	YBK605	Euroview	YYL775T	Leroy Coaches
WJI1723	Simonds	XGS767X	Hedingham	YBM930S	Buckland	YYL776T	Belle Coaches
WJI1724	Simonds	XHE754T	Neave	YBT849	D-Way Travel	YYL778T	Belle Coaches
WJI3488	Sanders	XHK215X	Essex Buses	YDE4	Reynolds	YYL783T	Belle Coaches
WJI3489	Sanders	XHK217X	Essex Buses	YDS650S	Go-Dons	YYL786T	Belle Coaches
WJM831T	Hedingham	XHK218X	Essex Buses	YDX101Y	Ipswich	YYL794T	Essex Buses
WJN565S	Essex Buses	XHK232X	Essex Buses	YDX104Y	Ipswich	YYL795T	Belle Coaches
WKH424S	Go Whippet	XHK235X	Eastern Counties	YEV308S	Essex Buses		
WKH426S	Go Whippet	XHK236X	Eastern Counties	YEV320S	Eastern Counties		
WKJ787	Brentwood Cs	XHK237X	Eastern Counties	YEV321S	Essex Buses		

ISBN 1 897990 38 3

Published by *British Bus Publishing Ltd*
The Vyne, 16 St Margarets Drive, Wellington, Telford, TF1 3PH
Fax orderline:- 01952 255669